CU00793282

# Walking in all of the Squares

# WALKING
## IN ALL OF THE
# SQUARES

## A BIOGRAPHY OF
## ALEXANDER THOM

ENGINEER, ARCHAEOASTRONOMER,
DISCOVERER of a PREHISTORIC CALENDAR,
the GEOMETRY OF STONE RINGS
and MEGALITHIC MEASUREMENT

# ARCHIBALD S THOM

© Archibald S Thom

First Published 1995
Argyll Publishing
Glendaruel
Argyll PA22 3AE
Scotland

Permission to use extracts from the *Glasgow
Herald*, *Scottish Sunday Express*, the BBC *Chronicle*
programme, *Cracking the Stone Age Code*, *Antiquity*,
*The Ley Hunter* and the *Journal for History of
Astronomy* is gratefully acknowledged. The Royal
Commission on the Ancient and Historical
Monuments of Scotland, where Alexander Thom's
survey material is held, have permitted use of
diagrams and photos.

**British Library Cataloguing-in-Publication Data.
A catalogue record for this book is available from
the British Library.**

ISBN 1 874640 66 1

*Origination*
Cordfall Ltd, Glasgow

*Printing*
Images, Worcester

Printed and bound in Great Britain by Bookcraft (Bath) Ltd.

to my mother
Jeanie Boyd Thom


"They also serve
who only stand and wait."

Milton

# CONTENTS

# PUBLISHER'S NOTE

Grateful acknowledgement is made to the Carnegie Trust for the Universities of Scotland for their contribution towards the publication of this book. For financial support thanks is also due to Brasenose College, Western Isles Enterprise, Robert Howie & Son, Thomas Mackie & Son, the University of Glasgow Library and to Beryl Austin, Marian Austin, Hamish Gorrie, Professor Austin W Mair, Lord Joe Maclay, Nancy Lady Maclay, Professor Barry Nicholas, Joseph J Snyder and Dr Robert Watt.

The following list of subscribers have also helped to make this book possible by buying copies before publication.

Clare Adams, Dunlop

Robert Adams, East Sussex

Penelope Ann Balfour, Edinburgh

Lindy Austin, Fort William

Vincent Balfour, Edinburgh

Hiram Barton, Iver Buckinghamshire

Stan Beckensall, Hexham

Mrs G Bingham, Stewarton

J Roger Blamire, Staveley

The Library, Brasenose College, Oxford

David A Brown, Newton Mearns

Dr David K Brown, Bearsden

James F Brown, Troon

Lindsay & Anne Brown, Harrow Weald

IL Buchanan, Wormit

Dr HAW Burl, Birmingham

Ian Campbell, Glasgow

WD Campbell, Stenton

Mrs James Cashman, Stewarton

Paul Chapman, Atlanta Georgia

Alan S Clark, Edinburgh

VCWR Clement, Glasgow

A Conoboy, Alloa

MW Couper, Dundee

Maurice J Coville, Stewarton

Dr EC Krupp, Griffiths Observatory LA

Alan Davis, Lancaster

Dr Elizabeth Dick, Edinburgh

James F Dick, Inverness

Christopher K Donald, Edinburgh

WA Dukes, Suffolk

Richard L Dunlap III, Paris Tennessee

Dr Egen, Bremen

Prof AAR Elagib, Glasgow

GB Elliot, Preston

Margaret Ellis, Fort William

Kay Fegan, West Kilbride

Lesley Ferguson, RCAHMS Edinburgh

Helen KK Findlay, Stewarton

Dr Tom Foord, Bearsden

H Forrest, Monkton

Alison Fraser, Kirkwall

Dr Marion Fraser, Glasgow

Prof RA McD Galbraith, University of Glasgow

Alasdair Gibb, Leighton Buzzard

JT Gibson, Dunlop

Prof Pierre Giot, Rennes

Rose H Glennie, Dunlop

Prof JE Gordon, Oxfordshire

H Gorrie, Kilbarchan

Drs Joy & Robin Grant, Edinburgh

James A Greig, Dundee

HM Gustin, Stroud

Mrs AJ Halstead, Dunlop

FMM Hamilton, Cairnryan

Henry Heaney, Glasgow University Library

Robin Heath, Bluestone Press, Cardigan

Ivan Ver Heyden, *Kadath* Brussels

Douglas C Heggie, Edinburgh

Irvin P Hooper, Terre Haute Indiana

Robert Howie & Sons, Dunlop

Dr CA Hunter, Stewarton

Jean E Hunter, Ayr

G Jarvis, Glasgow

John & Jennifer Hunter, Dunlop

Prof SP Hutton, Southampton

Jill Keeling, Caernarfon

DG Kendall, Cambridge

Alex & Sandra King, Dunlop

Dr & Mrs C Lamont, Edinburgh

Eila S Lauder, Kilmarnock

Mary Law, Stewarton

ME Livingston

EO Lundholm, Edinburgh

Magnus Magnusson, Balmore

W Austin Mair, Cambridge

J Millar, Peebles

Robert Miller, Stewarton

DJ Milne, Stirling

Richard Mooney, Soddy Daisy Tennessee

Ian More, Edinburgh

Dr LV Morrison, Royal Greenwich Observatory

Mr & Mrs Andrew Munro, Stewarton

Dr Neil Murray, Huntly

Roddy Murray, Isle of Lewis

Leslie J Myatt, Caithness

David McCardel, Edinburgh

Eòghann MacColl, Edinburgh

James & Susan MacColl, Edinburgh

Kenneth MacColl, Oban

L MacColl, Portree

James S McDonald, Dundonald

L McFarlane, Maybole

Alexa & Suzanne McGregor, Harrow

Dr Duncan MacInnes, Newarthill

Angus R Mackenzie, Edinburgh

Dr CJ Mackinlay, Kilbarchan

Nancy Lady Maclay, Kilmacolm

CE & Dr ZM Norwell, Stewarton

Angela O'Sullivan, Edinburgh

Dr JC Orkney, Stirling

John & Anne Phillips, Kilmacolm

Roger A Powell, Wotton under Edge

Douglas John Cranton Rae, Kilmarnock

Sheena & Laurie Ramson, Pembroke Pines Florida

RCAHMS, Edinburgh

Chris Robinson, Fort William

James Roy, Stewarton

Bill Rudersdorf, Houston Texas

Clive Ruggles, Leicester

Aasmund Sandland, Tonsberg Norway

Jack G Scott, Newton Stewart

A Seed, Glasgow

Ian C Shields, Milngavie

James L Shields, Stony Stratford

Robert Shields, Edinburgh

Michael Skupin, Houston Texas

Eleanor R Small, Tarbert Argyll

Don & Ivy Smart, Taynuilt

Catherine Smith, Newport on Tay

Robert Q Smith, New Zealand

Sandy & Lorna Smith, Bishopton

Ian N Sneddon, Glasgow

Mr &Mrs RR Steedman, Cupar

Jean Stevenson, Boat of Garten

Sheila R Stewart, Troon

MA Strang, West Kilbride

Ian Sykes, Fort William

Marlyn M Thom, Dunlop

Melanie Thom, Edinburgh

Steven Thom, Edinburgh

Prof AST Thomson, Ayr

James Thomson, Dunlop

Ian Tindall, Stranraer

Anthony JM Walker, Coalville
Leicestershire

Andrew & Frances Wallace, Edinburgh

E Wallace, Bridge of Weir

AL Watt, Edinburgh

JA Whiteford, Stewarton

Bruce Wilcock, Oxford

G Williamson, Linlithgow

R Wilson, Dunlop

Stuart S Wilson, Castle Cary Somerset

J Wright, Fort William

# ACKNOWLEDGEMENTS

Many people, perhaps too numerous to mention, have helped with the preparation of this book. In no particular order, the following come most immediately to mind.

Jack Scott, Archaeologist; Ronald Morris, for help on Cup and Ring Markings; Margaret Curtis and Ronald Curtis of Callanish; Ian C Orkney of Stirling; Peter Wroth Professor of Engineering, Oxford; and for his help, advice, wise suggestions, guidance and continual encouragement, Archie Roy, Astronomer, of Glasgow University.

Ian Sneddon, Professor of Mathematics; David K Brown, Engineer; Dennis C Gilles, Professor of Computing Science, all Glasgow University; David Clement of Edinburgh and Dunlop; RA Clement of Dunlop; Peter Swinbank, History of Science, Glasgow University; Tom Foord of Glasgow University; Hamish Gorrie; Ronald Halcrow of Glasgow University; Hilda Mary Gustin; AN Black, Emeritus Professor, Southampton University; SP Hutton, Emeritus Professor, Southampton University; Alan Davis of Lancaster Grammar School; EC Krupp, Director of Griffiths Observatory, California; Michael Ovenden, Professor of Astronomy, Vancouver University; Jim Tindal and Frances, Drumore, cousin.

John Hardie and NI Bullen of the Royal Aircraft Establishment; Daniel Martin, Mathematics, of Glasgow University; Arthur Beer, Editor of *Vistas in Astronomy*; Michael Hoskin of Cambridge; ICA John Cox; Chris Jennings, Photographer; Hattie Forrest, part-time secretary, of Monkton, Prestwick; Librarians in BNC, Bodleian, and elsewhere including Mrs Cooper White, of Greenock James Watt Library.

Clive Ruggles; Aubrey Burl; Lesley Ferguson of RCAHMS Edinburgh for her invaluable help with diagrams etc; Mrs M McMillan of Inver Guest House, Dunbeath, Caithness; Peter and Helen Lund of Oxford University Engineering; John Allen of Oxford University Engineering; Colin Renfrew, Archaeologist, for suggesting BAR type of publication in parallel with Thom's books, not in tandem.

Mr Frank Donelly, Rector of Kilmarnock Academy; Mrs Osborne, Head Mistress of Carradale school; Mrs Chris Jowett, of Dunlop School; Alex King of Dunlop; Jack Todd of Dunlop; Margaret Jenkins-Thomas of Dunlop; James Thomson of Dunlop; Dr Philip Strang of Canberra, cousin; Jack Maclay, cousin; Walter Tindal, cousin, Iona; Lexy Kirkwood; Mrs Anne Wallace; Dr John Mackinley; Miss Chrissie Gordon of Dunlop; Miss Fiona Young of Kilmarnock.

RL Merritt of Cleveland Ohio; Alfred E Livingston; Stuart Wilson of Oxford University Engineering; Leslie Styler of Brasenose College; Norris McWhirter, (of Guinness Book of Records) for his Foreword; Margaret and the late Bill Strang; Mrs Louisa Mackie of Dunlop; Mr Alex Whiteford, classmate in Dunlop School; Mr Albert McAughtry of Dunlop (one-time Boy Scout); W Cormie, a student of the 1930s; Mrs Jean McKellar of Fenwick; Miss Elizabeth Stewart of Dunlop; Mrs GR McKie of Largs (Trude); Honour Tindal; Andrew Tindal, cousin; Duncan Semple of Carradale; David Rachman; Beryl Austin of Banavie; Tom Hudson of Dunlop and New Zealand;  Catherine Dickman of North Carolina (Mrs RL Merritt); Susan MacColl of Edinburgh; Jean Hunt of Shreveport, Louisiana; HAW Burl, Archaeologist; J McCusker, a student of the 1930s; Marion Campbell of Kilberry Castle and Arthur McPherson's daughter, Dr Joan McAlpine.

Sandra King for searching for two quotations; Geoffrey Dixon for researching on Arab caravans; Eoghann MacColl (great grandson) for arranging the dust cover; Jennifer Hunter for help with translating Belgian French.

A great many people helped us in the field work on which Alexander Thom's work was based and this help has mostly been acknowledged elsewhere. I was appreciative of the able work over many years of Alexander Thom's secretary, Hilda Gustin. The preparation of this book was made all the easier by her earlier efforts.

I am indebted to Emeritus Professor W Austyn Mair of Cambridge for carefully reading my draft of the section on the war years. He has greatly helped me to revise details of my father's activities at Farnborough, half a century ago.

Stuart Wilson was my father's first Oxford graduate to teach, followed by Peter Lund and others. Both of these staff members have been very helpful in supplying me with details of the department at Brasenose College during Thom's years.

My thanks to Margaret Cameron for advice which set the book on its way to publication. And last, but by no means least, I express my gratitude to my wife Marlyn for her efforts, especially in the final stages, in bringing the manuscript and proofs to a satisfactory conclusion.

Archibald S Thom

# LIST OF ILLUSTRATIONS

# ALEXANDER THOM
# CURRICULUM VITAE

26th March, 1894, Alexander Thom was born at Mains of Carradale, Argyllshire, His father was Archibald Thom, farmer and dairyman. His mother was Lily Stevenson Strang, daughter of William Strang, muslin manufacturer, Bridgton, Glasgow.

1901 His parents flitted to The Hill Farm, Dunlop, Ayrshire and from 1901-1908 he attended Dunlop Public School.

1908-1910 attended Kilmarnock Academy.

1911 He was taken on by William Strang and Sons as a junior in the family factory at Greenhead Street, Bridgton. Sat the university exam for entrance to the Royal Technical College and began attending first year day classes in Civil Engineering.

1913 Passed second year College examinations. With two other 'sandwich' course students, sailed to Canada. There he worked on the Canadian Pacific Railway, engaged on railway construction and location in Ontario for about three months.

1914 Entered the third year BSc course in Engineering at Glasgow University. He took an additional course in astronomy.

1915 Graduated BSc in Engineering at the University of Glasgow, with Special Distinction in (a) Natural Philosophy and (b) Engineering and Drawing.

1915 April, joined Sir William Arrol and Company, Bridgton. Engaged on general structural engineering design and detailing work, including design of factory and workshop buildings, gun ships, heavy mammoth cranes, caissons, bridges, setting-out work, etc.

1915-1916 Lectured for two terms in evening classes in Royal Technical College, in the subject of Mechanics.

1916 Published his first paper (on astronomy).

1917 Joined Norman Thompson Flight Company, Sussex. Engaged in the beginning as leading draughtsman; later as designer on flying boats and plant for production of same.

1917 August, married Jeanie Boyd Kirkwood, b 26/3/1897, d 24/08/1975.

1919 February, about this time he left the above company and came back to live at Dunlop.

1919 August, engaged as draughtsman by De Haviland Aircraft Company, but was soon asked to go to Gosport.

1919 September, engaged by Gosport Aircraft Company as assistant designer and chief draughtsman on general engineering work, including flying boat design, light marine engine installation, motor cycle design, etc.

1921-1939 Engaged as lecturer, later as senior lecturer, by the University Court of the University of Glasgow, taking the subjects of Civil Engineering I and II, Civil Engineering Design, Mechanics of Structures, and the Additional Subject of Aeronautics.

1926 Graduated PhD, Faculty of Engineering, University of Glasgow. Thesis: "Windchannel Experiments, with special reference to rotating cylinders."

1929 Graduated DSc, University of Glasgow, by thesis "Experimental and theoretical investigation on fluid flow in two dimensions".

1930-1935 Carnegie Teaching Fellow.

1939 August, volunteered to visit the Royal Aircraft Establishment Farnborough for a month, to learn the ropes should war come. War broke out while he was there.

1939-1945 Engaged as Scientific Officer and then as Principal Scientific Officer, at the Royal Aircraft Establishment Farnborough. Initially he worked in the small low-speed tunnels, but in August 1940 he was appointed as the man in charge of the High Speed Tunnel for his all-round engineering knowledge. His enthusiasm and drive led to the completion of the High Speed Tunnel in 1942 and later that year, the first model aircraft (that of a Spitfire) was tested in the tunnel. From then on until after the war the tunnel was in continuous use.

May 1944 He successfully applied for the Chair of Engineering Science at Oxford University. He took up his teaching and administration duties in the autumn of 1945 and was "given the keys of the cellars" in his College, Brasenose.

1945 Honorary Degree of MA, University of Oxford.

1946-1961 Occupied the Chair of Engineering Science at the University of Oxford.

1960 Honorary Degree of LLD, University of Glasgow.

1961 Emeritus Fellow, Brasenose College and Emeritus Professor of Engineering Science, Oxford University.

1976 Honorary Degree of DSc, University of Strathclyde, formerly Royal College of Science and Technology.

1961-1983 Lived in retirement at Thalassa, The Hill, Dunlop, where he wrote up his work on megaliths and enjoyed his hobbies, telescope making, woodwork and gardening. His wife Jeanie (Sis) died in 1975. By December 1983 it became too difficult for him to live alone and he moved to live at Banavie with his daughter Beryl Austin.

1985 Died peacefully in Fort William Hospital on 7th November.

# FOREWORD

Dotted over the islands of Great Britain there are not a few but many hundreds of Megalithic sites. These products of a culture dating back to 4650 BC had long remained brooding and enigmatic. The penetration of their purpose and their secrets was not even dented by scientists, however brilliant, who possessed but a single discipline.

The gloom remained impenetrable until the darkness was relieved in 1954 by a ray of light from a paper which appeared in the Journal of the British Astronomical Association (no. 64, 396-404) called *The Solar Observatories of Megalithic Man*. In 1955 the Royal Statistical Society received an illuminating follow-up paper, entitled *A statistical examination of the megalithic sites in Britain* (A118, 275-95). These shafts of light came from the Professor of Engineering at Oxford, a man who had gathered a quite extraordinary and unique combination of knowledge in archaeology, astronomy, hydrography, metrology, physics and statistics — Alexander Thom (1894-1985).

Here was a man, born in Argyll and living in Ayrshire, who was thrice blest. In addition to an intellect so wide and deep, he had physical vigour, even when an octogenarian. And he had the support of his next two gifted generations who shared his enthusiasm for exploring Scotland's western seaboard in their well-found, deep-keeled, sea-worthy yachts

In the chair of engineering science at Oxford, Professor Thom lone-handedly, in the years 1945-61, narrowed the wide gap between the reputation of his tiny school and those at Cambridge. Under his leadership and ability his department flourished to an academic staff of fifteen, with some one hundred and sixty undergraduates, one of whom, CJ Apelt, collaborated with him in the publishing of the classic work *Field Computation in Engineering and Physics* (1961).

This year also saw his publication *The Egg-Shaped Standing Stone Rings of Britain*. This was followed by *The Megalithic Unit of Length* (Journal of the Royal Statistical Society, 1962). Other papers followed until, in 1967, the Oxford University Press published his *Megalithic Sites in Britain*. The book presented an immediate challenge to those who consciously or sub-consciously find it hard to accept that nature deployed her minute ration of mathematical geniuses, even six or seven millennia before the present. Those settled in their certainty that the discovery of Pythagorean geometry was the product of a Greek philosopher, born on an Aegean island c560 BC, have difficulty with evidence that not merely $32^2 + 42^2 \sim 52^2$ but that $122^2 + 352^2 \sim 372^2$ was harnessed by these 'pre-Iron Age primitives'. Those to whom another Greek, Menaechmus of c350 BC, was the father of the ellipse were similarly incommoded. Alexander Thom's contention for their fixed unit of measurement, a Megalithic yard of 2.72 feet, carried from one end to the other of the 710 mile long islands of Great Britain, and found in Brittany, aroused much heat but precious little by way of subsequent light.

In 1967 there appeared *Megalithic Lunar Observatories* which raised archaeoastronomy to a science and Thom to the status of father of that science. If his first book strained the credence of archaeologists, the second almost ruptured it. He now invested Megalithic observers with the ability to extrapolate the turning values of lunar and solar declinations which they could not, in general, observe directly. One of the problems of his critics lay in understanding the life and death role of tides and tidal currents among mariners of thirty and forty centuries ago, in their frail, undecked vessels. Once the correlation between the tides and the moon was understood, the understanding of the movements of the moon loomed large. To make accurate predictions Megalithic man had to have an accurate calendar and Thom showed that he made use of a calendar linked to the sun. Crossing wide stretches of open water between Orkney and Shetland, crossing the North Channel between Kintyre and Ireland and negotiating the exceedingly dangerous Pentland Firth and Gulf of Corriebhrechan, were ventures which demanded a knowledge of tidal forces. Use of levers, sheerlegs, slings and ropes, made the building of stone circles feasible.

Thom with his wife and family meticulously pioneered the surveying of some three hundred megalithic sites. By any definition the life of Alexander Thom was one of great importance and fulfilment. Apart from the high standards he set, his greatest contribution was that he became the living epitome of the power of versatility in a scientific world which today appears increasingly dogged and dominated by those who possess but one discipline.

Norris McWhirter

# PREFACE

When my father was born in 1894, Queen Victoria was on the throne. The law of the land decreed that a mechanically propelled vehicle should have a man walking before it with a red flag to warn the public of its approach. Powered flight was still a dream. The Yukon Trail was known to only a few men. Edison's electric bulb was not long invented and later feats such as the man-walk on the Moon and sending probes to visit Halley's comet or explore the poles of the Sun were mere fantasy. Calculations were done longhand, by abacus, by Napier's bones, logarithmic tables or by slide rule. Wireless telegraphy was in its very infancy. In 1894 Sir William Ramsey with Lord Rayleigh discovered Argon, Gladstone departed from No 10 Downing Street, Hawaii became a Republic, Robert Louis Stevenson died, the Manchester Ship Canal was opened and Rudyard Kipling wrote *The Jungle Book*.

Shortly after Alexander Thom's death in November, 1985, I was invited by Professor John Carlson, of The University of Maryland to write a personal note for publication. John Carlson was the editor of the journal *Archaeoastronomy* devoted exclusively to reporting research in prehistoric astronomy.

About the same time Dr Clive Ruggles of Leicester University offered to edit a *festschrift*, later to be called *Records in Stone*, subtitled *Papers in Memory of Alexander Thom*. My personal note duly appeared in both publications. Lists of my father's published material were carefully compiled for these and about this time I began to think of writing a full biography. What an interesting, productive life he had lived — as engineer, aircraft designer, inventor, yachtsman, mathematician, astronomer, archaeoastronomer, telescope lens grinder — and what interesting times he had lived through!

Friends and relations encouraged me. They felt that a biography would be of general interest. Who better to write it than myself?

My father lived for nine decades and for a year and seven months into his tenth decade. I thought of his life in three sections of three decades each. I then wrote of Spring, Summer and Autumn. The summer was extended into Indian Summer, and the Autumn simply had to have Fallen Leaves.

He really had two careers, the first being in Universities and the Civil Service (with six years of very hard industrial engineering as introduction), the second being archaeoastronomical. Considerable overlapping occurred, but in the main, he began his second career in his Indian Summer.

Most of the world's population has little or no interest in history or prehistory. I myself can not remember when I began to pay attention to my own family background. Perhaps it was the very way in which my parents spoke of their past and of their families, but I seem to have donned the mantle of family historian. For five years I was the only child, and as young children often do, I called my parents Sis and Sandy. This was not encouraged by their peers. It was unfashionable in Georgian times. Soon they were Mummy and Daddy.

For many years, heirlooms, photographs, busts, amateur paintings, family bibles, family albums, toys, baubles, tools, home made harness, racing trophies, letters, school reports, etc, have come my way. After my father's death I began to make notes of thoughts relevant to the biography which came to mind at any time of day or night. It became obvious that a family tree was necessary; the collection of details for it brought more and more to mind as it grew. Anecdotes arrived unsolicited, and some of the relevant happenings in my own life and in the lives of my contemporaries are recorded, where these amplify the biography.

Often while searching through my own papers for records of some particular piece of work already done, I have been amazed to discover how much work I had previously done on other jobs, research projects, preparation of lecture material, etc. In the same way at home here, on The Hill Farm, I find evidence of the many achievements of my grandparents and my parents, and I feel nostalgic about their efforts. I would like others to share these feelings in some way. We are all more closely related to farming stock than we know.

Where does archaeology begin? With family heirlooms? With

buried artifacts? With standing stones? Where does history begin? What a wealth of interesting material has been destroyed by selfish, thoughtless, uninterested and ignorant men. For example take the destruction of the broken fragments of Pilcher's glider, seen once in a cupboard by my father in the University of Glasgow. He was lecturing in Aeronautics, and went later to look for it. But a janitor or cleaner had thrown it out for firewood! He himself had built a glider when he was in his teens. I still have a length of bamboo pole, part of the framework, seen in a photograph taken in the Home Park, near the site of his windmill.

At an international symposium on Archaeoastronomy held in 1981 at Queen's College, Oxford, a day had been arranged for visiting Avebury, Stonehenge and Silbury Hill. I well remember standing enthralled listening with the others to Professor Richard JC Atkinson's description of the discoveries made during the excavation of the sloping tunnel leading right into the very centre of the base of the mound. A feeling of belonging came over me, because, as an inhabitant of Britain, I realised that my forbears had built this mound, that their descendants were out there within walking distance of the site; out there at our feet in very Wiltshire itself; out there all over the British Isles. In spite of the many invasions of wave upon wave of conquering tribesmen, the genes of the builders of Silbury Hill were locally extant. Invading conquering men would have wiped out the local males, but many females would have been spared and these women would have had much more to do with the bringing up of the following generation of children than the strong men who had won them in combat. The minds of the next generation, who were perforce half native to begin with, were imbued with the traditions and the habits of the mothers. Incoming conquering males, whether they liked it or not, had children who grew up having, culturally and nationally, less than half of their fathers' culture, although they had half of their genes.

The phrase "Songs I learned at Mother's knee" aptly describes the process. No invader could therefore bring and completely perpetuate his own culture.

More parochially, I feel that I belong to the West of Scotland, to Ayrshire, Renfrewshire and Dumbartonshire, as did my parents. Our recorded family tree has roots which go back here for four hundred years.

Lady Mollie Butler, in her Memoir *August and Rab*, quoted Rab who said, "talking at length about the ordinary details of life" is the "stigma of many biographers". She disagreed — "to another generation the ordinary details can become fascinating revelations".

I can only but make a biographical sketch of the life of a young Victorian who lived on for nine decades after Victoriana.

Inevitably there came a time when the author had to find a name for this memoir or biography. It happened that in December 1924 a kind and thoughtful person, (unknown to us,) sent us at Thalassa, AA Milne's delightfully illustrated book, *When we were very Young*. The donor was anonymous and no thanks could be returned.

Since then the book has been enjoyed by four generations of Thoms and their young friends. In view of the long, richly varied and interesting life led by Alexander Thom, a life rooted in specialisms but crossing over and between them, it seems appropriate here to quote the first half of one of the poems and explain the title of this biography.

> *Whenever I walk in a London Street,*
> *I'm ever so careful to watch my feet;*
> *And I keep on the squares,*
> *And the masses of bears,*
> *Who wait at the corners all ready to eat*
> *The sillies who tread on the lines of the street,*
> *Go back to their lairs,*
> *And I say to them, "Bears,*
> *Just look how I'm walking in all of the squares!"*
>
> Lines and Squares, AA Milne, 1924

Archie Thom
The Hill
Dunlop
June 1995

# Introduction

How did the mind and brain of this man Alexander Thom actually work? What kind of man was he, this man who carved out two careers? What was his philosophy? How did he think and work? The reader must judge for himself from this biography.

WR McGlone and PM Leonard, in their book *Ancient Celtic America*, page 229 wrote —

> However difficult it is to discover, recover, and analyse the material culture and the biological remains of past humans, it is yet more difficult to discover and formally state the mental culture of these people. Yet it is this mental culture that archaeologists wish to know.

McGlone and Leonard discuss speculation. "To many, it is an evil that should be avoided at all costs, while to others it is a way of life. Scientists often shun speculation for they fear they will be branded as non-scientific if they do not, while inventors and other highly creative people make possible improvements in our daily lives by unshackling themselves from thinking only in terms of the proven and known."

McGlone and Leonard believe that speculation is healthy and essential. Although when conclusions are drawn, these should follow the orderly development of proof, speculation is a way to pose new ideas.

Alexander Thom went beyond speculation. He was sure that prehistoric men had brains as good as modern men. He put himself in their position and thought out how they would approach their problems. He made strictly accurate surveys of standing stones and applied strict statistics to his analyses. He insisted in using his own objectively obtained data to substantiate his scientific speculation about the mental culture of neolithic people. As a mathematician, an engineering surveyor, and an observational astronomer, he was a leader. He was intellectually honest and had great concern for accuracy.

Standing stones intrigued Thom. Near Stromness on Orkney the Ordnance Survey map shows 'standing stone' in the middle of a field on the lands of Hall of Clestrain. An eight feet long menhir was found at the edge of the field leaning at an angle against the dry-stone dyke. The menhir had been on the point of toppling and so the farmer, with the safety of his cattle in mind, moved it away. He had ignored the biblical instruction —

"Remove not the ancient landmarks, which thy fathers have set." Proverbs: 22:28

The 'ancient landmarks' caught Thom's imagination. He surveyed stone rings, single stones, alignments, ancillary mounds and ditches, and always included indicated profiles of horizons where necessary.

Gradually he began to realise that many circles were D-shaped, egg-shaped, etc. He analysed the diameters and ended up with the megalithic yard. The flattened circles in some cases were built on radii from the corners of Pythagorean triangles.

He thought deeply, formulated his hypotheses and published his results. He would not publish his findings, however, until he had satisfied himself. People began to sit up and take notice. His publications were likened to delayed action bombs.

The only way that we know how a man thought, say five hundred years ago, is for us to read what he wrote. Prehistoric people left no writing as such, but they did leave standing stones. Alexander Thom maintained that the relative positions of stones had 'messages.' He spent half a century deciphering these messages. He became convinced that the inhabitants of north west Europe in prehistoric times were numerate, used a metrication system with a standard unit of length, (megalithic rods, megalithic yards and megalithic inches), had a 16-month solar calendar, recorded lunar, solar and stellar risings and settings on the horizon and could have predicted eclipses. Thom maintained that the evidence was there in the relative positions of the stones.

Thom showed that prehistoric people possessed this quality of mental culture.

He wrote out the following after he became Emeritus Professor of Engineering in 1961 and before his Hon DSc from the University of Strathclyde in 1976. It was probably the introductory material for one of his early papers and shows how convinced he was that he was right. Thom wrote —

A statistical analysis of the sites shows that they were so carefully erected that we can from them deduce

(1) the obliquity of the ecliptic

(2) the inclination of the lunar orbit

(3) the mean amplitude of the lunar perturbation, and

(4) the mean lunar parallax

with an accuracy better than one arc minute.

I have shown elsewhere that Megalithic Man had a highly developed knowledge of geometry. It now appears that his knowledge of how to apply it put him intellectually in line with the greatest civilisations of antiquity. This is a statement which will shortly be fully substantiated.

An open air man, Sandy loathed the descriptions of the underground cave explorations described in *Aku Aku*, Thor Heyerdal's book on Easter Island. He experienced claustrophobic reactions while reading the book.

He attempted to 'grow old gracefully.' When he was beginning to slow down, he maintained that "middle aged people do not realise that the mechanics of living take more and more energy as we grow older!"

When he was worried he would retire into his shell and "relax" by using his brain. For example the day his wife Jeanie died in August, 1975 he was sitting at his table in his Study Cabin. At a younger age he would have been found "doing something".

Margaret (my wife) and I had been at the inquest, in Woodstock, on the tragic death of my brother Alan. I was always collecting tree seedlings and before we came north, Sandy was giving me some small saplings to take back to The Hill from the garden at Sunview, Chestnut Grove, Fleet Hants. He said something which I never forgot.

"Perhaps a grandfather in the future will make wooden brick toys for his grandchildren from some of these trees when they mature."

About that time he was beginning to make a huge set of one-inch cube blocks and matching bricks. My late brother Alan also had a hobby of wood carving and wood turning.

I often wanted to call him a "thrawn old beggar" to his face, but can not remember ever doing so. He had an excellent pawky sense of humour.

Like Robert Burns, Sandy had a charm for most females. If they did not exactly fall for him, they liked him.

The night I came home from Edinburgh on the day my son Alasdair died, Sandy sympathised with me, saying, "I am sorry for you: I know exactly how you feel. I lost my son too."

My sister Beryl maintained that our father's independent nature was such that he could not be taught how to do a thing — he had to find out how to do it himself.

In the biography I use all of the following names for my father — Alexander, Alex, Alec, AT, Feyther, Sandy, Thom, The Professor, The Skipper, Skipper.

The following initials are frequently used —
ARTC: Associate of the Royal Technical College
AT: Alexander Thom
BAA: British Astronomical Association
BNC: Brasenose College
EM: Euan MacKie
GD: Glyn Daniel
HST: High Speed Tunnel
HTV: Bristol Television
JBT: Jeanie Boyd Thom
JHA: Journal for the History of Astronomy.
MLO: Megalithic Lunar Observatories
MM: Magnus Magnusson
MSB: Megalithic Sites in Britain
MRBB: Megalithic Remains in Britain and Brittany
MR: Megalithic Rings
OUP: Oxford University Press

RAE: Royal Aircrat Establishment
RIS: Records in Stone
RJCA: Richard JC Atkinson
RTC: Royal Technical College
SRSS: Stone Rows and Standing Stones, publication
U of S: University of Strathclyde
U of G: University of Glasgow
VISTAS: Vistas in Astronomy, publication.

Much of the value of Thom's work in archaeoastronomy arises from the rigorous scientific and mathematical standards he set in his observations of neolithic man. While wishing to keep his life and his work of interest to a general reader without a mathematical background, the maths is important and should not be compromised. Technical and other more esoteric detail is amplified in the Notes.

For the same reason, extended quotations have been made from the transcript of Thom's interview by Magnus Magnusson for the BBC *Chronicle* programme. And features from the *Glasgow Herald* and the *Scottish Sunday Express* have been included as appendices. Although it is not a regular feature of the biographer's, art, the scientist in the writer makes me want to include the evidence of several notes of appreciation and obituary notices. The facts enable the reader to deduce the truth. All of these appraisals might enable more readers to undertake, like Alexander Thom, a walk in all of the squares.

# PART I
## SPRING
## First Three Decades
## 1894 – 1923

'A poor thing but mine own'
Alexander Thom

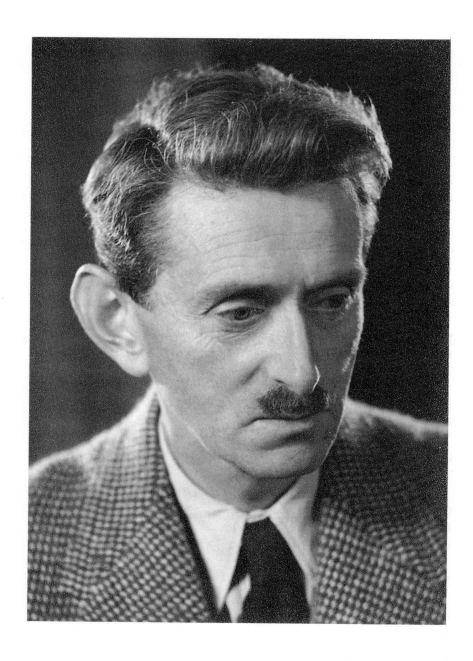

*Professor Alexander Thom, at Oxford in 1960, aged 66*

The young Alexander Thom had opportunity aplenty to use his ingenuity in his youth. In a sense he was like the young boy in the legendary story about the early days of steam engines used to pump water from mines. A boy was employed to open and close the valves required. Although an easy task, it took concentration. One particular boy wanted to play marbles. In a flash of inspiration he saw how he could make the engine work by itself and he could still play marbles. With a piece of string he successfully linked up two moving parts — the engine then worked by itself. A budding engineer, the boy was simply attempting to make life more easy for himself.

Sandy's upbringing on the farm undoubtedly developed his practical abilities. His father Archie's energetic example was always there. When a thing was needed and it was expensive to buy, Archie Thom made it or improvised!

Later in life Sandy maintained that if a man was going to develop new ideas they would come to him before the age of twenty. As an example he quoted the life of Isaac Newton.

I have been told that his reply to the question, "Did your parents help you with your studies or encourage you?" was simply, "No". The inference is that he liked learning.

Alexander Thom was born on 26th March, 1894 at Mains of Carradale in Kintyre, the farm rented by his father Archibald Thom. His mother was Lily Strang. His brother William Albert Strang Thom was born at Carradale on 22nd April,1900.

His grandparents had come to Carradale from the farm at Finnock Bog, Inverkip around 1870.

In making up Alexander Thom's family tree[1] I have been very conscious that farming was a most important occupation of all of our ancestors from the late sixteenth century on my mother Jeanie's side and from the early nineteenth century traceable on Sandy's side.

Alexander Thom of Finnock Bog Farm, Inverkip, flitted with his family of six to Carradale about 1876. I have a beautiful davenport with engraved silver plate "Presented to Archibald Thom by his well wishers in Carradale, 30th December, 1884." By this time the Thoms had been in Carradale long enough for Archibald to have gained the respect of Carradale folk.

Alexander Thom's father, Archibald had not been encouraged by his parents to go to school in Inverkip. Sandy actually used the words 'punished for going to school' while describing his father's education. Completely free state education was not available at that time. Pupils had to pay daily or weekly fees at schools, and I wonder how a farmer's son could do this without his parents paying his fees, unless he was old enough to be able to pay for himself. Perhaps a church school was involved. Perhaps he went to school after he had grown up sufficiently to be able to work on the farm and and earn the fees. This might have caused friction.

Whatever happened he could write well and keep account books. The population of the Inverkip parish in 1851 was 3,018. There was a public library. He had a well worn volume on farriery which I presented to Alyce Turnbull my American cousin, a girl who doted on horses. Later my father Alexander was to develop an engrossing interest in study. He loved to explore and extend the frontiers of the continents of knowledge. Did he perhaps inherit this from his father Archibald? According to Alexander he himself got little or no encouragement from his parents to proceed to secondary and tertiary education. My father always maintained that had his father Archibald been educated he would have been an engineer.

At Carradale the Thoms ran a successful dairy farm, retailing the milk daily. I have the till, a shallow hardwood bowl, used in the milk house at Carradale Mains, and a painting by Maggie Tindal, of Mary Thom her sister's sister-in-law, making butter there in a vertical churn, called a plump churn by folk in Banff. They sold cattle. In 1891 Archie was looking over a farm in Ayrshire with a view to renting it and saw two of their own Carradale cows there. They also bred horses.

My grandfather Archie had developed a special potato, registered as 'Carradale Thom'; like the McKelvie varieties developed by the Arran family into which cousin Isobel Dow married. Archie had considered going on the Gold Rush to the Klondyke. In 1898 there had been tension for ten years between the Thom tenants and Mackenzie, the Carradale laird who wanted the Carradale Mains Farm for his own use. The Thoms finally left Carradale in 1901 for Dunlop.

A branding iron for marking the horns of sheep with a T came from Carradale to The Hill. The Mains sheep were also marked with blue keel. Clippers for sheep shearing are extant, along with a specially shaped stool upon which sheep were shorn.

In 1984 at Banavie some eighty three years after the flitting to Dunlop took place, Alexander Thom reflected on his origins. His words are worth quoting.

> My grandfather William Strang 'took the Manse in Carradale for the summer' and that is how my mother came to meet my father. She first saw him on the roof of a shed he was building and from that minute his fate was sealed.
>
> I was born in The Mains Farm, Carradale. This was the home farm of the estate and when a new landlord (Austin Mackenzie) bought the place, he thought he would work the home farm himself. He hadn't a clue but we had notice to go about the turn of the century.

Archibald had received a letter from the Sheriff Officer for Argyll on 19th May 1893. Alexander, his father, had died on 19/11/89 and a solicitor's letter came addressed to Alexander in April, 1899. The arable lands were required at the term of Martinmas 1900, the house by the term of Whitsunday, 1901.

> I remember being taken (it would be 1897) by my father to see a bonfire. It was the sixtieth anniversary of Queen Victoria's Coronation, her Diamond Jubilee. A few years later the pulpit of the U F Church was draped in black for her death. (It was early in 1901, when Sandy would be in his seventh year.)
>
> I remember my mother telling me she had been talking with one of the boys in the village and she said to him, "But who is your mother?" and his reply was, "She's fine!" The question was repeated again and the same answer was forthcomcoming. (Who, Hoo and How had the boy and Mrs Thom in a verbal misunderstanding. The boy's parents in all probability spoke the Gaelic.)
>
> I remember the coal boat, a sailing vessel, deliberately

beaching on the sand in the bay. The farmers then rolled up with carts and bought all their coal at low water.

I remember going out through Shinaval (or Shinavar, as Duncan Semple calls it) and walking from the wood to Ballymeanach (the middle field).

I remember two boys falling into the tar boiler near the pier and being badly burnt before they were pulled out.

The minister was Mr GS McLeod. He lived with his sister, and my mother had to turn the heels for her when when she knitted socks (stockings).

Another minister called Mr Levac lived up the glen at weekends and when he came down to get the steamer to Glasgow he was always late. I remember the fishermen holding the gangway out from the end of the pier as the *Davaar* was leaving and he used to run along the gangway and jump.

All the fishermen spoke Gaelic. They used to congregate on the bridge at The Mains and blether in Gaelic.

One day a passing ship carrying crates of oranges was wrecked at Portree, south of the pier. Oranges had not been seen in Carradale before and the people there found the taste horribly bitter and fed them to the cattle.

I remember my father built a water wheel to assist the threshing and he also used it to drive his turning lathe. The mill dam was up in the wood and I remember being impressed by seeing my father carrying a pail of sawdust which he sprinkled on the water. As the level rose this sealed all the little leaks in the weir.

My grandfather Alexander Thom was poorly for many years before he died and he passed the time by knitting stockings. He knitted so many pairs that they stopped bringing him the wool, but he had enough knitted to keep my father all his life in stockings. They were great things and ran right up the thigh.

I do not think I was in Carradale again until I took a short vacation there during the war in 1916. I was very lucky to get a night out with the fishing boats. When a boat had caught a netful a flare was lit to attract the herring screw (which vessel took the fish to the railhead). I was given a sweep with which to beat the water as the fishermen hauled the net till they came to the 'bag'. The net was floated on corks and the two ends hauled together at the bottom. The result was a bag of fish. My splashing was to frighten the fish into the bag.

When my father flitted from Carradale to Dunlop he took his goods in a cart and a one-horse wagon. Tom MacKinnon accompanied him. They took the steamer to the Broomielaw and off-loaded there. They then proceeded to walk the horses from Glasgow to Dunlop. Meanwhile my mother and I were in Glasgow staying with her parents.

Sandy did not pick up any Gaelic in Carradale. I do not know if the school children spoke Gaelic but their parents did. The Thoms had no Gaelic. Although the Thoms, being farmers, did not keep a boat, they heard all of the village traditional fishing legends; and one which was passed down to me was about the total loss of a whole fishing fleet in the Sound of Islay. Boats were wrecked; all the men were lost. They were caught in a storm and there were no harbours of refuge in the Sound of Islay. That day many Carradale men were drowned.

One yarn spun about locals caught trespassing through the laird's land told that if the trespasser saw the keeper first he instantly turned round and proceeded in the opposite direction. As the keeper could only challenge the intruder and ask him to go back the way he had come, the interloper had only to turn round again and proceed in the direction in which he originally wanted to go.

Ships and shipping in the Firth of Clyde were the life and blood of the population and were always topics of conversation. Vessels of all types were built in places as far apart as Stranraer and Campbeltown, Maybole, Tarbert, Fairlie, Bute, Dumbarton, Greenock and Glasgow. Local newspapers printed shipping information and much heavy cargo was carried by coastal vessels. Each village had its harbour, large or small, and many villages, like Carradale, had a pier. Upkeep was financed by pier dues paid by each passenger on landing or boarding. Where no piers existed, local ferrymen rowed out to meet the competing passenger steamers. Carradale was on the Glasgow, Gourock, Lochranza, Campbeltown run. The company was called the Campbeltown and Glasgow Steam Packet Joint Stock Company. All their vessels had been paddle driven until 1869, when the *Kintyre* started the vogue of screw propulsion and yacht-like hull design, even down to the bowsprit. *Kinloch* followed the same pattern ten years later and the *Davaar* carried on the tradition which was to end with her demise. *Davaar* possessed only moderate speed but made up for this deficiency by her seaworthiness which was a necessity for her all-the-year-round duties. The Kilbrennan Sound could be a dirty stretch of water in the winter months.

With *Kintyre* and *Kinloch* using the Glasgow terminal, *Davaar* maintained a daily service to Campbeltown from Greenock, with calls at Gourock, Lochranza, Pirnmill, Carradale and Saddell until 1907 when *Kintyre* was lost off Skelmorlie. *Davaar* then went up river to join *Kinloch*. The partnership of the three graceful sisterships had ended. The Thoms would know them all. Campbeltown was the nearest market town to Carradale but Gourock was the nearest big town for the whole of Kintyre. Many landsmen feared sea voyages. Even in summer storms the seas at Ardlamont, Garroch Heads and in Kilbrennan Sound can be very rough, but travel to Kintyre by land was out of the question. It was so much quicker by sea.

Inverkip had been well served by steam vessels. As early as 1836/7, five vessels ran services daily, or three days a week, to Largs, Millport, Ardrossan, Troon, Ayr, Gourock, Greenock, Port-Glasgow and Glasgow. The Thoms, living on the Clyde estuary would know much about shipping, from the local newspapers and by word of mouth. Legends would be passed on. Maggie Thom who retired with her elder sister Mary to live at Wemyss Bay in 1901 had a good knowledge of river shipping and whenever a new ship did her trials on the measured mile at Wemyss Bay, everybody was watching. Tradition has it that if someone bumps a glass on a table with an article of cutlery and it rings out, it must be touched instantly to stop it ringing, "to save a sailor's life at sea".

Sandy loved Kintyre, and especially Carradale. He did not visit it often. Near the end of a cruise in 1934 he anchored at Carradale, having rounded the Mull of Kintyre en route home from the Hebrides. A drought had closed the Crinan Canal. He went ashore with son Archie to visit Mrs Oman, an elderly lady whom he had known a generation before. (Mrs Oman was to live long enough to have seen five generations of the Thom family). His next visits to the area would be with RL Merritt in 1969. This time he was hunting standing stones at Brackley. The farms Brackley and Rhonadale had been rented to his forbears nearly a century before.

Later, in 1968 or 1969 he was to take his grand-daughter Marian Josephine Austin to Carradale House, where Lady Naomi Mitchison (née Haldane, b1/11/1897,) entertained them both to dinner. She was still running the Home Farm, Carradale Mains, just as the previous owner MacKenzie had done, but she seriously asked Sandy, "How did the Thoms make it pay?"

Sandy's mother, Lily, was the third child, the oldest daughter of the family of eleven of William Strang and Lilias Symington, who lived in Craignairn, a house named after William's maternal grandparents, a Mr Craig married to a Miss Nairn. Their daughter Marian married James Strang and their son was William Strang, Sandy's grandfather. Sandy was among the first grandchildren.

William Strang began manufacturing muslin in the specially built factory in Greenhead Street, Glasgow Green, in 1876. Family legend has it that in his youth when he came to the city from Eaglesham he was, to say the least of it, impecunious. The family had been muslin manufacturers since the beginning of the eighteenth century. The new factory was a success. Later, five of his sons were to be deeply involved in the company, William Strang and Son; William, James, Robert Winning, John Nairn and Sam Fulton. Sandy said that his grandfather had once tried to extract ammonia gas from the urine in the factory urinals. The men, however, objected and the scheme fell through. The factory was demolished about 1960.

Nineteenth century rail and steamer services enabled well-off people to rent a house at the coast for summer weeks or months and frequently to commute daily or at week ends to the city. William Strang and his family were no exception. In 1890 they rented part of the Free Church Manse at Carradale and this is undoubtedly how Lily Strang met Archie Thom, farmer at Carradale Mains. During, say a three months' holiday, the vacationers joined in all the local activities. They had, of course, their own hobbies and ploys. At Whiting Bay, for instance, where there was no pier, the steamer would disembark its passengers (only in good weather) into the waiting ferry boat(s), along with luggage including hampers full of linen, cutlery, etc, and on occasion, a piano. The locals knew before the ferry-boat was rowed ashore, that the Strangs for instance had arrived because they had seen the piano! Aunt Marian's piano practice was to proceed uninterrupted during the summer!

It is pleasing to think that Alexander's parents met while singing in the church choir at Carradale. They met, however, and the Glasgow industrialist's daughter married the Carradale Mains dairy farmer in 1892. Alexander was born in 1894, and William Albert Strang in 1901.

Archie hired labour locally. The farm was big enough for him to own a four-horse automatic binder for harvesting the oats crop. He was an impatient, impulsive hard-working husbandman. My father related that as a boy of perhaps five or six, one fine harvest morning Archie had sent out a man to 'open' the corn field by scythe so that the horse-drawn binder could be used efficiently. On that dewy morning there was no particular hurry. The dairy round had to be finished before the horses were yoked to the binder and driven the half mile to the corn field. With his son, Archie found the field incorrectly 'opened'; a big row ensued and Archie drove the binder outfit over the unopened oats in the correct pattern thereby damaging some considerable amount of the standing crop. But what else could he have done? The child Sandy was sensitive to 'atmosphere' and remembered the incident long enough to tell his son about it many years later. Being his father's son, he would realise the implications — pressure on the husbandman in good weather at hearst, waste of the initial time spent on the scything, waste of valuable grain, and difficult untidy swaths (seen by his neighbours) to be tidied up at the end or left with the stubble for grazing as foggage later.

Sandy did not attend Carradale Primary School. No record of his having been at Carradale and Saddel School can be found. Mrs Marion Osborne, the headmistress in 1988 sent the author relevant school papers. Evidently his mother taught him at home at Carradale Mains. He was able to write by December,1900, because I have a letter from his grandfather dated 20th December, 1990, written in reply to one of Sandy's.

William Strang wrote from Viewpark, West Kilbride, to his grandson at Carradale —


My Dear Alexander,
    I got your letter telling me that you got safely home. I was afraid that you would have a great storm when you were going home. Grandmother and I were often looking towards the Garroch Head, and we thought that we saw the waves breaking against the shore, but we were both glad when we got your mother's letter telling us that it had not

been stormy. What are you busy with now. Write me another letter telling me all. I like to hear what my little grandson is doing. Tell me when you are going to school and all about baby William and his little tricks.

I am sending you a book for the New Year which I hope you will like. Mother and Father will read the story in the evenings when the lamp is lighted.

I am
Your loving Grandfather
Wm Strang

Baby William (Wastle) was born on 22nd April 1900.

The twelve months before the flitting to Dunlop must have been fraught with worry and indecision. The laird, Mr Mackenzie, of Carradale House, wanted Carradale Mains for a home farm for himself and was pushing Archie out. Archie was unsettled and spent much time looking for another farm.

A century ago most families had close connections with the farming community. Mrs William Strang (née Lilias Symington) was a grandaughter of Laird Robert Stevenson of Townhead of Shutterflat.

(The term 'Laird' implies that Robert was not a tenant farmer; as a 'Bonnet Laird' he farmed his own land; he would presumably at that time pay only feu duty to a superior. Bonnet Laird is now archaic, but I do remember fifty years ago cousin Margaret Strang addressing Sandy as 'Laird' when she saw him attired in kilt and the fashionable head gear, a Balmoral).

Two brothers Symington had each married Stevenson girls, and another brother William Symington had married a Jean Brown of The Hill, Dunlop, in 1848. Also Elizabeth Stevenson, widow of James Cunningham, a daughter of Robert Stevenson, had married, in 1844, widower Andrew Brown of The Hill.

Thus the Strangs had many country connections and contacts and so would hear at the turn of the century that Jack Brown of The Hill was selling up and going to Ontario. It was not therefore entirely chance that made William Strang buy The Hill for Lily and Archie Thom in 1901. They had two sons by this time and Archie's qualities were evident; and so The Hill was bought. Archie was no longer a tenant farmer. He could apply his energies, his ingenuity and zeal to improving the place to the best of his ability. There was plenty to do.

His father Archie had a busy summer before him. There had not been much farming maintenance done for some years and the steadings had to be prepared for use. John (Johnnie) Brown of Hill, (b7/10/1835, d27/4/1885) had spent an amount of money on The Hill in the middle of the nineteenth century. He had been a business man in London. Yet Hill had been described by George Robertson in 1820 as 'the best seat of the small proprietors in the parish.'

The farm yard, bounded by the three-storied dwelling house on the east, by the stable, calf house and bothy on the south, and the byre on the north side, had been enclosed on the west side in 1817 by a breast high wall with a pair of beautiful wrought iron gates. Against the wall were two loupin' stanes, platforms for ease in mounting a horse. The gates are at the top of the 1,050 feet long straight avenue leading from the main road through a fine pair of wrought iron gates five feet high hung on heavy sandstone masonry pillars.

Above the calf-house was the dovecote, with three entrance holes tastefully sheltered by a stone-apexed projecting roof. (In earlier days fresh meat was scarce at certain times of the year. A pigeon was always welcome. Often the cattle had such poor winter feeding that the weak ones had to be carried out to spring grass). Drinking water was pumped from a deep well in the north east corner of the yard. The midden occupied the area to the west of the byre, and the house privy was on the north west outside corner of the byre — a warm walk down the byre but cold and draughty privacy in the outhouse at the end. Two small pig-houses lay immediately to the north of the byre. To the east of the byre and north of the dwelling house was the two-storied part of the house, integral now with the main house and byre and with its own stairway to two bedrooms.

This is the oldest part of the whole steading, dating from 1692 and probably much earlier. Three of the windows have iron bars to this day. Here are the remains of the cheese presses made and used after Barbara Gilmour brought the recipe from Ireland for what was to be called Dunlop cheese, a cheese made from full cream milk, not skimmed milk. Her initials are on a lintel in the wall on the byre side of the gable, over what appears to have been initially a window. Until recently the hemispherical customary cast iron boiler was in situ with its chimney. Clothing would be boiled here, and food cooked for livestock.

All of the present steading shows evidence of various additions,

*The Farmhouse at The Hill, Dunlop*
*the drawing by Alexander Thom's grand-daughter, Susan MacColl shows*
*part of the old cottage and the entrance to the byre; the lintel stone is*
*marked AB JA 1748*

alterations, etc. Beside the main kitchen fireplace, in the warm part of the wall, were two dry cupboards, one used as the salt cellar at elbow level. The stackyard, with surface drains for water shed from the big 'sow' filled the area to the east and north of the dwelling house. In 1803 the present large barn was built on the south side of the stackyard, its gable being only five feet from the east side of the dwelling house. The barn has half a dozen three inch wide vertical ventilators in the form of embrasures suitable for defence by small firearms. It has an arched doorway to allow a gig or buggy to be housed under a timber-beamed ceiling/floor above. A solid eight feet high random rubble wall divided it from the barn proper.

Market prices for corn would be high at this time. A square area of fireclay tiling indicates where winnowing took place on a platform supported on beams between the door lintels. Winnowing would be done with both doors open, preferably when the wind was from the south. Tension ties of wood were craftily dovetailed into the sloping rafters of the barn in anticipation of iron nails rusting away. A cart shed was added later at the east end of the barn.

Four plantations of elm, ash, beech, alder, lime and sycamore were tastefully planted around the steading, providing nowadays good wind breaks but perhaps too much shade about the dwelling house. A garden of some one third of an acre lay to the north of the steading. Here a ten feet high random masonry wall with two twelve feet long wings sheds the flow of cool frosty air which on occasion can flow down the field from the north.

Sandy remembered the customary gravel paths, edged with low trimmed box-wood hedges. Perfect havens for slugs, he said. His father did away with almost all of the box-wood and laid narrow concrete paths suitable for wheelbarrow use. One of the sandstone pillars for the wrought iron gate was decorated with a small sundial.

This was the farm Archie had to work for the remaining twenty five years of his life. Here his two sons were to grow up, develop and mature with plenty of scope for work and play. Sandy said that he had helped to harvest crops on all of the fields at one time or another, either building corn stooks or forking hay into 'coils', the small temporary stacks made in poor weather. A bottomed road led from the steading to nine of the ten fields. Each field was named.

Rubbing stones existed in six of the fields. The Meadow, a five acre lot allocated to The Hill in bygone days during a drainage scheme

52

*The Cheese Press 1760*
*also from a drawing by Susan MacColl, this cheese press at Dunlop solved*
*the problem of disposing of large quantities of milk. After the railway*
*opened in 1871, the milk could be sold to Glasgow. But Dunlop cheese is*
*still famous today*

in that area, lay on the west side of the railway, at about 415 feet above sea level, while the summit of the land at the northeast corner of the Pump Park, the small plantation near to the site of the (now non-existent) lime kiln on Sidehead Farm, was at 522 feet. Ten fields totalling in all ninety acres, made up the arable acreage while the area of the access road, garden, stackyard, bull-pen, woods, etc, amounted to about five acres. Most of the fields were ridged (rigged), pitched at eighteen feet. Practically all of the riggs had rubble ('rummle') drains, part of the perpetual fight in areas of boulder clay to keep the heavy soil in good tilth.

The fields in the area had frequently to receive lime. Often tenants on other farms had to undertake to apply lime at intervals. In dry weather, water shortage was serious. The run-off stopped — the farm was, after all, called The Hill — and with no high ground behind, there were no streams running through the property. Practically no surface water flowed on to the property from neighbours' land. A dam near to the steading, called the Horse Pond, would be used for watering cattle and horses in droughts. It was also used in dry weather to soak gizzened cart wheels and always to wash the muddy feet of the horses and the cart wheels at the end of the day's work.

The Hill Farm is roughly triangular. At the southern apex were the remains of The Toll House, where there had been a Check Bar. The ruined cottage was owned by the proprietors of The Hill, who had bought it in 1880. Mrs Hugh Storrie, of Pointhouse had spoken to James Thomson about the life of a man who had lived in the Toll House. A mining engineer, involved in a serious pit accident, he had broken down and in his deranged state of mind, had murdered his wife. Convicted of manslaughter he had served his sentence in gaol.

James Thomson, who lived at Pointhouse at one time, found the Toll Board showing all prices payable by users of the highroad. Around 1932 he presented it to Sandy, who photographed it carefully and later donated it to Edinburgh Museum.

When Archie arrived in May 1901, he found that no hedge trimming had been done for years. In Sandy's words, "they were simply rows of little trees". He had more than four miles of fencing and hedging to maintain. He had read about the English method of layering sapling hawthorn hedges and so he made a special long-levered hooked tool with which, after notching overgrown bushes by saw, he could bend each one over in turn and thus fill the gaps.

He was partially successful. Hedge cutting was a continuous task. Of course when a hedge is allowed to grow too high it does stop wind and give more shelter to grazing stock. The hedges were again neglected during the 1914–1918 war and much tidying up had to be done in the late 1920s. Allan Kirkwood, my mother's father used to help a little in the summer by cutting weeds (thistles and bunweed or ragwort). Rather than carry his scythe all the way home he used to hang it in the centre of a huge hedge.

Archie had brought sacks full of early yellow, scented double daffodils and snowdrops from Carradale, and promptly planted them on both sides of the avenue. I reckon there are now on The Hill about 500,000 of the narcissus family of flowering bulbs. At that time there were no avenue hedges and Archie planted hedges on each side, alternating thorns, privet and beech. The gates at the end of the avenue had to be kept shut at all times. Used as a meeting place by village children they called the spot 'Tam o' The Hill's'. Reaching the gates after the walk from the railway station would be like arriving at The Hill for Mary and Maggie, Archie's sisters, when they visited from their home at Forbes Place in Wemyss Bay. They knitted underwear for Archie but left the parcels at the gates because they did not want Lily to know they were helping him in this way.

The daffodils multiplied. People came to ask for bunches. People stole bunches and dug out bulbs. The young Sandy wired up an electric bell which rang in the house when the gate was opened. The illicit flower lovers were then able to be observed at the very least and pursued by bicycle on occasion.

Archie had numerous tools — for blacksmith's work, for carpentry, for shoe-making, for saddlery, for veterinary work and for farriery. He made his own harness, using palm and rozet end. There was a pair of sheep shears, a shearing stool or bench specially shaped for man and sheep, and an instrument with a choice of three blades specially designed for castrating ram lambs or bull calves, but not stallion foals.

Archie had brought his lathe from Carradale. He could turn his own hay fork shafts, using the special angled chisel required. He supped his porridge with home made spoons fashioned from cows' horns. He made his own wheelbarrows, carts and wagons, but acknowledged the craft of the wheelwrights and bought ready-made pairs of cart wheels.

Keeping the iron treads or tyres on cartwheels in all weathers was quite a task about a farm. In summer the oaken spokes and rims gizzened and the cartwheels had to be hauled through the dam to keep the oak rims and spokes always swollen tight. The horses loved that exercise. I can remember the pungent smell of the axle grease used to lubricate the axles, which on rough ground gave out a distinctive clonk-clank with each step of the horse. An old wooden axle found in the barn was donated to an Edinburgh museum. It was much thicker than a modern iron axle — the nave of the wheel would obviously have been bigger too. There were sections of a leather bush still on it, held in position by tacks. Iron axles would have been very expensive when carts became numerous and replaced sledges on the muddy North Ayrshire clay.

Archie made two larger windows in his workshop, which had been the bothy. In it he had a huge oaken workbench with two vices, and a huge stock of adzes, wood bits, augurs, drills, saws, chisels, awls, shoe-maker's last, etc. I well remember a pair of huge wooden plier-like tongs or tweezers with the inside surfaces of the jaws serrated, their purpose being to pull out dockens, thistles and bunweed or ragwort from growing oats or hay. These weeds could not be cut amongst the long crop. He had a special forked weed-digger used like a spade for digging out deep-rooted weeds; a most effective tool.

A paraffin-heated 'Glevum' incubator which could hold ninety six hopefully fertile eggs was kept in the workshop. Candling each egg in turn to see how many were fertile after a week's incubation was always an exciting operation. The infertile ones were used for baking.

For his saws he had a tooth-setting tool. His anvil is still very useful and the ratchet drill with a two feet long lever handle is still in the workshop. He was adept at buying good second-hand timber, galvanised sheeting, cast iron steam piping (for hay-shed columns), and so on.

My grandfather had a special four-pronged hay fork for his own use. A huge hay-shed and sheep-shed were soon built at the south side of the bull-pen, now the stackyard. The sheep-shed had a wall of hay built inside for warmth. Robert Watt's steam-driven threshing mill was hired after harvest time. When animals had to be fed in an out-house where no hay had been stored, the hay would be carried by hand from the hay-shed in 'buttles' or tied armfuls. The hard bottomed road along the east side of the Avenue Park was broadened for the Big Mill to come in to thresh the oats. He built himself gates using lengths of scrap angle-iron, riveting them together. An extra large gate was made for the Big Mill, a steam-driven threshing machine with huge iron wheels, hired by the day.

On the north side of the new stackyard, by the burn, Archie built a corral for dipping sheep, an operation which had to be done with the policeman present. Three extra byres for wintering kye were put up, along with two henhouses placed 'up the Old Road'. Many breeds of hen were reared, all in the effort to obtain good laying stock. Strange and faraway place names come to mind — Anconas, Rhode Island Reds, White Leghorns, Black Leghorns, Barneveldes, Wyandots, Buff Orpingtons, Sussex — all names of fashionable good laying birds.

On occasion he would fell a tree, saw it into manageable lengths and haul the logs to the Aiket Sawmill (water-wheel) for cutting into planks. Perhaps he would hire the local carter who would use the adjustable four wheeled 'monkey', as it was called, drawn by two horses in tandem. Tom King, the carter, might also have used his huge jack on the 'janker', a two-wheeler towed behind a two wheeled tug, the tree trunk suspended below the specially shaped high axle. These wagons were seen regularly on the local roads.

Archie used willow withes to make baskets which he used for his fruit, mainly blackcurrants and gooseberries. His supply of withes came from saplings growing in the verge of the public road to the east of the Mid Park. Perhaps he had planted cuttings there. They grew to a height of fifteen feet.

He was expert at making coggies, little staved wooden buckets held together by iron hoops, with one longer stave used as a handle. These were used for feeding calves with milk and meal. Luggies of larger capacity were used while milking. Like the ten gallon milk cans they had to be kept scrupulously clean. Small milk cans, cream cans, cream ladles, butter-pat moulds — these were all part of the dairy farm's paraphernalia. A beautifully turned hardwood bowl had been used for the till at Carradale. A wooden box in the form of a truncated right pyramid was used for carrying approximately a bushel of coals or logs. Called a baikie, it had two outside handles.

He wanted to keep The Hill yard clean and more like a garden and so he cut new doors opening to the south out of the stable and calf house. A new stable midden was built in the wood to the south. The stable loft was made more suitable for storing hay by the construction of an out-shot door in the sloping roof, through which the rucks of dried hay could be forked from the slipe or cart. This fragrant fodder was later to be forked down through a trap door, into the long heck, with its shiny oily triangular-sectioned wooden spars, shared by the two stalls. As a schoolboy I can remember packing the hay tightly up against the wooden roof sarking (planking) and having to take care not to bump my head on the projecting wooden slate pins. A small boy has his uses about a farm.

Hay seed and dust were all that was left by the late spring. Robert Hall, late slater, related how slaters cut wooden slate pins while unemployed in winter, for 'pin money'. They were sold later to the master slater.

The stable had what was called a loose box (louse boax) where calf or foal could be fed over a low barrier. A huge covered locker full of grain for winter feed filled the three feet wide space beside one of the stalls. Harness and collars were hung on suitable brackets or on round wooden pegs turned on the lathe in the workshop next door.

Archie later fixed a drinking trough for his horses at the stable door, supplied with fresh water continually flowing from the overflow of his new storage tank.

Archie liked to keep the place tidy, but when the hunt came down through his farm he lost his temper. Horses in a hurry can make a quagmire in a few seconds. He closed the gate at the top of the avenue, waiting until several huntsmen were held up, and then gave them his mind. The gate was opened, and he repeated the ticking off next time round!

In Carradale Archie had been a pioneer in using a large self-binding reaper drawn by four horses. It had been successful on the flat fields on Carradale Mains. He realised however that it would function only with difficulty on the deeply rigged fields at The Hill and so he did not take it with him to Dunlop at the flitting in May 1901. He used a conventional reaping machine drawn by two horses. Two men at least were needed, one to drive the horses, the other to work the tedder. When ploughing a field he always arranged the furrow on top of the rig, eventually flattening the rig.

Later at Dunlop he had a successful potato digger, the first one to be seen in Dunlop Parish. It was lent to someone about 1922 but it was never returned.

About 1906 he had a ploy for threshing his corn. Instead of using a horse-driven threshing machine he wanted to use a water-wheel. A dam was made in the small burn running down beside the Old Road — it had a catchment area of about seventeen acres. He laid a five-inch fireclay pipeline to the west side of the byre leading the water to a wheel which appears to me, in a photograph, to be about seven feet in diameter. Two things militated against its success: (a) the wheel diameter was too small and (b) the rate of flow of the burn was not high enough. Undaunted, he began again, this time with more practical experience behind him. Surely, he reasoned, he could get the equivalent of the power output of about one and a half men to drive his man-powered threshing machine! This time he succeeded by using the storage capacity of the Horse Pond; a substantial dam breast was made; a new six-inch fireclay pipe-line led to a new eleven feet diameter wheel. With thirty buckets discharging about nine or ten feet below ground into a ten-inch fireclay tile discharging down the Home Park, he obtained the power he needed. Jim Tindal remembered that he could run from the Horse Pond more quickly than the water could flow through the pipe after he had opened the sluice. I can corroborate this.

The water wheel was installed about 1908 or 1909 and ran until about 1932. I remember Archie still using it to thresh corn in 1923/24.

A chopping machine driven by a belt from a pulley on one of the line shafts was used to chop hay or turnips for fodder, or straw for bedding. I well remember the noise of this dangerous machine which could be cranked (called) by hand. I treated it with great respect, having been told how my uncle Allan Kirkwood had unfortunately lost the tips of two fingers in a similar chopper at The Grange, where my mother was born. The lack of his trigger finger on his right hand made Allan unfit for military service.

Archie had many other activities. I have a piece of linen cloth made from flax grown and spun at The Hill. Presumably it was woven in the Strang factory in Bridgeton. He grew tomatoes in a heated greenhouse built in the north-east corner of the big garden wall.

Thieves approached the greenhouse through a nearby garden gate. Wastle attempted to deter them by arranging a huge pile of tin cans to be pulled over in the dark by a string from the opening gate. History does not relate whether or not the thieving stopped.

Archie grew soft fruit for sale. One year he sold half a ton of blackcurrants which he cultivated in a four acre section of the Home Park.

Fertility of the soil had to be maintained. Archie bought 'Glasgow City manure' (Glesca dung) by the railway truck load. Carted from Dunlop station for spreading over the pasture lands for ploughing under for cropping, it was stored on the few square yards of Hill property on the west side of the railway by the curling pond, ready for use on the fields at the correct season. As it originated in the tenement ashpits of the city, every kind of small broken trinket could be found on the fields. One orraman, Charlie Hutchison, was fortunate enough to pick up, in the field, two dirty pound notes, equivalent to a week's wage.

Archie was musical. According to his cousin, Jim Tindal he used to sing at work in the fields on The Hill and at harvesting the blackcurrant crop.

He taught singing by the Sol-fa system. I have his expensively framed certificate from the Tonic Sol-Fa College issued to him on 31st July 1890. The impressed stamp states clearly on the roundel "Music for the People : easy, cheap and true, incorporated 1875." Four signatures are clearly seen, those of two local examiners, the President, and the Secretary. It states in scrolled printed writing that "Archibald Thom has passed the examination for the Advanced Certificate of the Tonic Sol-Fa College Branch I, a Certificate of attainment in Reading Music at First Sight, in Writing Harmony from Ear, in the Cultivation of the Voice, in the Elements of Musical Composition, Musical and Verbal Expression, in the Analysis of Classic Harmonies, and the use of Staff Notation."

Evidently Archie studied his music by a correspondence course, receiving forms to study, in sets of three, with exercises for each set to be submitted each fortnight. He taught singing in Carradale and also in Dunlop, at The Hill, in the workshop (or bothy), where there is still a big open fireplace. One can picture him there, an enthusiastic teacher striking his tuning fork on the huge oak workbench, winding up and setting his metronome and making the young ones sing their parts. If he taught like his son Sandy did years later, he would be a good teacher and he would be enjoying it all. Two paraffin lamps at least would have been needed, and a big log fire would have added extra brightness to the white-washed room. The tools hanging on the walls around would make a good acoustic background. Jim Tindal reported that his uncle would walk to Dunlop of a Saturday evening to buy sweets — striped balls — in Nellie Gemmill's shop. Did he dole out sweets in the bothy during singing practice?

Archie had attended church in Carradale. The Thoms felt strongly enough about their worship and had once helped to cart stones for a new church. Archie would, as a singer, be in any choir in the church, and it is almost certain that this is where he and Lily Strang would meet. Lily was an accomplished pianist.

Lily wrote in her diary that when they were courting, Archie would sing *The Village Blacksmith* at evening sing-songs. He insisted that the Scottish song about the Bonnie Bonnie Banks o' Loch Lomond should always be rendered as *On the Bonnie Bonnie Banks o' the Lomonds*. He reckoned it made better sense of the words and sentiment of the ballad.

John Dunlop of OverHill, as The Hill was called, married Barbara Gilmour in 1692, a date carved on the lintel of a window in the historical Cheese Press room in the steading.

Barbara's part in developing Dunlop Cheese is detailed in the 1851 Imperial Gazetteer of Scotland —

Dunlop Parish is separated from Beith by Lugton Water and from Stewarton by Corsehill Burn, and is bisected into nearly equal parts by the Glazert. About 30 acres are moss. Nearly all of the area of the parish is under cultivation. Dunlop has been long celebrated for its cheese. Barbara Gilmour — a woman whose wit was sharpened and whose range of observation was varied by exile to Ireland during the troubles in Scotland between the Restoration and the Revolution — settled down in Dunlop as a farmer's wife. She successfully attempted to manufacture from unskimmed milk a species of cheese unknown in Scotland and altogether different from the horny insipid produce of skimmed milk still in use among the present people of other secluded districts. Her manufacture was speedily imitated by her neighbours and in a short time came into such general demand under the name of Dunlop cheese that whether the produce of her own hand or that of her neighbours or persons in adjoining parishes, it found afar and near a ready market. Even Mr Cobbett himself has pronounced it "equal in quality to any cheese from Cheshire, Gloucestershire or Wiltshire." About 25,000 stones are now produced annually in the Parish.

It was Barbara Gilmour who first introduced into the parish the famous Dunlop cheese and by her ingenuity and perseverance rendered an inconceivable blessing to her people and country. The story is an old one and is well known in every dairy.

Previous to the revolution of 1688 the manufacture of cheese of fine quality was generally unknown in Scotland. The people were contented with a hard unsavoury stuff made from skimmed milk. During the dark and drublie days of Charles II when conscientious people suffered for their religious beliefs, (1678), Barbara was driven to Ireland to escape the persecutions and took up her abode in County Down. While there she gained a thorough knowledge of dairy procedure and especially the art of making cheese of a sweet fine nature from unskimmed cow's milk.

Returning to her native Dunlop when the commotions were at an end she became the wife of John Dunlop of Overhill, Dunlop (Hill) and turned out with complete success the famous Dunlop cheese. From the issue of John Dunlop of Overhill and Barbara the present Browns of Hill are descended. The late John Brown died in August 1883 at Hill being the great great great grandson representative of the worthy couple. Over the dairy house door at The Hill is inscribed in old characters the following initials with the date: ID BG 1692. No monument has ever been erected to her memory, not a line to the woman who rendered a greater service to the world than Alexander The Great but the old cheese press which turned out the first Dunlop cheese and which is still preserved in the dairy house at The Hill remains as her memorial. Inscribed on a gable stone at Dunlop Churchyard are the following records. 'This is the burying place of John Dunlop of Overhill and Barbara Gilmour his spouse and their children 1732.' Underneath is the other. 'Here lies the body of Andrew Brown of Overhill grandson to the above John Dunlop who died 15/3/1794 aged 72 years also Jean Anderson his spouse, who died 6/1/1801 aged 74 years.'

Growing up in this richly stimulating, stable, established but now vanished farming environment, what would the boy Alexander Thom make of formal schooling? We know that Alexander did not attend Carradale and Saddell Primary School and that his mother taught him at home.

No records are available for Dunlop School, but it seems likely that Alexander went to Dunlop Primary School in May 1901 when the family arrived from Carradale. Undoubtedly the attendance officer, nick-named 'The Whipper In' would soon be on the doorstep. Probably this was the time that Sandy was reported to have said upon arrival home after his first day at school, that he didn't need to go to school, he knew it all already. In his eighth year of age by this time, he would think nothing of the half mile walk to school in the village. The teaching was good — his first teacher was Minnie Heriot, his second, Jenny Robertson.

The headmaster was Mr Rattray, who had been promoted to Dunlop from Kingsford School in 1876. According to John Dunlop Reid, Mr Rattray ran evening classes on various subjects of interest to the village populace. The next headmaster at Dunlop School was Mr Archibald Logie Brown, a full cousin of John Logie Baird, inventor of television. Mr Brown is said to have told his school class about 1927 that his cousin was able to send pictures through the air.

Country schools exhibited a special sign depicting the torch of learning to advertise that they were branches of the County Library. Books were issued to the public and pupils frequently carried these books to their homes for their parents to read. The schoolmaster was in charge and gave out the books.

In the infant classes the pupils wrote with a slate pencil on wooden-framed slates stored in special vertical slots in their desks. Slates were cleaned using a damp cloth or sponge. Saliva was very often applied. Pencil on paper was not used until the third class. Inkwells and pens were for bigger children. Merit places were given daily in class, the top pupil sitting at the back of the room. If a child gave an exceptionally good answer at any time during the day, the teacher would say, "Good, take your books and move up one!"

Infant teacher, Jenny Robertson, arrived rain or shine in her pony and trap. She would unyoke the outfit and stable the pony for the day in her cousin Kerr's stable at the Old School House opposite the school. Most of the village-based children enjoyed watching Jenny leave each day after school, her blond hair piled high on her head. She would yoke the buggy, but the pony would not move until it had been fed a crust of bread. Think of Jenny driving over that rough hilly track on a pouring wet morning, or in deep snow and ice! She came from Balgray, a farm several miles away to the west.

Frequently many of the children at Dunlop School had no footwear and although Sandy had boots, he pled with his parents to be allowed to go barefoot to school in the warmer weather, solely because he could play and run with his barefooted class mates and not be ostracised. Obviously he was not popular wearing boots at games in the playground!

In winter the classrooms were heated by coal fires. Gas illuminated the rooms when necessary. Christmas Day was not a school holiday. Sandy learned quickly and passed the qualifying examination as it was called in these days, in June 1907. He was kept on at Dunlop for another session and, as 'a pupil over fourteen years of age' on 17th July 1908 was given a certificate of merit signed by his teacher, headmaster Archibald Logie Brown MA, and James Symon, the Church of Scotland Parish Minister who was on the Parish Council. Sandy had been taught English, Arithmetic, The Empire and our Colonies, Nature Study, Drill and Singing and had taken a Special Course in Book Keeping, Geometry and Mensuration and Algebra, gaining good marks in everything. 'Character and conduct had been exemplary'.

Four of his contemporary classmates in the junior school were James Howie, Alexander Whiteford of Gabroch Hill, Tom Kirkwood and Alexander Brown, the school master's son. Mr Whiteford tells me that about age 11, the master gave four of them some special tuition in Latin. While learning to decline 'mensa' Sandy could not grasp why the Romans wanted a Vocative case to address a table as 'Oh Table!' His sense of humour of eighty five years ago was still remembered by Alex Whiteford.

Sandy was allowed to stay on at Dunlop school while his classmates went to Glasgow Academy, Kilmarnock Academy, Boys' Hutchesons' Grammar School, etc. Others of his contemporaries were W Reid of Kirkwood Farm and Jessie Dykes. I know he visited Jessie once about 1980 at Gunshill Farm, three miles away.

About this time self-education came into his life, in the form of *Editor Arthur Mee's Harmsworth Self-Educator*, a complete set of magazines in forty-eight fortnightly parts, bought at newsagents' shops. The set was kept, almost intact — a seven thousand page source of information and what is now called 'know-how'. He subscribed to *English Mechanic* about which he later frequently enthused to the author. It seems to have been a mine of information for a keen young man.

When he reached the end of the Advanced Division or senior class in Dunlop School Alexander Thom's betters wanted him to go to a public school. But Alexander refused. Instead, on 25th August, 1908, he entered Class Ia in Kilmarnock Academy. His number at school was 539. I wrote to Mr Donnelly the present Headmaster and he kindly sent me photocopies of both sides of Alexander's record card.

In the column headed 'Fees' there is entered for two years, "Int. Burs." signifying a bursary.

In class Ia he took Maths, English, French, Latin, Physics, Drawing and Woodwork. He won a book prize on 25th June 1909, for excelling in Drawing (First), Physics (Third), signed by RC Grant, MA. The prize was a 487 page book *Victories of the Engineer*. For sure this volume stirred the boy's imagination and made him take up engineering in October 1911. Many of the works described were in the New World. Did this prize book influence him four years later in his decision to go to Canada in 1913?

There is no record of his achievements by Class IIIa, other than his class examination results. These are of interest because in the third class examination in January 1911 he was marked 'a' for absent in English, Maths, Physics, Mechanics, French, Drawing and Chemistry. The columns for the 4th Class Examinations are empty. It is obvious that he left school at the Christmas vacation, 1909.

Evidently Alexander did not like Kilmarnock Academy. One reason would be the waste of time because of the poor train connection. About 1952 he gave a set of large volumes of an encyclopaedia to the pupils' library in Kilmarnock Academy. This had been presented to him early in the century. He spent much spare time in the Reading Room in the Dick Institute in Kilmarnock thereby educating himself. Many of his Journals and Proceedings were donated to 'The Dick' in 1988.

The year 1911 in my father's life is not easy to detail exactly. Obviously his Uncle Willie had talked it all over during the Christmas vacation in 1910 and persuaded this six feet tall callant to come into the Strang muslin factory in Bridgton. The boy did not like it or could not stand it. He was, after all, in the eyes of the other uncles who were directors, the son of a daughter of their father William Strang who had built up the business. The uncles had sons and it could be that Alex was not made wholly welcome. Perhaps Alex did not like weaving. Maybe the wages of an apprentice weaver were not enough. He would enjoy the machinery maintenance part. Perhaps he could see too many faults everywhere. Perhaps had he stayed in the business it would still be a business now, but he left. The business lasted for another half-century. None of the owners had seen ahead far enough to keep it viable after that.

Exactly how many weeks Sandy stayed in Bridgton is not known. Uncle Willie was very fond of him and by this time realised that he was very bright. There must have been many discussions about this country boy's future and in the end he took a crash course at Skerry's College to study for the Preliminary examinations for university entrance. He sat the 'Prelims' and in September 1911, aged seventeen, entered first year classes in engineering at The Royal Technical College. He had gained University entrance in little over three years after leaving the primary school in Dunlop, an academic feat in its own right, proof of good teaching by the staff and headmaster.

Sandy told me that at College he was in classes on a level with boys of his own early school years — he had made up the years wasted between Carradale and Dunlop School. Four sessions later, in March 1915, he graduated BSc in Civil Engineering at Glasgow University.

No history of happenings at The Hill in Alexander Thom's early years would be complete without mentioning his cousin, Jim Tindal.

Aunt Maggie Tindal was very fond of her sister Lily Thom. Throughout the years she had learned to look after Lily when she took her spells of depression. As a result there was a continuation of the friendship into the next generation. One of the Tindal boys, Jim, born in 1900, was not strong during his childhood. He spent many of his formative years at The Hill, which he called his second home. His first visit to The Hill was to the steading. He remembered getting lost in his uncle's blackcurrant bushes.

Jim was to take up farming later. He got honours in dairying at Kilmarnock Dairy School. He learned much from his uncle Archie. One dark cloudy night about 1907 he and Sandy were out in one of the fields some distance from the house. Sandy took Jim under the armpits, swung him round several times and planted him down, saying, "Show me the way home." Jim was completely disorientated. No lights were visible in any direction. Country people at that time thought nothing of the darkness. They did not realise how privileged they were. When the author walks about The Hill in the dark now he is continually blinded by his neighbour's powerful anti-burglar lamp some three hundred and fifty yards away. I can read with its light. No longer is the aurora borealis seen from The Hill. The skies at night are not dark enough any more. In days gone by the beam of Toward Lighthouse twenty miles away on occasion lit up the horizon clouds on Irish Law (1600 feet), some eleven miles distance from The Hill.

During one of the war winters Sandy had a job lecturing once or twice per week in the evenings at the Royal Technical College. It is very probable that he slept on these nights at Brackley, the Tindal's home in Newlands instead of travelling home. There was frequent contact between the Tindals and the Thoms. Jim Tindal told me that his parents obtained oatmeal by the sackful. The grain was grown on The Hill and ground by Mr Picken at Ladysteps Mill in Dunlop. Grain or hay was cropped on all of the fields at one time or another. Jim shot a hen once in the cattle creep, below the railway. It was eating seed corn in the Laigh Park.

Jim talked of the curling pond at Netherhouses, remembering Sis and Sandy there. They were good at waltzing on skates. The curlers, however, were not too pleased about skaters. They skated on moonlit nights.

Jim explained how his Uncle Archie built a hay rick in the Laigh Park for the sheep to eat in the winter. They devoured it evenly, its shape being like a huge puddock stool. A sheep shed was built in the stackyard with framed compartments for hay which served as protecting walls for warmth. The Meadow was sold about 1926. It had no access road, and with the Dunlop dairyman Mr Graham grazing his cows there and herding them daily through the Netherhouses field, objections were raised and the easiest way was for the Thoms to sell the field to Netherhouses.

Jim talked of going to see a cinematograph show in Stewarton and of the return walk in the dark when Wastle attempted to startle Jim at the big rubbing stone in the Laigh.

In a letter dated April, 1986, Jim wrote that when Sandy was at

'The Tech', one of Jim's duties was to get him up in time for the Glasgow train. Sandy had it all timed to the minute.

It was the same in all that he did.

I well remember the old Albion. It was to be loaded on a rail truck. There was no petrol. A bottleful was found, the carburettor was filled and the engine started the second time. I also remember the electric clock on the wall in the dark room. Every thirty seconds an electric magnet operated which gave the pendulum a push which kept it swinging for thirty seconds. The pendulum was a cane with a Fry's cocoa tinful of lead at the bottom. Sandy and Sis were keen on skating and could waltz quite well in our eyes. We just skated. One night I fell through the ice. Sandy fell through trying to get me out of the two feet of water and hurried us home to The Hill.

The daffodils and snowdrops which lined the road to The Hill were a great temptation to the villagers. Sandy wired an alarm which rang when the gate was opened. I don' t know if The Hill was ever surveyed but I do know that Sandy's measurement of the base line was very exact. The theodolite kept the line straight and each length was marked on a 56lb weight with a pencil. Two 56-ers had to be carried.

The story goes that Sandy flew a kite at night over the village with a light hanging from it. I do not know. As you know Sandy built his own radio sets. He made his own coils and tried them all over the room. I remember the glider being built. Two pram wheels supported the body. The idea was that you ran behind pushing the tail in a level position and when you got to a high speed you depressed the tail and hoped it would get off the ground. It did not.

Your first appearance in Scotland, Archie, was when Sandy and Sis and you arrived in a side car from the far south. I think you would be under two months old. This mode of travelling was not approved for young babies but you seemed to thrive on it.

Sometimes your father played the fiddle along with your Grannie. The *Spring Song* was the favourite.

About 1911 a Flying Meeting had been held at Lanark Race Course. A flyer called Hamil landed in a field just south of The Hill. Sandy took a photograph of the machine, with most of the population of Dunlop lined up, before the the the pilot took off. The photograph, made into a postcard, sold by the dozen in Jimmie Wyllie's shop for long enough. People had two reasons for buying it — they were in it!

Sandy was born before the end of the railway boom. He was always interested in railways, and treasured a photograph of the Lugton viaduct which collapsed before he was born.

Passenger rolling stock on the railways had gas illumination in glass domes on the roof of carriages. Cast iron foot warmers filled with hot water were loaded into compartments at the beginning of winter journeys. Electric lighting, when it was installed in each carriage, was by belt-driven dynamo charging lead acid cells which, during the Hitler War, deteriorated, and were not replaced. They gave very uncertain illumination, especially if the unit had not been usd for a few hours or minutes. The step by step four voltage drop was very evident as two-volt cells progressively discharged and reversed polarity. Once the train got moving things brightened up immediately.

Millions of people commuted daily, weekly or quarterly and from the earliest years Sandy was no exception. Sandy had to walk to school daily.

Rail travel enabled people to live much further away from their work place. The railway came to Dunlop in 1871 and allowed much greater freedom of movement. Until the opening of the Neilston to Kilmarnock line the nearest railheads had been Neilston and Cunninghamhead. Before this the steep gradient known to be required through the Barrhead Gap had been too much for the engines of the day. As the engine builders applied yet more modern technology to design, the steady increase in power enabled trains to come through the Barrhead Gap. During the construction of the Barrhead to Low Neilston block, the level of the Barrhead platform had to be raised by nearly two feet in order to make the pull-away gradient out of the station at the south end as small as possible.

At Stewarton it took several years to build the great viaduct over the River Annick. The line south from Stewarton was not opened until 1873. I was told about one young man who started his apprenticeship as a stone-mason when the bridge was begun and his time was out before the work was completed. Beith was joined to Lugton in 1873 and Glasgow's St Enoch's Station was opened in 1876. Until then Gorbals was the terminus on the south side of the Clyde.

Dunlop station and its block of track employed about fourteen men. Trade developed rapidly and the railway carried goods, live stock, parcels and of course passengers. Each morning exactly at 09.00h on the clock in the signal box the signalman pulled a lever which rang a large bell installed at the end of the platform. Intended for station use of course, much of Dunlop heard it and one's watch was set by 'railway time'. Until the advent of the railways, exact time was not really necessary for day to day living. Train guards were supplied with best-quality watches engraved 'Railway Time-Keepers'. Before altering the time, the back of the watch had to be removed. This prevented accidental alteration. Timetabling made it desirable to have standard time throughout the land and the railway telegraph helped to achieve this. Sundials can only be used when the sun shines. One farmer shouted through the house from the muddy outside, 'What's the time Jean?' Looking at the grandfather clock and saying aloud to herself, 'Half an hour fast and ten minutes slow', she then shouted back, 'It'll be Quarter to Four in the Toon'.

We take much for granted nowadays. The difficulties of timetabling might be illustrated by the following observation made once in my presence about Sandy's parents. When his mother Lily went shopping to Glasgow she frequently caught the train before the one she went for. When his father Archie went to Glasgow (usually to markets to buy second hand building materials,) he invariably caught the train after the one he had intended to catch.

For two and a half years Sandy commuted to Kilmarnock Academy by rail. Unfortunately the morning train arrived an hour earlier than school opening while the evening train left an hour later. On good days he used his bicycle for the round trip of sixteen miles. Later he commuted by rail to Skerries in Glasgow, to The Royal Technical College, The University of Glasgow and to Sir William Arrol's in Bridgton. On occasion he would be met at Dunlop Station by his father's farm hand, Peter Neil. It would be raining heavily and Peter would have used the horse and trap to get himself to the village. Peter frequently carried a canful of milk to the creamery at the station. Sandy would drive the trap home, unyoke either Dobbins or Dick or Nellie, hang up the harness and make for the house.

After the Great War he again used the railway at Dunlop, but there was a period when he decided to rent a house, and the problem was, where? He applied reason to determining the best location and did this by plotting a graph of the sum total of weekly travel from the university and weekly rent of houses as advertised in the daily press, against distance from the city of Glasgow. The graph showed a minimum at West Kilbride and so he rented the house advertised in that seaside resort for the winter of 1921-22. Living in West Kilbride was not however to his liking and so in 1922, he built his own cottage, Thalassa, on The Hill Farm. He was once more commuting by rail from Dunlop to the University of Glasgow via St Enoch Station.

Passengers were treated better in these days. There were no queues at terminus barriers — there were no barriers. The trains into Glasgow's St Enoch's station stopped always at Gorbals station and a large team of ticket collectors swept rapidly through the train. On the Up Line (to London) the same thing happened at Kilmaurs, to save the time of passengers alighting at Kilmarnock.

Travel by rail was superior by far to the time-wasting, tiring and sometimes dangerous conditions that commuters by road subject themselves to nowadays. The convenience of the horseless carriage blinds many of us to the benefits of rail travel, even although rail commuting might still be available. Sandy, for instance, worked steadily every day in the train. He allowed himself a certain amount of socialising, travelling with friends and meeting people, but he never joined card-playing groups nor the crossword puzzle experts. (Professor) Adam Thomson from Barrhead was impressed by Sandy sitting in the train looking at an equation — no movement — but he would be thinking it all out.

Railwaymen were important members of each local community and partook in all local activities. Use of the network's internal communication system led to a good turn to Sandy one dark morning in 1928. His aunt Maggie Thom had died during the night at Forbes Place in Wemyss Bay. Her kind neighbour, a signalman in the railway, sent a message to the signalman in Dunlop, Bob Gordon, who opened the window of the 'Box' and passed the message to the surfaceman who was passing on his track patrol. This man, when he reached that part of the line going over Hill Farm ground, laid down his key hammer (for striking home any wooden key between the rails and the chairs shaken out after dry weather) and walked up the fields to Thalassa four hundred yards away. We were wakened by his rapping on the front door. Sandy was able to begin his duties as executor that very morning.

Sandy could remember horse-drawn trams in Glasgow.

John Boyd Dunlop's invention of the pneumatic tyre had been made only six years before Sandy was born. His marvellous addition to the comfort and speed of riding the penny-farthings, velocipedes or bone-shakers as they were called, had made the new 'safety bicycle' a real and useful vehicle for personal transport.

The late Hugh Archibald, in the first decade of the century, rode from Dunlop to Stranraer with a friend. When they arrived they sent a telegram home on the same day to report, "All well".

Exactly when Sandy got his first bicycle is uncertain, but between 1908 and 1910 he frequently cycled to Kilmarnock Academy, some eight miles away. The school train arrived in Kilmarnock at 0800h and left at 1700h, which meant that pupils had time on their hands. This did not suit the six foot tall schoolboy, although he probably did his lessons in the Dick Institute Library in the afternoons on non-cycling days. In frosty weather he frequently skated on the ice on Kay Park Pond in the mornings, at lunch time and before train time in the afternoon.

The bicycles of the day had 28-inch wheels, and the tyres would have beaded rims. One of the bikes found later at The Hill had a very effective back-pedalling brake, an excellent device but useless if the chain came off! One bicycle had been fitted with a shaft drive, the main shaft with a tooth wheel at each end, with a ball race on each tooth, was in the scrap heap here for years. Front wheel braking was primitive — a rubber brake pad firmly pushed radially down on to the tread of the tyre. These bikes had 'back steps', used by the not so young to assist mounting. They were frequently used by a rear standing passenger (disallowed by law nowadays).

About 1916, William Strang, his uncle, gave Alexander his Albion motor car. (Albion was one of the big names in the original home-financed Scottish motor industry along with Argyll, Arrol-Johnstone and Beardmore). Uncle Willie did not drive himself. He had a chauffeur, Willie Heaps, remembered to this day in the Mugdock area. There had been a Minerva before the Albion. Heaps had a big moustache. He would have been called up for more urgent war work, and so the car came to The Hill. It was of the sit-up-and-beg kind, with black canvas hood, running boards, starting handle, etc. Sandy drove it — he did not like to crash the gears and reasoned out how to double-de-clutch, much to the amazement of another of his uncles.

The Albion would not be driven much at this time. Sandy went south to work in the aircraft industry in 1917 and his company bought the car to be converted into a works lorry.

Some time towards the end or just after the end of the war, Sandy acquired a motor bike and side car. It was a 598cc 1913 Baker Precision, with belt drive and Sturmey Archer hub gear box. In its youth it had a clutch in the hub but it had to be started by pushing it in middle gear and stepping on. By 1919, Beardmore of Glasgow advertised their 'Beardmore Precision', the up-to-date model, with a rear-frame spring device. A merger with FE Baker, Precision Works, King's Norton had been made. Baker failed in 1925, owing Beardmore a large sum of money. Beardmore were successfully making cars and taxis at this time.

Some time in 1919 Sandy's aircraft factory job folded up and he headed north this time with wife Sis and six month baby Archie. The four hundred-mile journey took four days — quite an accomplishment, considering the state of the roads which were in poor condition. They had been badly mauled by munitions traffic with heavy solid rubber-tyred wheels. An accident over-turned the combination somewhere in the Midlands. Fortunately not one of us was hurt. A protesting yell from the youngest member of the party astonished a fourth party, "Goodness me, there's a baby in the nose of the side-car!"

Later as a civil engineer, Sandy could set out road and rail centre lines and part of his contribution to safety was the publication, in 1935, of *Standard Tables and Formulae for setting out Road Spirals*. His use of the road system would have drawn his attention to the necessity for such design. He knew of course how railway engineers set out transition curves on the rails, having done it himself in Ontario in 1913.

Once, on his way to visit his aunts in Wemyss Bay he was driving his motor bike and side car carefully down the Haylie Brae above Largs when he came upon a cyclist whose brakes had failed. The poor man had crashed against the cliff at the top hairpin bend — a painted cross could be seen there for decades. Sandy took the dying man to hospital.

In the late 1930s Sis and Sandy used the tandem for visiting friends, just as nowadays one uses a car. They rode several thousands of miles.

In the 1950s and 1960s Sandy drove all over the island of Britain, sometimes with company, on surveying expeditions. With Alan Clark as helper and passenger, he was heard to remark forcibly, just having been passed by a faster driver, " Drive on Ya Pugger. Plenty seats in Hell!"

On his first day at 'The Tech' (the Royal Technical College in Glasgow) in 1911 Sandy made the acquaintance of two men who were cousins, Sandy Prain and Sandy Martin, son of the gunsmith. Prain and Thom would be made to sit next to each other in class, alphabetically arranged so that attendances could easily be taken. Class attendances were taken in each lecture. Each student had to cover his own number in the long pews in the tiered rows.

Prain's father was a saddler in Montrose. Prain was to retire with the rank of Brigadier, RE. Another class member was Binnie, later to invent the Rail-Plane. Another was Logie Baird, later of Television fame. Baird, born in 1888, was 'working his way through college'. He was a baker. On occasion he fell asleep during morning lectures and his classmates took a carbon copy of the notes for him to use later. Sandy remembered Baird's attempt to make money by selling his special socks. Sandy is mentioned twice in the *Secret Life of John Logie Baird*.

George Moncur had been put in charge of the RTC Civil Engineering Department in 1905. Each summer a Surveying Camp was held near Lochgoilhead. In 1912 the camp was held at Loch Eck, the use of which site was acknowledged to Sir Harry Lauder by the College. Here Sandy was taught the basic principles of field surveying which served him well in Canada in 1913 and indeed for the rest of his life. He had a high regard for Professor Moncur and took the author to visit him in Seamill in 1935. We rode over on the tandem and I well remember the elderly gentleman's welcome. Moncur edited a series of twenty two text books of Civil Engineering between 1912 and 1941. Moncur was promoted to Professor of Civil Engineering in 1910 and he retired in 1933.

Sandy soon practised his surveying knowledge at home. Jim Tindal saw him use a steel tape tensioned in catenary form while measuring a base line for a survey at The Hill. Sandy talked of another staff member at Camp, Mr David Clark, 'an awful nice chap'. Clark wrote a book on Geodetic Surveying, in the second volume of which Loch Eck appeared in many examples. Clark had come to RTC in 1911. He was Professor Moncur's chief assistant from 1911–1921. Clark must have taught the young Thom the field Astronomy which he was to use so much later on, first as Lecturer in the University of Glasgow and secondly in his own archaeoastronomical field work.

Professor GG Henderson taught him chemistry. Henderson taught the author chemistry in 1934–35 at Glasgow University.

Some evidence of personality clash comes to light here. Either during the summer of 1912 or the summer of 1914, Sandy worked for Forman and McCall, a firm of consulting Engineers established since about 1890. They had designed parts of the West Highland Railway to Fort William. In Sandy's day a strict apprentice training system was adhered to — a youth was signed on as an apprentice and had to work for five years for an impossibly low wage. Whether Sandy had signed on with this firm or not, I do not know, but I do know that later in life he asked the firm to give him a reference which was refused for the reason that they thought he should have joined them in 1915 after his graduation. He went to Arrol's instead as a draughtsman. Perhaps Sandy refused to be regimented. Perhaps he had come against the same apprenticeship system in his grandfather's company in 1911. He never joined any of the engineering institutions, but he did see to it twenty years later that I so arranged my training in various engineering activities to be under men qualified as Chartered Engineers who could sign my papers for me to graduate CE myself in due course.

In October 1914 Sandy entered the third year BSc course in Engineering at Glasgow University. He took an additional course in astronomy under Professor Becker.

In April 1915 he graduated BSc in Engineering at the University of Glasgow, with Special Distinction in (a) Natural Philosophy and (b) Engineering and Drawing. He won the George Harvey Prize, one of the special class prizes. He won the First Walker Prize, buying a planimeter with this money. He was to use it soon on his analysis of light curves of variable stars.

In April 1990, the author met Dr Alasdair Gibb who remembered Professor Thom in 1968 at his father's farm, Dunadd, Kilmichael Glassary, when everyone stayed up all night to watch the Moon Walk. Sandy was an overnight guest at Dunadd, on one of his many surveying expeditions to Argyllshire. The boy Alasdair, aged nine, remembered the great interest of the Professor in it all. Alasdair was the expert in tuning the television set — which screened a fairly 'snowy' picture in Argyllshire at that time — and he was not to know that Sandy had sketched some of the moon's craters on 29th January 1912 while looking through his own telescope.

Sandy had shown interest in astronomy from an early age. He kept a log-book from 14th January 1912 until September 1921. His first entry was — "Looked at Saturn through the telescope. Also looked at Zeta Ursa Major."

The telescope had arrived for his 1911 Christmas present from his Uncle Joe Maclay. It was a three inch refractor, with a small finder telescope and three eye-pieces of differing power, namely 7, 45, 61 and 130.

At this stage he was a boy in his eighteenth year of age. Some of his notes show his abilities and steady interest until the log-book was laid aside in 1921, after his appointment to the lectureship in Glasgow University. Four notebooks written between 1914 and 1921 contain calculations and graphs about variable stars, double stars and comet paths. In 1916, incorporating some of his own observations, and using his planimeter, the prize won the year before, he published his first paper *Variable Stars: Some features of light curves.* (JBAA 26, 162-4). His interest in observing variable stars continued until May 1920, the last recording.

He possessed a four-screw theodolite, sold by Adie of Edinburgh, with which he measured the latitude of his observatory. It had a five-inch circle graduated in half degrees with verniers which allowed readings to minutes of arc with a final precision of thirty seconds. A compass needle was incorporated above the plate.

His notes show his constant efforts to obtain Greenwich Mean Time, measured then from noon. Commuting daily to The Royal Technical College, he could check his watch using the big clock in the shop window of Edwards, Jewellers, in Glasgow. Two time checks of his watch are logged on 29th January 1912, the first at 0905h, the second at 1305h, some seven and eleven hours after he recorded the lunar occultation of Mars. Once he had established his observatory he could check his watch at home by careful observations.

The log book clearly shows from the very beginning Sandy's talent and ability — how in essence he was unknowingly preparing himself for the lectures he would be giving in field astronomy from 1921 onwards. His early notes indicate the promise of what was to come much later, namely his deep thinking and reasoning on lunar movement, refraction, etc, so necessary for the full analysis he presented of his archaeoastronomical discoveries which was to stir the interest of thinking men and add to archaeology, the new dimension of archaeoastronomy.

Mr Thomas Reid lived at Borland at this time. He sold up and went to Canada in 1912. In the 1890s the Reids had visited a lot with the Browns of Hill and later became acquainted with the Thoms who had bought The Hill farm in 1901. The dates fit and it is assumed that Thomas Reid lent Sandy the telescope. I have checked with two other Reid families in 1990 and neither of them have knowledge of a telescope having been in their families about 1912.

The *English Mechanic* published information on Gale's comet from September 27th until November 6th. Sandy observed it on October 17th, October 18th, October 21st, October 28th, October 29th, October 31st, November 9th, November 10th, November 11th, November 12th, November 13th, November 17th, and November 18th. Each time he made sketches of its position.

When Halley's Comet was returning in 1985, Sandy knew that astronomers were watching it approaching, but he did not live long enough to see it for himself and besides, he was registered as a blind person by this time. He was one of the small number of interested people alive in 1985 who had seen Halley's comet in 1910, but he told Ed Krupp that there was a brighter one after Halley. No wonder he remembered it. He had observed it on thirteen occasions. Ed Krupp of Griffiths Observatory, California was visiting Sandy in 1985 and was delighted to talk with someone who had seen Halley in 1910.

He mentioned several times in his log book the telescope that Thomas Reid of Borland House had lent him. On 10th November 1912 he 'got the diameter (of the field of vision) of Reid's telescope as 6 minutes 30 seconds in time units.' Obviously he needed a telescope with cross hairs on a diaphragm and graduated circles for angular measurement.

On 14th May 1912, while examining Jupiter and its four moons, he fixed a thin wire vertically across the focus of the telescope. He counted the double beats of his watch (130 beats per minute) that Jupiter was hidden behind the wire. He then recorded 16 seconds time between initial vanishing of Jupiter and the vanishing of the inner moon and 45 seconds for the outer moon.

Undoubtedly he felt the lack of a good diaphragm and so he learned how to use the next best thing, the edge of the field of vision. He timed appearances and disappearances of heavenly bodies in the field. He knew the angular diameters of the four fields as seen with the three different eye-pieces and the 'finder', which small telescope had cross hairs.

In his 1921 book of calculations a postcard was found dated 24th June 1921, written to A Thom Esq at Dunlop by ACD Crommelin of Blackheath, London. They were evidently both observing Reid's comet and corresponding, but on the above subject of field diameters Crommelin remarked, "I was glad to have the illustration of the method of using edge of field as a ring-micrometer." Sandy had written to him on the subject of comets.

Many observations are recorded in his log-book between May 1921 and September 1921, a period between jobs when he lived at The Hill.

His interest in astronomy was life-long. In the company of Professor Macaulay of RTC and Mr Macaulay Senior, we drove, in their car, on a camping expedition to Yorkshire in order to observe the 1927 total eclipse. A cloud obscured the early morning phenomenon. We heard an aeroplane above the cloud.

Not long before Thom left Thalassa in 1983 he purchased a score of slides illustrating all that was then known about the solar system, the information having been sent back by space probe *Voyager*, which is now completely away from the Solar system. In the ten years before he died he read many modern popular books on astronomy. He was keeping up to date with discoveries as they took place. What an advance on all fronts since the first decade of the century, when his interest had first started.

The following letter came on 30th August 1984, from FW Markham, British Rail Area Manager, Bristol —

Dear Professor,
        During 1985 the Western region of British Rail is

initiating and countless members of Local Authorities, Cities, Clubs etc, are responding to the 150th anniversary of the passing of the Parliamentary Act that authorised the construction of the London to Bristol section of the Great Western Railway

The whole celebration is meant to highlight the success of GWR throughout the 150 years and to project this into the future, but inevitably much attention will focus on the works of its first Engineer, IK Brunel.

We believe it may be fitting to launch the celebration on the anniversary of Brunel's birthday on 9th April, 1806.

In any event, Brunel worshippers will gather, as they do every year, at the Western entrance to Box Tunnel. They do so because it is said that on this day the sun as it rises can be seen through the tunnel which is nearly 2 miles long and is dead straight.

Are you able to confirm this phenomenon, and if it is true, at what post-equinoctial day a similar event may occur, since it might be appropriate to close our celebration on this date.

I realise that this is a request outside the normal scope of your office, but would much appreciate if you could give the matter some consideration.

I do hope you are able to help.

Yours sincerely,

FW Markham

The author worked it all out carefully to find that the sun shone through Box Tunnel two days after Brunel's birthday.

During the last two years of his life at Banavie the Professor kept on using his mind as much as he could. He was gradually going blind but kept mentally active by dictating his thoughts. The following paragraphs are recorded here —

Since a boy I have been interested in astronomy; from an early age I knew the principal constellations and first magnitude stars and so when I was reading Civil Engineering in the University of Glasgow and found I could incorporate a class in Astronomy, I did so. In this way I got to know the Professor of Astronomy in the University, Ludwig Becker. I found him to be a very good teacher and later on made much use of his advice. When I got into difficulties with calculations I went to him.

I remember one very amusing incident. By that time I had acquired a thorough grasp of the use of surveyors' instruments. I had measured the position of a new comet on three different dates.

This meant that on each of the evenings I knew the direction and position of a line crossing the solar system and on this line must lie the comet, controlled, of course by the gravitational attraction of the Sun but I got stuck on the solution of the equation. Becker took a piece of paper and solved the thing in two minutes.

I took the solution away with my tail between my legs, but what Becker had really found was the orbit of the earth, since the earth at each one of the times had obviously been on one of the lines. This was evidently a possible solution. I eventually obtained the other solution and so found the orbit of the Comet.

It will be obvious from the above that, later in life I was in a position to deal with the geometrical knowledge of Megalithic man. He has left us no written information and so we must base our knowledge entirely on the lines which we find on the surface of the earth. These sometimes consist of a circle of stones with with one or more outliers, each giving a direction or we may find a line of stones, perhaps of only two; an example of the last case is Dunskeig where the two stones in Kintyre point to peaks of the Arran hills peeping over a ridge.

The difficulty with all these lines is that altitude is low and so the refraction is high. In fact you cannot use an alignment if it is very low.

Each alignment gives us a declination and right ascension and it also gives the hour of the day when the moon crosses the horizon.

In seeking a solution we must use a time at which the Sun will be below the horizon or at least very low.

One Hundred Days in Ontario

Civil Engineering apprentices had to be indented with a consultant, and the universities and colleges so arranged their courses that engineering students could do practical work in the summer months. In practice there were about five months in this 'Sandwich System' when undergraduates were free of examinations and classes. Sandy and two class mates, George MacPherson and George Mann decided to spend a long vacation in Canada. Forthwith, in the spring of 1913, they booked passages from the Clyde on the Donaldson liner, *Letitia*, and for £12 each crossed the Atlantic to Saint John, Nova Scotia.

Disembarking, they entrained for Quebec en route for Montreal. For some miles the rail track passed over US territory and Sandy would say gleefully later, "Oh, yes, I've been in USA! They locked me up when I was there!" Frontiers are frontiers.

George McPherson took employment near Montreal. Mann went elsewhere. In Montreal Sandy stopped a passer-by to ask for directions but found the man spoke no English, only French.

He made use of a letter from his lawyer Uncle James A Love Tindal to a director in the Canadian Pacific Railway who arranged for him to go as chainman on a new stretch of the Canadian Pacific Railway which was being built in Ontario to facilitate the hauling of grain to the eastern ports. A fairly long loop was to be shortened by a stretch of new track passing through Forrest Mills, which lies eleven miles south of Napanee, today a town of 4500 population, itself lying some two hundred miles south west of Montreal. The small city of Belleville lies some twenty five miles further west.

The new line was opened for service in May 1914. It is now CP Rail's main line to Toronto. The original line, built in 1887, has been partially abandoned.

Alexander Thom dictated an article in the spring of 1985 when he was living at his sister, Beryl's in Banavie. It was sent to Canadian Pacific in Ottawa. By this time he was ninety-one years old, registered as being blind. He had finished writing the paper, to be his final one, on *Moving and erecting the menhirs* and proceeded to prepare the article which ended up in CP Rail's archives in Montreal in the summer of 1985.

In a letter dated 22nd June 1985 to Mr Omer Lavallée, Corporate Historian and Archivist of the Canadian Pacific Railway, the Professor wrote, " . . . I enjoyed my stay in Canada greatly, and the impressions and the experience which I gained there have been of great value to me throughout my life. . ."

Eleven of his letters posted to his parents, to his Aunt Margaret Strang and to his cousin Lily Tindal have survived.

A summer vacation in Canada, in Alexander Thom's own words is instructive.

I duly presented myself at the residency at Forest Mills, in the middle of a ten mile section. The railway had already been located, with a Residency every ten miles. Centre line location had been done by a different party altogether and had taken place months previously.

The staff at the Residency consisted of Mr Garnet the resident engineer, Mr Harry Walkam the transit man, Scottie Young the rodman, and me the chainman at the end. On my first morning we walked out four miles, nearly to the west end of our section. There I received from the transitman my first instruction, "Get your bloody shite hooks on that chain and take it up the line." I thought very hard for an instant and decided to lift the end of the chain, which was lying in the ditch by the side of the railway, and pull it forward. I had passed my first test.

At night I found I had omitted to bring a camp bed and so they gave me a broken down affair that had been left behind by the previous chainman. We propped it up with some books and that sufficed but one night the whole thing collapsed. I simply pulled in my pillow and went to sleep again. Next evening I built up the pile of books but found when I was turning in that there was a rope stretched across the floor leading to Harry's door. After I got into bed I bent over and loosened the rope from the improvised end of the bed. The transit man had hoped to precipitate another disaster that night but this time I won out!

I soon decided to build myself a canoe. I designed a frame, made it and covered it with calico. The local farmer took it to the Salmon River for me where it worked perfectly to begin with. I soon learned on the river to look out for 'snags'. These are logs with the branches shortened and floating just under the surface. The stub branches could have punctured the canoe very easily.

There was a boy in the neighbourhood who had been at Quarrier's Homes (the Orphan Homes in Bridge of Weir). I remember how impressed he had been by my cousins Lilias and Janet. Their father Joe Maclay, my uncle, had a lot to do with running the Homes. Of course this boy wanted to use my canoe. I told him he could, if while he was moving it on the beach he was careful to drag it on its keel. I think he was only a half-wit and simply trailed it over the beach because when I went the next time it was leaking very badly. Luckily I was able to repair it.

Hazel, the daughter of the farmer who took my canoe to the river, did the cooking for us. The kitchen stove pipe came up through the bunk room. In hot weather its heat was unbearable.

I remember being very impressed by a large rock cutting which we had to make near the beginning of the section. Unfortunately there was a curve inside the length of the cutting. The line had been set out on the ground surface as usual and the rock cut from each end but the ground was very uneven and in the event the two ends did not meet in the middle on the grade line. Some mistake or another had been made. So the whole thing had to be carefully surveyed and the curves reset with proper clearance. The resident engineer then set out on paper a curve with its two spirals, new hubs, etc, all to suit the bottom of the cutting. We then set this out carefully by theodolite and measured, every fifty feet, from the new centre line to the base of the cliff. The contractors then cut away the base of the cliff until they got the necessary clearance. The cliff above this was thereafter excavated to give a slope of 1/4 in 1. Presumably that is how it stands today.

Circular bends had a transition curve or spiral at each end and so each curve was marked by four 'hubs': the beginning of the spiral BS; the beginning of the (circular) curve BC; the end of the curve EC; and the end of the spiral ES. We had to locate each hub for the contractor, but before the rails could be laid down these hubs had to be carefully 'referenced in' to points outside the track. Also, every point along the railway had to be excavated to grade level. (The length of spiral had to be equal to the nominal name of the curve, the radius.)

We picked up all the hubs we could from the references of the location gang and then set them out carefully using, this time, theoretical values for each relevant length. Thus we obtained the final values for the lengths of the curves and final values for the straights.

At the residency in the evenings or at the weekends we had to calculate the area of each cross section so that the contractor could be paid for the amount of material he had moved. Each section was marked out and checked independently. We had to keep track of the total cut and total fill. It is worth noting that we did not work any definite hours, but just worked the whole day and evenings and weekends also when necessary.

While we were calculating the amount of fill we found that there was an error of one foot in the grade level. To put this right I suggested simply adding on a slab of earth one foot thick and equal to the width of the railway. The resident pointed out that it would have to be equal to the width of the railway and embankment at ground level and so the error was corrected.

Looking back, I feel somewhat doubtful about the resident's qualifications. I remember watching his attempt to put a transit theodolite into perfect adjustment. I saw that the method he was using was contradictory and, greatly daring I pointed this out. He huffed and told me to do the whole thing myself.

When the rails were down it was easier for us to travel. We were provided with a hand car. This four-wheeled vehicle runs on the rails. There is a lever in the middle, pivoted at its centre with two handles at each end. By pumping these up and down the car was driven along the rails. The fence gang and other gangs of labourers also had hand cars and when we were coming home at night it was their delight to ram us. With four big hefty lads pumping, they had no difficulty in doing this. When we saw we were going to be rammed we slowed up, and then pumped furiously to reduce the crash. Once they had 'bumped' us, they jumped down and lifted our car off the track, moved theirs forward and lifted ours on again.

There was another type of vehicle used on the railway. This had two wheels running on one rail with an out-rigger. It was driven by one rider pushing with his feet at the bottom of the lever and pulling with his hands at the top. Of course we never had one of these. I do not know how one man could get it off the rails when a train was heard approaching.

I believe the ballast trains had been taken over the Salmon River on a timber trestle. This was being replaced by a proper steel riveted bridge, and the workmen were Red Indians. As I watched, one of them threw his sledge hammer into the river from high up on the bridge. I thought that he had lost his temper, but to my surprise several others scrambled down into the water. It occurred to me that these Red Indians were very accommodating — one loses his temper, throws away his hammer — and his friends go to recover it. But the friends did not worry about the hammer. They produced a pike that he had hit fair in the middle. I realized I had seen a real 'tomahawk throw'.

I took to sleeping outside under the trees because the slop bucket, a great big galvanized iron pail, was never emptied. Perhaps it was my job to empty it, but I refused to do it, and no-one else would either. It got fuller and fuller and stank atrociously.

When I slept under the trees I would see the girl coming down from the farm with the milk every morning.

I remember one night when we got home the resident told us we had to work in the other direction in the morning. Unfortunately we had left an instrument behind, and so the chainman had to go back and get it. I bought a dozen bananas, and ate the lot whilst walking to fetch the instrument — a total of 8 miles.

I worked for about three months on the railway and in that time we completed the ten mile section.

At the end of 'the vacation' I took a liner home from Montreal. I remember coming down river from Montreal to Quebec but I fell asleep and did not see the heights.

The field work during that summer of 1913 was undoubtedly arduous. Sandy's boots gave out in a few days and he invested in a pair of suitable boots and canvas trousers. Walking was often on rough rockfill on the bankings. Mud and water abounded. One week he estimated he walked seventy two miles. He learned cuss words in Irish, Italian, Swedish, Hungarian and Polish, which indicates the internationality of the working force. A homesick Scottish labourer asked how St Mirren were faring. Large dynamite charges were detonated at night or on Sundays but in daylight he saw dozens of smaller blasts. He wrote, "The men did not trouble much but went back a hundred yards or so and held a jacket to their face. Familiarity breeds contempt." Again he wrote, "I got to the head of the chain today because the rodman was unable to take his position due to a staved thumb. He knows he got it on Saturday night in Napanee, but how and when and where, he has not the faintest notion." The same man drank three quarters of a bottle of whisky every night and seemed never to be drunk. He quoted a rhyme which Sandy caught immediately with his aural memory.

*Surveyin's worse than slavery,*
*It sure beats hell at the best.*
*You're up wi'the sun*
*And you're never done,*
*Wi' never a minute to rest!*

On a really hot day, a match-stick, which had been stuck into the ground for the transit man to sight on, ignited in the sun.

Work on the steel riveted bridge fascinated him, but he left no indication as to its span. His work in the residency office would be highly valued. He would revel in the relatively simple calculations to work out the cross-sectional areas of the bankings and cuttings and he would soon tumble to the tabulation needed for making a mass-haul diagram, so necessary to optimise the grade level required to balance cut and fill, ie excavation in cuttings and dumping on bankings. Allowance would be made for settlement of fill so that the final grade was correct. Office work was frequently done at the end of a hard day's field work and often on Saturdays and Sundays. 'Estimates' had to be prepared each month too. The rodman's rhyme was correct — they were never done.

Distribution of the ballast intrigued him. The train had many trucks with one long platform loaded with a long mound of ballast from end to end. Unloading was done skilfully by the engine driver pulling a plough by winch and cable through the ballast and adjusting the train speed to ensure even longitudinal distribution of the ballast.

Telegraph pole distribution nearly killed the survey gang who were busily engaged taking levels on the embankment when a puffing train approached. To their dismay a gang of men were rolling single poles off the moving train at regular intervals, oblivious of the men on the slope. The engine driver was not going to stop and the pole heavers' attention was on their work. Where was the next pole coming off? They survived.

Farmers' fields in the vicinity were still full of old tree stumps and he found himself wondering what all they had seen. In his canoe expeditions on what he called Salmon River, he found himself quietly thinking of the Indians who had inhabited the region, and pitying them in the swamps swarming with mosquitos. Government had granted one quarter of a square mile (160 acres) to each settler who could build a small homestead and show successful cultivation of ten acres after two seasons. Each 'quarter' as it was called, had a long shape, a strip, which ensured that the settler took the rough with the smooth. His land would then be as nearly representative as possible. As it turned out, Mr Jack Brown, from whom Sandy's parents had bought The Hill, Dunlop some twelve years before, owned a quarter (160 acres) at Brighton, through which Canadian Pacific was building the new line. History does not relate when Sandy found this out.

The wooden 'snake' fences amused Sandy. He wrote a description of them for his father. On occasion he would lift a top bar for making surveyor's pegs for the company. Roads were atrocious, with great holes at each wooden culvert. The locals drove light buggies everywhere. What a change has taken place — Canada Highway 401 passes through the area nowadays.

Sandy described an expedition when during an off-day the residency staff went fishing with dynamite. A fuse fastened to a stick was lit and thrown into the river and they all ran. After the explosion they went back and collected the dead fish. That day a gun had been carried for game.

He loved to paint and must have found it relaxing. Two only of his quickly done water colours survive. He must have given many away.

He was in a strange land and saw the ten mile section daily during working hours. It was not long before he decided to explore the river and so he built himself a canoe. He already had a canoe at home, in the Horse Pond, and knew what he was about. His theoretical studies at 'The Tech' (to become the University of Strathclyde) now helped him. He knew how to draw out the sections and calculate stability, displacement, etc. The local sawmiller cut out the bulkheads, ribs and frames and the boat took shape. He covered it with calico, tarred it and launched it in the river some two miles from the residency, about eight weeks after arriving in Forest Mills and four weeks after beginning to build it.

He learned how to paddle using the single paddle on one side of the canoe only, and went on many excursions, getting four miles up river before rapids stopped further progress. A paddle in the moonlight was an experience worth recording. On one daylight trip he discovered upon launching the canoe that the 'Homes boy' had been remiss and had dragged it over the beach and holed it. Sandy had difficulty getting it back to Roblin. By this time it was 10.15 pm, he had to cross the steel bridge, it was dark and he nearly lost himself in the bush on the walk home, where he arrived before midnight. En route he used the Pole Star to orientate himself. The 'Homes boy' was not popular as Sandy was badly bitten by mosquitos and he still had to repair the rent. To cap it all that night he was so restless that at 3am his makeshift canvas bed collapsed again. The residency men ragged him well and said he should do his 'coming down trick' in Napanee theatre!

About midsummer he had a haircut for the first time since coming out and promptly the sun began burning the back of his neck.

He had offers for his canoe before he left. One fellow wanted him to build him one. He overheard somebody say it was the slickest boat around Roblin.

Of necessity he was in close contact with the residency staff all the time. Perhaps he painted, built his canoe and wrote letters in order to get some privacy. Letters took ten days to reach Scotland. His accounts of the alcohol consumption of his fellows can not be greatly exaggerated. But he did write, "Perhaps this will give you a false impression of my companions. They are very decent fellows but have a blowout every time they visit Napanee which isn't very often, of necessity."

They had certain levels of cleanliness below which they did not descend. Socks were considered to be dirty when they stuck to the wall after having been thrown hard against it. Some of them shaved. Sanitary arrangement was simple — a dry closet.

The previous rodman had been a heavy drinker. Mrs Garnet in the company residency must have been working on him, but to no avail. He had rigged up a bottle chute of wire for carrying empty bottles to an old barrel without Mrs Garnet seeing them. Sandy wrote, "Last night the transit man sent the alarm clock down the chute. It stuck, and there it was in the morning, humming away in mid-air."

Although he wrote in April saying that they were very comfortable in an old farm house, things changed for him as the warm weather arrived. The upstairs room was too hot, because the kitchen stove chimney was led through it. Windows were removed and mosquito nets fitted, but it became unbearable. They moved out to the barn, but had to vacate it when the hay was put in. Sandy ended up sleeping below a tree for night after night.

He had left home with about fifteen sovereigns kept hanging round his neck in the soft leather pouch which he kept for another forty five years. He wrote to Lily Tindal saying, "It is rather nice to know that I am keeping myself and saving over a pound a week, not to mention the muscle and knowledge."

He took with him a pigskin sewing kit which still exists, with some of the original spare buttons still in situ.

Within one hundred days in Ontario he felt a change in himself, from that first day the faltering Scottish farm boy spent among strangers on the Section, to the day he left, a young confident engineer. He had grown up.

No wonder he fell asleep in the train en route from Montreal to Quebec, where he visited George McPherson. He was going home a month before George to sit again the preliminary examination in French.


Sandy liked sketching. His mother's cousin Sam Fulton, was a well known artist whose forte was painting dogs. He was one of the 'Glasgow Artists' and had visited 'The Hallowday' Inn at Dunlop with them towards the end of the nineteenth century. He seems to have had a cottage in the Campsies where he would keep his dog 'subjects' for a few days before he painted them. Quite possibly the painting of the sheepdog and the orphan lamb before a roaring fire with the shepherd's clothing drying below the mantelpiece was done in the cottage.

Sandy's Uncle John Strang had sailed to Australia about 1908 to visit the family connection in Sydney. Hornel the painter was in the party. While the ship was coaling at Colombo, Hornel began a painting of a group of Ceylonese girls which he finished when he returned home to Scotland. John bought it for £8. Thirty years ago it was sold by John's widow, Aunt Agnes, for £1,100.

Dates on Sandy's sketches show that he began using his sketchbook in 1912 during the hike over the Black Mount on the Wade road from Inverarnan Hotel to Balachulish via Glencoe with his Uncle Sam and cousin Willie Tindal. Quick sketches were made of Loch Tulla and Loch Leven on 22nd April, 1912.

Sam Strang was the youngest of the uncles. A keen outdoor man, he introduced many young people to the joys of the open air. Many of these youngsters, like Sandy, carried on in the same tradition, introducing more and yet more friends to sailing, hillwalking and mountaineering.

In August of 1912 Sam took Sandy sailing in the yacht *Thora*, and Sandy sketched Tarbert Loch Fyne, West Loch Tarbert, The Green Rocks in Sound of Mull, Ardnamurchan Peninsula from the Sound of Mull, Loch Teacus, and Gylen Castle on Kerera.

Two water colours remain, *Creek in Ontario* and *Concession Bridge, Forest Mills*. These have dates 11th and 18th May 1913, about a month after he arrived in Ontario. No other paintings exist of his Canadian visit, but he reported painting quite often. A sketchbook was left in Bellville station waiting room. Perhaps it had just that day been bought, because later McPherson had to send him 'a block' from Montreal. The pocket sketchbook had been too small for him.

A pencil sketch of a lifeboat on the deck of a ship could have been done on the Atlantic voyage in 1913, along with the face of a beautiful sleeping girl.

In 1914 Sam built a yacht named *Betty* after his daughter. A sketch of *Betty* dated July 1914, one of Lochranza, one of yacht *Sayonara* and three of west Highland castles probably in Loch Craignish, are next in the book. Quick sketches of Castlebay Barra and Loch Skiport follow.

War broke out while Sam and his crew had *Betty* in the Inner Otter Vore at Barra, where coastguards boarded the yacht to question the crew. Sandy's final sketch in the book was drawn in Seil Sound on 9th August 1914 en route for the Crinan Canal and home.

A framed water colour of sailing yacht *Betty* by Alexander Thom hung in his study for years.

*an artist and sailor — a sketch by Alexander Thom from 1923*

He used oil paints too. His paint box was well preserved and is still used by his artist grandaughter, Susan. His oil painting of Carradale herring fishermen in yellow oilskins hauling in their net in the Kilbrennan Sound in the dark, lit by a paraffin flare and with the 'herring screw' in the background, was done about 1915. The herring screw bought the fish at sea and rushed the catch to the nearest railhead. It would be on this night that he was served with a herring cooked in oatmeal. There was no cutlery. The cook merely said, translating from the Gaelic, "Your fingers will get a fork when they get home." On this visit to his birthplace, for which he always had a soft place in his heart, an elderly fisherman haltingly making conversation, said, "Your hand to the plough you'll not be putting it?"

Two of his artistic remarks remain fixed in my memory. We were on a surveying expedition in late March in Argyllshire. Although it was a bright day, he remarked that the prevailing colour was brown, of each and every tint. Again, on a winter's day, looking out from the cabin window, he was sitting resting his eyes looking into the distance, when he remarked on the beautiful tracery of the elm tree boles and branches against the dull sky. He loved the outside world, appreciating all of its facets. Although the trees appeared to be hibernating they were really beautiful while consolidating their position for the spring to come.

Many of his original pen drawings of standing stones, and sites with mini-views are little works of art in their own right.

When Sandy began to publish his plans of stone rings and menhirs he produced dozens of these little works of art. A number of them were used in their original form by various editors and many must still exist hidden away in archives. Frequently however, the publishers employed specialist artwork draughtsmen who produced line drawings worked up from Sandy's originals. His hobby of drawing and painting helped him in all of this, and of course he had had years of drawing-office experience himself. At committee meetings his habit of drawing and sketching led him to 'doodle' on a clean sheet, producing amazing imaginary sketches.

Two of his grandchildren and one of his great grandchildren have inherited his artistic talent — Susan MacColl makes her living by painting; Jilly Luff is a mapmaker. Great grandson Eoghann MacColl is a promising young professional artist.

The years of the First World War were very full of activity. As a young graduate Alexander Thom joined Sir William Arrol and Company immediately after coming down from Glasgow University in 1915. Arrols, of Forth Bridge fame, made their name on bridges and their money on roofs. Sandy gained experience in setting out steel buildings, in steelwork design of all kinds and in drawing office work. He worked, for instance, on the redesign of the flooring on the Forth Bridge, and on the redesign of the circular crane rail for the rollers on top of the huge four-cornered braced column supporting the 175 ton Finnieston crane. A landmark on the Clyde, this crane was used for lifting boilers into the empty hulls of ships, and for loading huge steam locomotive engines and tenders, etc, on to, or into the holds of, cargo vessels.

By the summer of 1917 Sandy was feeling the need of a change. Arrol's was interesting enough but he felt that he could use his abilities and better himself. He had plenty of interesting work and was applying himself diligently to it all. For instance he had bought himself a very useful set of the American Smoley's Tables of Logarithms and Squares, consisting of the sides of Pythagorean triangles of all shapes and sizes laid out in feet, inches and 1/32 of inches. This book was in great demand in the drawing office. It was difficult to procure.

He applied for a position as draughtsman with The Norman Thompson Flight Company, Bognor, Sussex. He was successful and was soon deeply involved in the design and construction of flying boats. Experience in Arrol's came in with a smile, especially in the organisation of drawing office plans. Later on in life, on yachts, he kept his charts in apple-pie order, remembering how to handle huge rolls of many large drawings without damaging them.

A photograph of an experimental amphibious flying boat with 'NT2B about 1916' written on it by Thom, built by Norman Thompson, is in the archives — a forerunner of the four bladed pusher propeller biplane *Walrus* used at the beginning of the Second World War. This particular machine was not put into production. When the First World War ended every company involved in manufacture of aircraft attempted to jump on the postwar civil air-transport bandwaggon. A future aircraft industry was seen by men of vision. Sandy left Norman Thompson, which company had been involved mainly in building special research flying boats for military requirements. Their expertise was not sufficient and suitable work did not materialise.

Whatever happened, Sandy departed, later joining The Gosport Aircraft & Engineering Company, helping in 1919 and 1920 in the design of several biplanes and one triplane flying boat. The Gosport Company also designed a sixty one feet span single engine pusher-propeller biplane flying boat.

The Gosport Company also specialised in motor cycle work which made Sandy interested in their design, especially front and back springing, speed wobble and damping. A file has come to light containing a ten page unpublished paper on *Stability of the Bicycle*. He had been working on it in 1924, by which time he owned and maintained two motor cycles. I remember seeing him swinging a bicycle frame suspended like a pendulum in the Sheep Shed at Thalassa about this time. But by this time his mathematical energies were being directed towards his aerodynamic work and he dropped the bicycle calculations.

With the expertise gained in the design work involved in all of the above flying boats, Sandy was more than qualified to write his lectures for the class in Aeronautics in Glasgow University where he was appointed lecturer in October 1921. It is evident from correspondence that the aircraft industry knew of his research work in December 1923.

Later Sandy talked a lot about his days in the aircraft industry. He had a yarn about Mr Constantiscu, the inventor, who devised an interrupter gear which allowed a centrally mounted machine-gun to be fixed on the fuselage of a single-engined fighter so that it could be fired through the propeller while the pilot aimed his aircraft at the enemy. Legend has it that on one occasion the gearing slipped. The bullets kept on firing through the wooden propeller which survived because each time round the gun fired through the same hole and went on firing through the same hole.

He also spun the yarn about the pilot whose engine overheated while he was flying north over the English Channel. Undaunted, the pilot managed to urinate into the cooling system. The aircraft returned safely. The pilot was decorated.

Jeanie Boyd Kirkwood (Sis) was born on 26th March 1897 at South Grange, Dunlop, where her parents were farmers. She was born there in the front room, where the infamous Kirsty Cochrane, murderess, had been locked up a generation before. Jeanie's parents had set up home first in Irvine. Allan, her father, had inherited a fortune from his Uncle Allan and had invested it in South Grange. He was not a successful farmer and his wife Jane persuaded him in 1902 to build her the cottage of Glencairn in Dunlop before his fortune evaporated. Grandfather Allan Kirkwood kept a dictionary beside his chair in the parlour in Glencairn, and used it often.

Males dominated the Kirkwood household. Jeanie had three older brothers and two younger sisters. She had long hair in her youth and prided herself that she could sit on her tresses. Being the first sister of the three older boys, she was called Sis. Another family nickname for her was Toosh.

After Dunlop School, Jeanie attended Hutchesons' Grammar School for Girls in Glasgow for at least two years. She studied German and reached the end of Form IIA before leaving to begin working at her one and only paid job, typist secretary in a tea-blending company in Glasgow. There she trained to be a touch-typist, learning with a hood over the key-board of the machine. Later she was to type Sandy's theses for him.

Little pocket-money was available. She remembered being given half a crown by her father to go to the 1911 exhibition in the building now called The Art Galleries in Kelvingrove Park.

She had to make the tea for her bosses, the tea tasters, and described the whole procedure — a long row of freshly brewed cupfuls with no milk, no sugar. She enjoyed the Dunlop village policeman's rhyme about grocer Allan Gilmour's tea, knowing how tea was blended. Mathew Anderson, who wrote two books of poems, is reputed to have composed the verse for advertising on Allan Gilmour's paper bags —

> *Gilmour's tea's the best o' a',*
> *It tak's the shortest time to draw;*
> *Ane spinfu' gangs as far as twa*
> *O' any ither.*

Jeannie's mother had to be frugal, and she had been taught good habits. The food rationing and shortages in the war developed certain behavioural patterns, such as — no jam on the first slice of bread, no sugar in tea, etc. Jeanie used the word 'harigals' for a meal made out of leftover foods. Many of these wartime habits persisted for a generation. The main enemies were hunger and cold.

She never went hungry and she discovered that outdoor comfort was increased in winter if she donned her outdoor clothing some time before venturing forth in winter. Her homes were never overheated. Using her body warmth to heat her clothing when she was already warm was sensible. It was fashionable to wear a fur muff carried at waist level by a loop of cord hung from the neck.

Sandy and Jeanie were acquainted for years. They were three years apart in the school where all pupils knew one another. Jeanie would be travelling to Hutchesons' Grammar School for Girls while Sandy was a student at 'The Tech'. Later she would be travelling to her work in Glasgow while Sandy was a student, and while he was working in Arrol's in Bridgeton. They enjoyed skating togther in frosty weather.

When Sandy went to work in England in August 1917, he promptly asked for leave of absence to travel north over a weekend. He met Jeanie by arrangement on Saturday, 17th August 1917 in Glasgow, where they were married in a registrar's office. They had two friends for witnesses, who must have known about the wedding in advance, but nobody knew about it in Dunlop.

The newly wedded couple travelled out on the last train and Jeanie went into Glencairn and announced she was married. History does not relate whether Sandy went into Glencairn or not. He arrived home at the Bungalow. Presumably the house was in darkness except for the loft, because Jim Tindal related that he and Wastle were there when Sandy poked his head up through the trap door.

"He usually came home about 6pm but one night he was late," wrote Jim to the author. "We were in bed when Sandy came up the steps to the loft. Wastle and I asked him why he was so late. His reply was, "Getting married!!" We celebrated by smoking State Express cigarettes, 333s. Sis had gone to her home!! Uncle Archie asked me later if I'd known about the wedding. I said, No."

Next day Jeanie went to church, and sang in the choir as usual. Walking home from church with her friend Louisa Howie, she could not keep her news to herself any longer and told Louisa, just out of the blue, that she "got married yesterday". The honeymooners travelled south immediately. Sandy had his new job to hold down.

Jeanie had a fair knowledge of the constellations. Sandy had

*Jeanie Boyd Kirkwood who married Alexander Thom in 1917*

taught her. He was courting her when he was learning astronomy himself. Her interest dwelled on in her mind because in old age she watched the daily newspaper reports of when satellites were to be visible and sometimes managed to view the same sputnik twice of an evening.

From my point of view, they were both young enough to be companions to me and for us all to enjoy energetic activities.

PART I FIRST THREE DECADES

# PART II

## SUMMER

# Second Three Decades
# 1924-1953

"It is a growing subject."
Alexander Thom

The First Career

At the age of twenty seven, in 1921, with his undergraduate years and wartime initiation into the world of practical engineering behind him, Alexander Thom was appointed to a lectureship in engineering at Glasgow University. By this time he was well prepared for what was to be his first career, an academic life in engineering. His second career in archaeoastronomy was to begin many years later. It overlapped his first career by some twenty years and it began as a hobby.

He applied himself with energy to his lecturing, began research work, built himself a home, a wind tunnel, was awarded PhD and DSc by theses, and supervised research students. He attended an international conference "Aerodynamiker Tagung" held at Aachen from 26th to 29th June, 1929. He realised that good work was being done in Germany on Fluid Dynamics and forthwith began to learn German by the Pelman Method. He also learned by listening to Linguaphone gramophone records.

He conducted an excellent course in field astronomy and statistics and began construction of a hydraulic scale model of the Clyde Estuary.

After wartime service on wind tunnels at Farnborough, he was appointed to the Chair in Engineering at Oxford University in 1944/45. Here he completed his academic career, his first career. But by 1954 Sandy had enough material on his researches into the geometry and astronomy of standing stones to begin publishing.

Alexander Thom's first experience of instructing was when he became assistant Scout Master in Dunlop. Thereafter, in session 1916-1917 he gave a course of lectures on the Theory of Structures at the Royal Technical College, Glasgow. For each evening's work he received £11. Laboratory work was included.

JD Cormack, appointed Professor of Civil Engineering and Mechanics in the University of Glasgow in 1913, had reason to be pleased when in 1921 he arranged Thom's Lectureship in the Department. Having been appointed Chief Contracts Officer of Military Aeronautics in 1915, Cormack became Director of Aircraft Supply and Equipment. He resigned in 1919 with the ranks of Hon Brigadier General and Hon Group Captain, RAF. Cormack needed an experienced man to take the sixty lecture course in Aeronautics. Dean of the Faculty of Engineering and Director of the Engineering Laboratories, Cormack was holder of the Rankine Chair in Civil Engineering and Mechanics, founded in 1840 by Queen Victoria. As it was a Regius Professorship, Cormack had been appointed by the Crown.

Glasgow had been an engineering centre of some note long before 1840. It had had a university since 1451. Unquestionably the second city of the Empire, Glasgow was an obvious choice in 1840 to be given the first chair in engineering. Professor Lewis DB Gordon was the first holder of the chair, followed in 1855 by world famous Professor WJM Rankine who in 1862 obtained approval for the award of a Certificate of Proficiency in Engineering Science. This did not satisfy Rankine and he pushed for a degree in engineering. Under his pressure a BSc in Science was established in 1872, made to embrace biological, geological, and for a time, legal subjects, as well as engineering.

In 1921 Thom's appointment was ideal. He lectured in Civil Engineering, Civil Engineering Design, Theory of Structures and Aeronautics. He had been trained in Field Surveying. Field Astronomy was his hobby, and so the practical side of the classes presented no difficulties. During lectures, like his peers, he made use of standard four-inch square slides which could be projected in each classroom. He soon wrote his lecture notes on Aeronautics, applying the expertise gained from 1917 onwards in designing flying boats, etc

Classes were held in Engineering over three sessions of twenty weeks each. The Sandwich System was in use; students were supposed to work with engineering companies during the long summer vacations.

A photograph of the members of the Engineering Department taken in the science quadrangle in April 1922 shows 290 students, with the following fourteen staff members: A J Small, HM Spiers, AF Hewett, J Scobie, J Wilson, RM Brown, Professors Howe, Cormack, and Goudie, and J Vost, A Thom, J Small, E W Geyer, and the attendant janitor, J Edwards. One student, NY Keanie, made himself famous because he managed to appear twice in the picture, by running along behind the others from left to far right while the camera was panning the large angle.

The subject of Aeronautics was optional to students. Few electrical engineering undergraduates took the class. Some naval architects attended, but mechanical engineers came in greater numbers. Sandy's civil engineering students augmented attendances. He encouraged his civil engineering students to take the class, because of the structural aspect of the course. As it turned out, a number of his civil engineers later attained high positions in the aircraft industry in the 1939–45 war to come. One of these, Archibald M Ballantine, came on to the staff and finally became secretary of one of the Aeronautical Institutions.

Some of the men who became outstanding in their later careers were J McCusker, T Blench, A Andrews, James Orr, JFC Conn, W MacGregor, Billy Latto, MacMillan, W Cormie.

(Professor) SR Sen Gupta, Peter Swart from South Africa about 1937 and Archie M Ballantyne were his research students.

Much of the work done in developing aircraft is theoretical calculation, with the help of scale models. Some twenty years before, the Wright Brothers had performed wind tunnel experiments to study the aerodynamics of their flying machine. Sandy was no exception. He needed a wind tunnel badly. In 1920 and in 1921 he had published theoretical investigations into aerofoil characteristics. This attracted the attention of Handley Page Ltd, Aeronautical Engineers, Crackle, who wrote him on 1st December, 1923 —

Dear Sir,

We have been particularly interested in the R & M Report No 837, Dec1921 recently issued by the Aeronautical Research Committee. This report deals with your *Empirical Method of Predicting Aerodynamical Properties of an Aerofoil* and the method used in the report appeals to us as having considerable possibilities.

Our immediate object in writing to you now is to enquire whether the derived sections A and B shown in Figure 15, the ordinates being given on page 6, have been tested

independently in a wind channel in order to check the
accuracy or otherwise of the results obtained empirically.
Aerofoil B in particular would be, as suggested in the report,
a very useful section, owing to the considerable depth
available for the spars, and we shall be particularly glad if
you could let us know of any wind channel data which may
have been carried out on this section.

Yours faithfully,

For and on behalf of HANDLEY PAGE Limited (GRV)

For sure the above letter would encourage Sandy to build himself a
wind channel. No university capital in the form of a lump sum was
available, but a workforce existed, and so in the mid 1920s Sandy
built his own 24" x 24" tunnel.

Where was it to be erected? The only suitable space was in his
own office, the long triangular prismoidal-shaped space below the
large lecture room of the then James Watt Engineering Laboratories.
The wooden tunnel took up 70% of the floor length, leaving room for
his desk and book cases. He knew how to design the four bladed fan
— he was teaching the subject — and so he gave drawings to the
University Joiners' Shop, where the four or five laminations needed
were cut out and glued together. He carefully pared the blades to the
correct shape using his spoke-shave. A variable-speed drive was easily
arranged, as the electricity supply was direct current.

Like his father on the farm at Dunlop, he was never at a loss. For
instance, while building and using his wind tunnel he needed to have
an airtight sleeve joint round the stem of his rotatable Pitot head
projecting into the air stream. To save time he threaded the stem,
screwed it into the wall of the tunnel and fixed a lock nut. His tests
were not in any way delayed, and on went the experiment.

Students respect and recognise practical research work applied
to lecturing and some of them would be allowed to partake in practical
demonstration experiments on the tunnel. Apparatus was designed
and made to measure the air forces on models, and much research
work was done on measuring the forces on rotating cylinders. When
wind blows across a rotating cylinder, or a spinning golf or cricket
ball, a considerable side force occurs. Initially discovered by Magnus,
the principle was used by Flettner on his famous Rotor Ship. Sandy
built a bench-top demonstration model of a Flettner rotor on rails to

illustrate the phenomenon, making the wind with a fan.

Hailstone shapes intrigued him and he performed some experiments on wooden models of these in the wind tunnel.

Not satisfied with using air as the working fluid, Sandy built a 5" x 5" open-topped channel for water and oil experiments, again on rotating cylinders. From 1931 to 1934 his publications show that he was performing experiments on the flow past rotating cylinders in air, water and oil and developing methods of calculating the stream lines. He was the expert 'back room boy' on the subject and later, during the Second World War, his papers must have been studied by Barnes Wallace while designing the spinning bomb which so successfully skimmed over the torpedo nets protecting the Möhne Dam in Germany.

I once asked Sandy if Wallace had talked to him about it, but the reply was in the negative. The whole thing had to be kept secret, and besides, during World War II Sandy was deeply involved at Farnborough on the High Speed Tunnel. All he said was that he knew Wallace. Basic research should never be muzzled. Work done twenty years before, purely out of interest, had been extremely useful. Combination of teaching and research as Sandy practised it was, and still is, ideal.

A good lecturer keeps his students interested by any means at his disposal. At the Monach Island lighthouse the senior keeper was drowned in an unfortunate accident. The Monachs constitute a small archipelago in the Atlantic off the western side of North Uist in the Outer Hebrides. An enterprising photographer chartered a light aircraft and took an excellent snap of the Monach Light. Sandy saw the photograph in the *Glasgow Herald* and studied it carefully. He had anchored in the shallow sandy bay the year before, had been welcomed ashore by the keeper and shown all over the light, even being allowed to stand on the platform upon which the huge Fresnel lenses were mounted while the whole floating base was slowly rotating and the huge paraffin heated incandescent mantle was shining brightly.

That anchorage was a memorable one, and so the photograph had special interest for him. He produced it in his next lecture, along with the large-scale chart of the Monachs, showing the spot above which the film had been exposed, the altitude of the aircraft, the time of day, obtained from the shadow of the lighthouse cast on the easily identifiable rocks, and the state of the tide, seen by the sea level round the rocks through which he had navigated. He had also calculated the date of the photograph. Not many yachts ever visited the Monachs and when our black-hulled gaff-rigged cutter *Lufra* anchored, the Keeper was sure that he would be getting some French brandy that evening.

I relate the above anecdote in order to record that Bill Cormie, Consulting Civil Engineer referred in 1976 to Sandy's lecturing abilities in glowing terms. Bill had remembered the ten minute talk in the lecture given in 1936, forty years before. He admired the searching mind of the lecturer, the freshness of the approach and the opportunity seized of using a topical illustration of the principles of surveying, field astronomy and tidal information, all part of university training — to think.

Hydraulic scale models interested Sandy and in 1938 he began to design a scale model of the Clyde estuary for demonstration to students. A large part of the hardware had been made by the time war broke out in 1939. He did no more work on this type of hydraulic modelling until about 1957 when he arranged for a tidal model of the North Sea to be made in the Engineering Laboratory at Oxford. The model was constructed with an exaggerated vertical scale. Atmospheric depressions were modelled by moving a suction disc over the water surface. Modelled from Iceland to the English Channel, Norway and Sweden, the whole apparatus worked well and reproduced the natural tidal amphidromic points to everyone's satisfaction.

A short course in probability and statistics was given in the civil engineering surveying class. Sandy developed a simple apparatus to teach probability and the theory of error. A brass plate about 1.2m long by 150mm high was mounted at eye level in the vertical plane with its long axis horizontal. A long row of 2mm diameter holes was drilled about 20mm from the top edge of the plate. Each student was given fifteen steel balls and asked to place them in what he considered the centre hole, having stood initially about 4m away. Vertical divisions in a movable glass case out of sight behind the plate collected the balls which were duly counted. The resulting Gaussian distribution curve was used by him in all sorts of ways to illustrate the theory.

For a test involving, say, the division by eye of the length into one third, the movable glass case behind could be slid along to

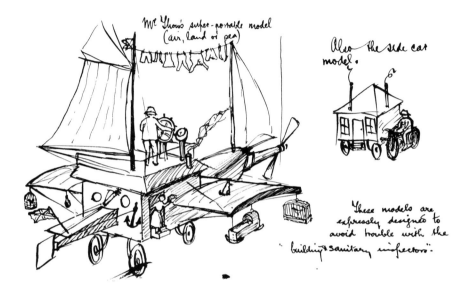

Building his own house, hydraulic models, inventive lectures, Alexander
Thom caught the imagination of students and colleagues — Professor
James Small (above and overleaf) depicted the ways of the man

The tragic domiciliary adventure of Mr Thom.

House drags anchor in gale.

Subject of great new film
"Over the Hill".

Pastoral scene
"By the Burn"
or "Sunrise after a storm"
Mr Thom studying the problems
of the nose dive

accommodate the chosen position.

Manufacturers of theodolites and levels keep on developing their instruments and Sandy saw to it that his students were trained to use the most modern types available. Many of these men would soon be setting out road and rail centre lines and, much more exacting, hydro-electric tunnel centre lines. He taught the theory of theodolites carefully and thoroughly, pointing out that this instrument is almost unique in that it can be made to check its own adjustment. He wanted each student to feel confident in using theodolites, and to this end placed great emphasis on field astronomy. Experiments were devised for determining latitude, longitude and for finding true north. A ship's chronometer was used for the timepiece, its rate being determined by the broadcast radio signals. The students did all of these experiments on the lawns and grassy banks in front of the university. No calculating machines were available and six figure tables were used. As a result, students went down with a real feeling of confidence.

In 1923 the sandwich courses were reorganised into four years, each with twenty weeks' teaching as before. The New Regulations allowed some more specialisation at all stages. More time could be spent in teaching, for example, transition curve design. Sandy developed his own way of setting out road transition curves, writing a small book on the subject in 1935. This was his first book.

Steelwork design, reinforced concrete design, fixed arches, masonry arches, piling, earthworks, road and rail curve design, transition curve design, chain surveying, hydrology, open channel hydraulics — all of these courses were taken by Sandy at one time or another. He was not fond of reinforced concrete theory and this was usually given to his assistant lecturer.

WAS Thom, Sandy's brother, joined an Arctic expedition to Franz Joseph Land in 1925. About this time Sandy became very interested in polar exploration. He bought and read avidly many books on the subject. Dunlop Literary and Debating Society invited him to lecture. This was his first lecture to the public. He used slides, some of which he made himself.

Sandy presented a paper on flow past cylinders at an international conference *Aerodynamiker Tagung* held at Aachen from 26th to 29th June, 1929. With his colleague MacCall he met Messrs Hopf, Karman and Prandtl, as seen on a photograph of those present. One of the participants had seen Alexander Thom's name on the programme and had associated it in his mind with a small man, like an atom. When he met this tall Scot, Sandy, he was greatly amused.

About this time Sandy was realising that good work was being done in Germany on fluid dynamics and forthwith he began to learn German by the Pelman Method. He also learned by listening to a set of Linguaphone records, using a very modern electrical pick-up on his pre-war *His Master's Voice* hand-wound gramaphone. He was using his aural memory, a sense not realised by teachers earlier in his life when he was having difficulty learning French. Much later in life he enjoyed reading German novels and detective stories, remarking that the stories lasted longer when read in a foreign language!

When Sandy was later appointed to the Chair of Engineering Science at Oxford University, he discovered quite a different traditional system than that which had developed in the five centuries old Scottish universities. In Oxford at that time, 1946, lectures in the arts subjects were attended only voluntarily. Sandy's background made him disapprove of this arrangement in engineering and he was relieved to find that attendance at engineering laboratory classes and lectures could be made compulsory. In many ways he had more responsibility than a professor in a Scottish university, in that he had more control over departmental finances. His administration duties were time consuming and he did not take on a heavy lecturing load. Having a wealth of lecturing experience behind him he could pick and choose what sections he liked.

In the spring of 1922 Sandy began to build his own house, Thalassa. He chose the site well, beginning with a small 24ft square bungalow. Having been appointed to his lectureship in the University of Glasgow in 1921, he knew he had security of tenure. He knew he could do the job well. Daily travelling to West Kilbride in the winter of 1921–22 he found too much and besides he loved The Hill. Forthwith he got permission from his parents to build, made architect's plans, and flitted from West Kilbride in the spring of 1922.

I well remember the journey, Jeanie driving the Precision motor cycle combination, Sandy driving the 4-cylinder FN motor cycle and combination. The feeling of dismay is with me yet, when they found the road from Auchentiber to Torranyard at the bridge over the Lugton Water to be temporarily closed. Shouted instructions, a U-turn and a slightly longer way home was taken. The mind of a forty five month old child stores in the memory what he thinks is important. The incident was nothing to my parents.

Sandy chose a good site on which to build his new home, in what is now called the Thalassa Park, immediately south of his father's hay shed in the stackyard. Two holes were cut in the hedge, a wire fence erected round the site, and the first sod cut. Eighty working days later we moved in. Jeanie was on the job daily, sawing and hammering, planing, mixing concrete, puttying in panes of glass, the lot. Many friends helped, some for a few hours, some for much more. Charlie Hutchison, grandfather's orraman also helped. Grandfather built the gate posts at the entrance and made two riveted steel gates. I remember grandfather Thom, David McCardel, Aunt Bessie Kirkwood, George McPherson, Wastle, James Hay, Bill Strang (Westbrae), Margaret Strang (Drymsdale), all being there.

The gate post concrete shone white beside the mossy drystone wall and someone suggested pouring bedroom slops on to help green moss to grow quickly.

Official permission was easy to obtain. Father had produced a well drawn plan and elevations. The sanitary inspector for the area made a few visits during the building and that was that. One man inspected the site, not the fifty five officials needed nowadays! A steadily running supply of water was located in the south eastern corner of the Mid Park. A collecting chamber of brick was built in a field drain running from a bed of gravel. A local drainer dug the thousand feet long trench for the supply pipe and refilled it, all for the sum of £5. Sandy laid the one-inch gas pipe himself. The pipe led to a cistern outside of the house with continuous overflow at eaves level. No hot water heating system or inside wc was fitted, but there had to be a kitchen sink and a bath which was fitted in the kitchen with a suitable waste pipe. A huge roaring Primus paraffin stove was used to heat the water. Initially the waste water from the kitchen sinks and bath went into a field drain. An outside dry closet was erected in the space between the hay shed and the boundary hedge.

My parents were rightly proud of their efforts in building a home, and while showing friends round remarked, "A Poor Thing, but Mine Own!"

Outer wall cladding on Thalassa consisted of 8'x4'x1/4" asbestos cement sheeting on four-inch timber framing, with 1/8" asbestos sheeting inside. A layer of thin tarred paper or felt, as it was called, was fixed inside the outer asbestos layer. Accommodation consisted of two bedrooms, one living room, one kitchen and one pantry — the bare minimum required by law. His main posts were supported in concrete, with dwarf walls built between them. The house plan was 24 feet square. One built-in fireplace in the living room was the only source of heat. Cooking and baking was done on a three-burner Valor Perfection Cooker and Primus stoves, fuelled by paraffin which was stored in a fifty gallon tank with a pump for filling reservoir casks. The paraffin was sold by Mr Allan, who ranged the countryside selling hardware of all kinds, including chamber pots, hence he was named 'Chanty' Allan. Paraffin lamps were used for lighting.

Tom Young was the butcher who brought a big choice of meat in his van for the housewife to see and choose from. Once purchased, the meat was kept outside, in a meat safe with gauze-covered louvres. Mr Wood, coal merchant, delivered coal, using the railway weighing machine.

Jeanie had a smoothing iron heated by methylated spirit. It was shaped like the bows of a liner, with rows of port-holes shining blue light.

His colleague James Small made a cartoon drawing of Thalassa withstanding a gale. Sandy was hauling on a rope, Jeanie behind him, Archie behind her and a wee dog pulling the seat of Archie's pants. Certainly the wind noises were more noticeable in the light frame building. Sandy had intended it to last five years. It lasted until 1989. In it he wrote his PhD and DSc theses, typed by Jeanie, who was a touch typist. Their second son Alan Watson was born in 1923.

Sandy began gardening, made lawns, built a specially shaped wind break in the form of a grassy mound. The dwelling was so successful that four years later he doubled it by adding an extension to the east, consisting of two more bedrooms, a bigger public room and a bathroom. He built a massive fireplace and brick chimney and fitted a hot water system. A septic tank was constructed to specification. The compound was enlarged to the east and he built a dry-stane dyke with circular corner pillars, a stairway stile and a wrought iron gate into the field. In 1926 Ayr County Council widened the main road, taking about a quarter of an acre of land from the Laigh Park of The Hill. Part of the bargain was that the stones of the dyke which was to be demolished would be carted up to the midden wood at The Hill. These stones Sandy used for the drystane dyke. He loved dyking, a mentally relaxing art. He proved the dyker's rhyme to be true.

*Twa upon wan, Wan upon twa;*
*Work a' day and ye'll shin hae a wa'.*

Beryl, my sister, was born in 1926. Cousin Margaret Strang, Uncle Andrew's daughter came to be nanny when Beryl arrived. Beryl's niece Susan Thom was born in Thalassa in 1946.

Andrew Tindal's fiancée Violet Purves lived in The Hut, a wooden outhouse erected in the compound. A greenhouse was made in the early 30s, heated by a long horizontal flue made from the cast iron water heating pipes from grandfather Thom's old greenhouse in the big garden of The Hill. Much earth was moved to level out the back lawn for badminton.

In the early thirties one clear summer evening at Thalassa we were using the telescope and looking at Pladda, thirty miles away. Alexander Thom had spent holidays at Kildonnan in his youth with various uncles aunts and cousins. He could clearly see the gable of a house on Arran, which he identified as the home of Findlay Bo. Suddenly he saw a flag on a flag pole, and the rest of us could see it too. To check that we were seeing a flag and that the air was so clear, he wrote to Findlay Bo, the postman, who replied to say that his flag had been flying at the stated time. Jim Tindal remembered Sandy saying he saw a donkey too.

Rust finally choked the small-bore water supply pipe in 1944 and it was replaced by a two-inch asbestos cement pipe.

Sandy obtained a very old type of two-way telephone which did not require any cells. Vigorous cranking at the Bungalow end made the bell tinkle in the Main Cabin. The overhead 30 volt lighting wires were no longer needed after the grid arrived in 1948. The heavy wires were ideal for the private telephone. A call from Oxford during vacation could get him to come to the Bungalow phone or he could be asked to telephone back later.

Sandy retired into Thalassa in 1961. It had lasted longer than the five years he had initially thought of when he had the idea of building a temporary home. He renewed the tarred felt on the roof once more, laid parquet flooring on five compartments and fixed insulation above the ceilings. Electricity had been installed in 1948, a boon for heating and power, and much more useful than his own home-made DC lighting supply. The hot cupboard with copper cylinder in the bedroom next to the living room fire kept the bedroom warm. He arranged a floor-level inlet vent to the hot cupboard from the living room and a shoulder-level outlet for convecting air and thereby increased the living room air temperature by some 8F degrees.

During this active period he was working steadily at archaeo-astronomy, so hard that Jeanie said plaintively, "But I thought we were supposed to be retired!" She did the cooking but after dinner Sandy would make the coffee. He ground coffee beans each time at table in a small electric coffee grinder which made a whining noise as it speeded up. Jeanie likened it to a ship making her way up the Sound of Mull. Sandy frequently added a little mustard and a pinch of salt to the coffee.

About the beginning of the war the hay shed had disintegrated. It was greatly missed. We had kept hundreds of hens since about 1927. Feedstuffs became scarce during the war and the hens were given up. There were three excellent timber sectional Miller hen houses lying unused and so they were moved one by one to the Stack Yard. One became Sandy's workshop, the two others became The Cabins, where Sis and Sandy spent three months every year while he was at Oxford. Fitted with a closed fire, electric cooker,etc, well carpeted and lined with suitable insulating materials, the Main Cabin was extremely comfortable, in summer and in winter, and when Sandy finally retired into Thalassa, the Main Cabin became his study. It was here that The Tub was finally placed, where a cold plunge each day was the rule for both of them. Its water supply came from the original continuously running Thalassa supply.

From 1948 onwards until Sandy retired in 1961, Thalassa was occupied successively by Jack Ralston and family, then by George and Molly Law and family, and finally by Brigadier Sandy and Mrs Joan Prain.

The three main dwelling houses were connected to the county water main after the serious drought in the early 1950s. Cattle drinking troughs were installed in the fields at the same time. What an immediate benefit this water supply was during droughts, in saving the labour of wheeling water pumped from the well to cattle drinking troughs at strategic points.

116

A bottomed road led to the north east gateway to the stackyard. Access to Thalassa on foot was along a path through the midden wood, across a slab bridge built by grandfather over the Bridge Burn as the burn was soon called.

Sandy never built a bottomed road to Thalassa. He simply did not see the need for it.

The Cabins were movable, and hence unrateable, but sooner or later they were taxed. Sandy had built himself a dwelling, this time without any permission at all. They were taxed separately from Thalassa. The homestead ended up finally with Thalassa, three cabins, a dry closet, two greenhouses, a coal house, Violet's Hut, and the telescope house.

Sundials had always attracted Sandy. In his youth he had one second-hand leather-bound very out-of-date volume of the *Encyclopedia Brittanica* which contained the section on sundials. A garden ornament rather than an accurate time piece existed on one of the gate posts of the big garden at The Hill. Made of sandstone, it had a brass gnomon.

In 1925 Thom made an excellent sundial for Thalassa garden. He etched a dial on a thick sheet of brass, soldered the gnomon in position, and etched a sinusoidal curve on the sheet from which one could easily read off the correction for application of the equation of time. The device was accurate to within one minute of time. He placed it on a sandstone pedestal bought from the demolishers of Hamilton Palace, wrecked by coal mines undermining the area. An elderly bookseller, Joseph McCardel, who had been a stonemason, cut and cleaned the stonework required for the sundial. He also prepared the stone chair made from a broken trough which in its turn had been made from one of the stone cubes used for the historical Dunlop Cheese Press in the steading. The sundial was very successful, being accurate enough to set one's watch to catch one of the frequent trains.

At Brasenose, Oxford Sandy perfected the College sundial, mounted with its dial vertical on the south facing wall of the quadrangle. Its gnomon consisted of a slender stayed rod, anchored at its top end on the vertical dial.

The building was being repointed and Sandy made the correction table and arranged for it to be fixed under glass in a sheltered coin of the archway nearby. Leslie Styler of Brasenose College has memories of helping Sandy by writing down his readings as he used a theodolite to shoot Jupiter on a clear but bitter frosty February night.

A biography of Alexander Thom would be incomplete without bringing in my Uncle Bill, my late brother Alan and my sister Beryl.

WAS Thom

Wastle as many of the connection called him, since his full name was William Albert Strang Thom, was born at Carradale in 1900, before the flitting to Dunlop. He grew up and attended the primary school at Dunlop. While on a visit to Brackley, the Tindal home in Newlands, history relates that the young Bill's voice was heard at breakfast asking, "Is this a Hull egg?" Aunt Maggie was ensuring that her family got fresh Hill eggs. They were sent in regularly by rail.

After secondary education at Glasgow High School Bill was called up in 1918 and served as a midshipman in the Royal Navy, on patrol vessels in the North Sea, based at Grantown. As sailors sometimes do, he built a model of his ship. Bill Strang saw the model in Bromborough when he visited Wastle during one of his sales journeys — he was a traveller for his uncle's factory products.

When Wastle and Sandy were together they referred to their parents as 'Mater' and 'Pater', pronouncing the vowel 'a' to rhyme with 'slater'.

After demobilisation in 1919, Wastle matriculated in the Faculty of Science at the University of Glasgow and after four years' study duly graduated BSc in Applied Chemistry in 1923. He shortly found employment as a chemist with the soap and margarine manufacturers, Lever Brothers, Port Sunlight, and stayed with that company until the early 1930s. Thereafter in 1934 he returned to his Alma Mater, this time to study medicine. Upon graduation he took up general practice in Peebles where he was a much-loved and respected family doctor.

Bill, like his brother Sandy, had a palky, dry, waggish sense of humour. He had met his Uncle Joe Maclay by accident in Glasgow one day and reported this at home. "What did Uncle Joe talk about?" he was asked. " I can't remember", said Bill, "I was too busy looking to see what my next suit was like!" He must have been a fully grown schoolboy at the time.

In 1924, travelling by train to Port Sunlight he noticed an

advertisement over the shoulder of a fellow commuter's morning paper. It was asking for volunteers to man a British Arctic Expedition in 1925. Joint leaders were to be Commander FA Worsley, RNR (New Zealand) and Grettir Algarsson (British Columbia). The ship was the auxiliary sailing vessel *Island* (pronounced Issland, meaning Iceland). Rigged as a brigantine, ninety-nine feet from stem to sternpost, one hundred and fourteen tons net register, and built of British oak fifty one years before, she had done yeoman service and had beaten to windward round Cape Horn, glory of glories for a small wind-jammer. A semi-Diesel engine had been installed in 1920. It drove her, when all was well, at six knots. She set thirteen sails.

Bill was chosen as second mate and scientist. Worsley had navigated the open lifeboat from Elephant Island to South Georgia in 1914, with Antarctic Expedition leader Shackleton and two or three others, bringing the bad news to the outside world that their ship had been crushed in the pack ice. I remember Worsley visiting Bill at The Hill some months after the Island expedition returned. Strange to relate, fifty years later, when I was on a standing stone surveying expedition for my father on the island of Eday, Orkney, while in the house of Mr and Mrs Burger, I was shown Captain Worsley's rifle. He had presented it to (that old) Burger after his ship had been wrecked nearby. I wonder if it had been used by Worsley in the 1925 expedition, or even in the Antarctic, in the open lifeboat? Mr Burger was a most interesting man. He possessed a flint arrow head, showing proudly the position printed on my 1:10,000 scale map, where he had found it.

Bill posted four letters home from the *Island*, the first one from Liverpool before they set sail on 21st June 1925, the second from Belfast Lough where they dropped the wireless fitter three days later. The *Island* sailed outside of the Hebrides, later taking her departure from North Rona on July 1st. Passing to the east of Bear Island the ship arrived at Spitzbergen on 15th July, 1925 tying up alongside Amundsen's ship *Fram*. The fourth letter, given to a sealer to post on July 30th, reported the damage to the propeller. This letter was posted in Tromsö on 18th August. Bill was having the time of his life. "Last night I sailed the ship for three hours among heavy pack ice with a good breeze, a most exciting proceeding."

While Algarsson and Worsley were navigating in Franz Joseph Land waters, near to the site of Nansen's winter hut, Bill unwittingly asked the name of 'that island over there?'. Though on the chart, it had no name and it was promptly dubbed Thom Island.

Bill had a friend, Mr Yuille, who visited The Hill on occasion. He was a member of the Flying Club at Renfrew Aerodrome in the early 1920s. On several occasions he flew his biplane over Dunlop, doing some aerobatics, to everyone's delight. My brother Alan Watson Thom was thumbing lifts coming north from Fleet, Hants early in the war, when by coincidence Mr Yuille gave him a good lift northward. It turned out that Yuille had become a pilot in Imperial Airways in the early days of passenger flying, but had given it up as he considered it a dangerous occupation, piloting on the London-Paris route in all weathers.

I remember seeing a Weir Autogyro fly over The Hill in 1928. It was during the Round Britain Air Race. Sandy took me to Renfrew Airfield to see the spectacle. He treated me to a five shilling flight — take off, round the airport and a landing. The machine, a Gypsy Moth, was literally a bag of strings; and the noise!

Like his father before him, Bill was good with his hands. He showed me how to fashion a whistle from a twig of rowan tree, the bark of which can be easily twisted free of the wood.

At Peebles, for a lucrative hobby he wrote adventure stories and novels. Some of the titles are *Squall among the Lochs, Wind Force Seven, The Monach Light, Adrift in the Arctic, Restless Tides'*. He wrote under the pen name J Strang Morrison. Morrison was his wife's middle name.

## Alan Watson Thom

> *They shall grow not old, as we that are left grow old:*
> *Age shall not weary them, nor the years condemn.*
> *At the going down of the sun and in the morning*
> *We will remember them."*
>
> Laurence Binyon, 1869–1943

My brother, Alan was killed in a tragic air accident on Friday 27th April, 1945, eleven days before Victory in Europe Day on 8th May, when the end of the war with Germany was celebrated.

When war broke out in 1939, Alan was a schoolboy beginning his sixth year at Kilmarnock Academy. He had been awarded a Speirs Prize in June 1939 for excellence in Mathematics. He and his school friend John McDonald loved outside activities. Once they did some

top: *The Thoms at The Hill in 1930*
*Jeanie and Alexander with children (in descending order) Archie, Alan and Beryl*

bottom: *the family pictured in Fleet, Christmas 1939 — the same cast joined by Archie's future wife Margaret. Alan (left) was to die in a flying accident 6 years later*

goods train jumping instead of hitch-hiking. On a dark night to their dismay they realised their freight wagon was crossing the Forth Bridge, not where they wanted to go.

Whenever the Higher Leaving Certificate examinations were finished in March 1940 (he had Higher English, Mathematics, French, German and Science with Lower History) he left school to work at the Royal Aircraft Establishment, Farnborough. He and John McDonald rode the family tandem to Oxford. In October 1940 he began classes in Engineering at the University of Glasgow, completing the first year in March 1941. He was awarded, for excellence in the classes of the first year, the George Young Bursary of value £45, tenable during 1941–42, provided he attended the course in General Engineering and Drawing. He returned to work at RAE for the summer.

By this time it was very evident that Alan had a first class brain and his father decided to send him to Cambridge. Entrance requirements necessitated that he pass a Latin examination. Alan had had three years of Latin while at Kilmarnock Academy but had dropped that subject in 1937. He had three weeks in which to cram for "Little-go" the popular name for the "Previous examination", the Cambridge University entrance examination of the time. A prospective student had to qualify in a number of subjects, either by taking the examination itself, or by gaining exemption from some, or all, by means of school Certificate credits or other similar qualifications. It was quite common to pass most of the necessary subjects at school and make up one or two (for engineers, very often Latin!) in "Little-go". Mrs John Adamson (of Farnborough) tutored him in Latin translation, to very good effect. He had intense powers of concentration. He passed the Latin examination and matriculated in St John's College in the fall of 1942.

Like other universities, Cambridge was by this time running classes through the long vacation summer terms. Alan began studying at St John's Cambridge in October, 1941.

After studying continuously for twenty one months, Alan was awarded in 1943 a first class degree in Aeronautics in Mechanical Sciences Tripos, which allowed him to graduate BA in 1944. At the end of the Third Year he was elected by St John's College to a £100 Scholarship, subject to residence and available in case he wished to return after the war. He was also awarded a Wright Prize (£5) for books. He won two university prizes, both in 1943: the Ricardo Prize in Thermodynamics (£24) and the John Bernard Seely Prize in Aeronautics (£15). He won one other distinction, although it was not an actual prize, by having his name marked in the Tripos results list as "Distinguished in Aeronautics." No mean accomplishment.

It was 1943. He was twenty years of age and on 12th July was directed to work as an assistant Grade III (£275) at the Ministry of Aircraft Production in London. While there, on 26th January, 1944 he was given a Certificate of Proficiency in the Home Guard. On 5th June, 1944, he was transferred to the RAE Farnborough, to report to Mr Perring, DDRE.

In February, 1945, Alan applied for Election to Fellowship of St John's College. The next Annual Election was to be 30th April, 1945.

Alan never graduated MA because this requires at least a further two years to elapse after the BA is awarded, nor was he elected a Fellow of St John's. He did not live long enough.

No aircraft had as yet been flown experimentally faster than sound. Genuine fears existed concerning the safety and wisdom of flying an aircraft as it approached Mach 1. In the High Speed Flight Department a single engine jet fighter, a Meteor, was being used for in-flight experiments. Jet propelled aircraft were still being developed but the Meteor was the aircraft for the job. Alan was involved in the design and development of an accelerometer, one of the many instruments fitted to this aircraft for recording its performance in a dive. During each successive test the pilot was asked to take the aircraft to a higher and yet higher altitude and to dive it a little faster each time. Work was proceeding well on the project but because the machine was by that time of great historic value, the Air Ministry issued instructions to stop using that particular aircraft as a flying test bed.

While at Cambridge Alan met Jill Shaw, a London University undergraduate evacuated to Cambridge. They became engaged on 14th January, 1945 and it was on a flight in a Lockheed Hudson from Farnborough to the north to visit Jill at her home in Chesterfield, that fuel starvation caused a crash just north of Oxford. Alan was killed. None of the three other personnel on board survived. The Lockheed stalled and rolled over as the pilot was attempting to glide over some trees prior to landing in a field.

Alan, like other staff members at RAE was encouraged to fly. He had logged some forty two hours pilot flying time but had to stop flying lessons because of ear pains while in rapidly climbing aircraft. Alan's death was a great loss.

Beryl Thom

Beryl was born in Thalassa on 14th November, 1926.

She attended Dunlop School, Kilmarnock Academy, St Paul's School for Girls in London, and Guy's Hospital Physiotherapy training Department, where she qualified as a physiotherapist in 1947. She married David T Austin on 14th July, 1947. They had three daughters and one son. David died on 2nd May, 1982. She nursed her father, Alexander Thom at Banavie in the winter of 1981–1982 after his twin cataract operation and broken thigh. She looked after him well at Banavie during the last two years of his life.

The Geyers and Jim Tindal

Ernest Geyer was appointed lecturer in Heat Engines about the same time as Sandy joined the staff at Glasgow. They became friends. Sandy took him yachting in 1923 and 1926. Ernie's mother was a nurse, daughter of Mrs Strong, who had been the highly regarded matron of the Dundee Hospital before she became matron at the Western Infirmary, Glasgow. Mrs Strong had been trained by Florence Nightingale. Ernie's father was Pastor A H Geyer, of the Austrian protestant church in Glasgow. His church was on a small piece of ground near the Domestic School of Science. It was demolished by the authorities in the anti-German frenzy in 1914.

A photographer, an etcher, a hill walker, Pastor Geyer had struck up a friendship after the war with Jim Tindal who had given the Pastor a lift one day near Loch Lomond. Jim moved the sheep dog into the back seat. At that time Jim was farming Blair Vockie, on Ben Lomond.

Pastor Geyer led a party of Scots to explore his own homeland area of Salzkammergut in Austria in 1929. Sandy and Jeanie went and enjoyed it so much that they returned again in 1930 and 1931. In their company were Dr JC Morrison, Agnes W Kirkwood (Aunt Nae), cousin Jean Boyd, and Mr and Mrs Verel (Maria Birrell), then farmers at Dunlop.

Elfriede Jeschko of Hof Mühle, Wels, Salzkammergut, Austria was Ernie Geyer's cousin. She was later to come to Scotland and live with us at The Hill for a six months' period. We all became proficient in German that year. Many years later Elfriede, a nurse, emigrated to USA.

Sandy acquired an ice-axe (at that time ice axes were three feet long), and adapted it for use as a camera stand. He climbed Dachstein, hiring a guide for the day in the snow.

He fancied an Austrian walking stick, bought it from a shop keeper and walked off along the street, followed by a dog. The shop keeper realised what was happening, followed the Scotsman, explaining, "Er kennt die Stock!". He kens the stick!

Ernie Geyer drove a three-wheeler Morgan car. He had been in 'signals' in the trenches in 1914–18, while his father had been interned in Scotland. Ernie pulled my leg on the yacht cruise on Ripple in 1926, tormenting me with the rhyme;

> *Why do the girls all look at me so ?*
> *Is it because of my Greecian nose ?*
> *Or simply because of my elegant pose ?*
> *Or just because I'm Archibald, Archibald, Verre de Verre ?*

Ernie Geyer, James Small and the Skipper were lining up in correct pecking order in the University Library prior to joining the procession into the Bute Hall at a graduation ceremony of the engineering students. Thom's gown was badly crushed and Small remarked, "I see Thom has been yachting in his gown!"

For travel to Glasgow while he was in Arrol's Alexander Thom wore his bowler hat. Accustomed to a felt hat, lifted by grasping the crown, he found instantly that he could not raise his bowler that way to ladies. Rather than learning to grasp the brim on such occasions, he perfected a way of grasping the crown by his five fingers.

Sandy had a kilt while he was assistant Scout master. He wore it occasionally when he came back to The Hill in 1922 to build Thalassa, and at the Carsaig camp. About 1933 Sandy fitted himself out in a tailored kilt, tweed jacket, balmoral hat, etc and wore it frequently as his 'good suit'. He realised the cost effectiveness of the dress. Kilts last a long time. That good kilt is still used by a friend of the family.

About this time he took up ballroom dancing. He and Jeanie

started going to dances and soon he obtained a Prince Charles jacket required for evening wear. On occasion he would don his full evening wear for social occasions in Oxford. It was simpler to use the tandem than to drive and park his car. The sight of a don in Scottish evening dress wearing a gown and mortar board on a tandem raised scarcely a glance in Oxford. In many parts of Scotland however, remarks like "Kilty kilty caul' bum" are thrown gratuitously at wearers of our national dress.

Jeanie liked men in old tattered kilts for casual wear.

For motor-cycling he wore riding breeches with ends laced at calf level covered by his hose and long laced boots. His head-wear was an airman's helmet, with fur skip, held in position by a leather buckled strap. In winter he wore a flying suit. He refused to wear the fashionable 'plus fours', best described as knickerbockers or fitted riding breeches with four inches of cloth added, which extra cloth made them resemble, above the calf and over the knee, the 'nickie tams' worn by drainers and navvies.


Alexander Thom at The Hill 1924–1939 and after the war

After the death of his father in November 1924, because he was living at Thalassa, Sandy took over the farm maintenance. The property belonged to his mother but Lily took nothing to do with it, and Wastle was with Lever Brothers at Port Sunlight.

Lily was not at home and Sandy moved over immediately to live in the Bungalow to hold the place together. Lizzie the dairymaid kept milking the cow and Charlie Hutchison was kept for the work of painting the farm machinery, etc, for the displenishing sale held at Commoncraig where Mr Reid had died. David McCardel, a student of Mining Engineering at RTC, lived in Thalassa acting as caretaker. I can remember AT reading out to me an adventure romance by RM Ballantine while we were both in bed. I had 'flu' and my father had lumbago.

Income from grass rents amounted to about £1.50 per acre and the rent paid by Mr and Miss Hay for the steading was £28 per annum. Sandy's father had scraped a meagre income, adding to the grass rent by keeping a few sheep, two cows, some calves, two horses, (Dick and Dobbins), some hens, and by selling soft fruit. One year he had sold half a ton of fruit. One of the horses, Dick, was sold at the displenishing sale along with sundry ploughs, carts, grubbers, etc. Sandy was not going to 'farm' the place, but he still loved the site and wanted to bring up his family there.

He decided to run a hen farm, as hens seemed to be paying reasonably well. A man was hired to work a five and a half day week and the family did the weekends.

By 1926 things had adjusted. He was extending Thalassa, and settling down to maintaining the property. The additional income from the hens with the grass rents and the steading rent held the business together, but the only one really to profit from it financially was the hired labourer (firstly Charlie Hutchison, then as time passed, George Beveridge, Tom Knight, James Thomson, Hugh Archibald). The hired man at least got his £2.50 weekly wage. Sandy had the pleasure of living on the beautiful site and had the fun of maintaining it. Jeanie and the rest of the family did of course do a lot of work.

Men working in the fields did not carry pocket watches but if they were within sight and sound of the railway, passing trains gave an accurate idea of the time of day. During the period of George Beveridge's employment at The Hill, a second way of knowing the time of day became available. A bus service was begun about 1929 in opposition to the railway. George obtained a bus timetable and soon had two ways of knowing the time of day.

Hugh Archibald possessed a muzzle-loading gun. He regaled us describing how it kicked his shoulder when overloaded with powder. It was sold by Martin of Paisley, a cousin of Sandy Prain's.

A sore point with Alexander was the very high payments paid annually to the Church of Scotland. Called the teinds, or tithes, they had to be paid. Fixed at one time by the price of corn, and so varying annually, the Church had managed to arrange for a stabilising of the amounts payable, the fixing being done during a year of high corn prices. Some farms had small teinds; others had large teinds. The Hill had teinds which were much higher than the average. In the 1930s the teinds took about 50% of the grass rents received.

Sandy's resentment over this unequal burden showed itself one day when he met Mr William Bain in St Enoch's Station, Glasgow. Willie was the incumbent minister of Dunlop High Church. The leading Greek scholar in Scotland at the time, he was friendly with Sandy's mother, who attended his church. Her brother James Strang had died some years before, and Lily decided to instal two beautiful stained glass windows in the High Church, in memory of James. This was too much for Sandy, even although he was very friendly with James Strang's son, William. When he met Willie Bain he accused him of being a snivelling little Roman Catholic priest. The author asked William Strang's opinion about putting this anecdote in this biography. William thought it should be included. Sandy was no churchman, although his religious education in his youth had not been neglected. He knew his scriptures well.

In the spring the incubators had to be maintained, the freshly hatched chicks reared, the cockerels sold off when they developed combs — sexing of day-old chicks was too expensive. Young female hens (poulets) were valuable. One with a broken leg was saved by splints and plaster of Paris. Always hens had to be fed, eggs gathered, hens shut in from the predatorial fox, eggs washed and marketed. It was touch and go. At the peak Sandy had six hundred hens. He joined the SPBA, (Scientific Poultry Breeders' Association) in a brave attempt to make it pay well. Every building on the steading was used in some way. The barn was converted for hens. He tried extra feeding there in the late evenings, lighting the petrol lamp and feeding the hens nightly. The extra food was supposed to make them lay more. Rats were attracted to food bins. Sandy lashed a spotlight to a sawn-off shotgun with which he shot many rats in the dark.

When physical energy permitted, there was firewood aplenty for the cutting. Trees could be felled for sawing into fencing posts, gateposts and planking. There is great pleasure and satisfaction in making ones own artifacts from home-grown timber, such as ash, elm, sycamore, chestnut, box-wood, gean and cherry.

Felling trees was a task enjoyed by everybody. In these days a huge double handed Canadian saw was the only means of cutting the thick boles. A horizontal cut was invariably made on the side of the tree towards the path of fall. A sharp woodman's axe was then swung to notch the bole so that finally it fell as if on a hinge like a thin plank when sawn in from behind. Frequently trees had to be felled from their positions too near to buildings, too near to other trees or too near to the public road, and ropes had to be used made fast to a chosen fixed place at ground level, the upper end being as high up the tree as it was possible to fasten it. The problem was, how to get the rope up there. Our ladders were often not long enough and tree climbing is not too safe. Sandy often overcame the difficulty by using his bow and shooting an arrow over a lofty branch. Attached to the arrow would be a long thin thread. Once the thread was over the bough a light string was made fast to the thread and pulled over. A yet thicker string was finally used to haul the guy rope over. If the wind sprang up from the wrong direction, a second rope was needed to pull the whole tree against the wind. Sometimes a four to one block and tackle was used.

Friends were often invited to spend a day at felling a tree. Many hands made light work, especially of the cross-cut sawing required at the stump. Timber felling is arduous but rewarding work. It is but the harvesting of a crop.

About 1930 Sandy began to cultivate the big garden in earnest. Vegetables of all kinds were grown — soft fruit, plums, apples. The garden had to be dug and I remember seeing him digging in the dark in a dry spell in February using the twin mantle pressure petrol lamp which helped to make night into day about the outhouses. This lamp was better than his father's paraffin hurricane lamp which served only to illuminate the darkness in the byre when he was milking Culleddy (Cowlady).

The 1920s saw the beginning of the age when many more people owned a motor car. Here was the horseless carriage which allowed much greater range of travel. The result was that friends and relations came in greater and yet greater numbers to visit The Hill. On occasion at weekends five or six cars would be seen parked at the top of the avenue. The family referred to these visitations as 'invasions'. At invasions the author met many of his uncles, aunts and cousins of all ages, The Connection.

My first memory of 'The Connection' was at Aunt Martha Maclay's Christmas party at Duchal in 1921. We had come up from West Kilbride by train. I was three years and five months old, a wee boy amongst all of the bigger folk. My party piece was given — "He was asked to a fancy dress ball, but had nothing too wear at all. He thought he would risk it and go as a biscuit, but the dog ate him up in the hall!"

Sis was always gracious and we younger family members enjoyed the 'invasions'. At meals it was "Deal sma' and serve a'."

Discussions at Thalassa were many and varied. Dr Alex Fraser who had known Sam Strang and Compton Mackenzie at Salonika in 1915, brought his friend Mr Hay, a mathematics school teacher from

Glasgow. Mr Hay related his experience while travelling home from a missionary post in China en route from Vladivostock to Europe on the trans-Siberian railway. He boarded the train and found he had been allocated a berth beside a Russian. He spoke to this gentleman in English, in French and then in German but the fellow traveller had none of these languages. Communication was thereafter made by sign language, until, a day later, Mr Hay tried Latin. The Russian spoke Latin and for the next three days of the journey they chatted in Latin.

Arboriculture appealed to Sandy. About 1955 he obtained several special Seqouia trees, named Dawn Redwood. They grow well on The Hill soil. Deciduous, they were unknown until about 1940 when they were 'discovered' in a valley in China. Until then they were known only to palaeontolgists who knew they had existed by identifying their pollen grains in sedimentary rocks — hence the name Dawn Redwood.

While the family was growing up Sandy often made them toys. He made me a wheelbarrow of sycamore planks and he made a scooter. He taught me to weave on a small border loom brought from USA by his Uncle Willie, about 1909. Many of his homemade toys, pieces of furniture and artifacts of wood succumbed to woodworm as the years passed. He made me a crane from Meccano, powered by the spring of a worn out alarm clock. He brought home a Christmas present of a model steam railway engine, an oscillating cylinder job, heated by methylated spirit. A circle of rail track with lengths of straights allowed an oval layout. Later a set of movable points arrived, with an X-crossing. He then made a second set of fixed points so that the engine could loop-turn unattended at the end of the corridor in Thalassa and retrace its track before being manually switched at the circle at the main end. The second set of points was carefully cut out of standard rails soldered successfully together.

One summer time cousin Bill Strang passed on his model steam battleship which sailed successfully on the Horse Pond. Home made submarines with propellers successfully driven by elastic added to the fleet.

Sandy made excellent paper gliders which demonstrated the principles of elevator and rudder control. He started me off on making propeller-driven model aircraft, powered by elastic. A Meccano tower was built with a vertical shaft round which rotated a 36-inch arm driven by a wooden propeller turned by a robust rejected winding-up Hornby railway engine power-pack he had picked up cheaply. Another power-pack arrived, this time in the form of a 6 volt dc motor. This required three 2 volt accumulators, charged by the water wheel dynamo. Meccano was an excellent toy, useful for teaching boys about structural design.

Sandy saw the boys and their visitors (John Tindal was one of them) playing with model boats made from thin wooden planks sharpened at one end. They had wooden masts and sails of thick brown paper stiffened by candle wax. The boys were racing the boats on the pond at Thalassa back door — The Cement — used in winter as a wee skating rink. Sandy promptly made his own, hollowing out the hull and leaving a long thin keel which made his model a winner. It planed, like the flying boat hulls about which he knew so much. He taught us about the 'step' formed in flying boat hulls to allow the craft to break away sooner for take-off.

A four feet high box kite was made and flown regularly on suitably windy days. Boomerangs were played with. Daughter Beryl was not forgotten — a pensioned-off pit pony called Donald arrived at The Hill, obtained from the childrens' uncle David McCardel, by now a mine manager. Donald was not really broken in for riding, but Sandy thought he would make a wee buggy for Beryl. He did this, using the frame of the side-car of the by now derelict FN motor cycle. Donald never pulled the buggy. Someone unloaded a bridle and saddle on the family, but truth to tell we were not horsey folk and Donald had a really lazy retirement.

After Sandy retired in 1961 he arranged for double doors to be made in the east gable of the stable building, below the dovecote, so that he could garage his car in the stable. The stalls were removed and the thick planks, covered with hoof marks, were used to make doors for the arched entrance to the barn.

Sandy had kept Dobbins until about 1927, a very useful one horse-power tractor as it were. After the war Sandy invested in a 10hp OTA tractor with a single plough attached and this machine was well used. Some ground was ploughed and Hughie Archibald was sowing oat seed. Jeanie was thrilled watching the old man relive his youth. In earlier days all seed was sown by hand from the canvas tray. Her description of his back view as he swung from side to side was graphic. Hughie had been a farmer of course, taught by his father. He was skilfully using hands and arms only, not a bow, for spreading the seed. The oats grew well and Sandy arranged the tractor to drive his father's threshing machine by a suitably arranged belt from one jacked-up wheel. The date would be about 1951.

Mr Allen of Oxford visited the Engineering Laboratory to discuss his design of rock-digging plant. I doubt if the Channel Tunnel was discussed, but Sandy learned about the Allen Scythe produced in Oxford. He bought one which turned out to be a very useful machine for reaping long grass. The Hill became much more tidy looking. Hay made earned a pound or two yearly for long enough until the huge hay-making machines used in open fields made the making of small amounts of hay by hand absolutely uneconomic.

Sandy loved making things work, making gadgets which functioned. The challenge was in the making of the devices. While making the concrete floor for the septic tank for Thalassa in 1926 it became obvious that the wet concrete was going to be ruined by water welling up from below. The tent was pitched to provide shelter, and a semi-rotary pump of his father's rigged up forthwith. This was pumped by us all in watches by hand, but at one period he rigged up a belt drive from the rear wheel brake rim on the Precision motorcycle which chugged away for a time on its own. When the cement had finally set, the hole left after extraction of the hose-pipe was sealed using quick-setting plaster of Paris. He was never stuck for ideas.

My father built a canoe for me when I was about nine years old.

This was his third canoe. Watching him draw out its 'lines', the cross sections, seeing the oak knees being cut out in Howie's sawmill and watching him build it was very instructive to a young boy. He used steamed green ash for the strakes and covered the lot with unbleached calico dressed with boiled linseed oil and painted.

He wanted me to be able to handle small boats and in this he succeeded admirably, because it taught me watercraft — in the Horse Pond at The Hill. He stepped a mast and taught me how to sail. The Horse Pond, called the Dam most of the time, because my grandfather had adapted it to store water for running the water wheel, was primarily a storage reservoir, but it gradually filled with silt and mud. During a dry summer, Tom Knight's nephew Jim Macaulay spent his week's holiday (he was a spindle machinist in Beith) digging the mud from the dam. The spoil was simply thrown out on the banks. The Dam was then of course much more useable for the canoe as well. Some time later a pair of gold-rimmed spectacles was found on the muddy bank, washed clean by the rain. Sandy remembered that a Miss Elder, while visiting The Hill in Edwardian times, had lost her spectacles; they had fallen into the dam and had eluded searchers in the mud.

A wooden sledge was built too, big enough for two grown-ups, suitable for use on some of the steeper parts of the fields.

When mains electricity was installed in 1948, lighting made the biggest impact, turning night into day in the outbuildings. Electric motors were next on the list of conveniences, followed by kettles, cookers, radiators for spot heating and rectifiers for battery charging.


Alexander Thom afloat

Uncle Sam Strang (1876-1957) built himself a cruising yacht, *Betty*, in 1914, naming it after his daughter. Sam frequently took Sandy sailing before the war. In fact they were in the parish of Barra, in the Outer Hebrides, anchored in Inner Oitir Mhor on 4th August, 1914 when war broke out. They were boarded by coastguard officers whose duty it was to investigate all ship movement. Officialdom was looking for radio transmitters.

Sandy had made himself a canoe for paddling in the Horse Pond when he was a schoolboy, and a better-designed canoe for paddling in the river in Ontario.

Before the war, on occasion Sandy had crewed on yachts *Raider*, *Sayonara* and *Thora*. On one weekend cruise a practical joker gave him a pill, a supposed laxative. Its only effect however was to make the victim urinate a bright green colour. His family were, needless to say, very concerned about this, and called in their doctor. Sam Strang took great exception to this trick, letting the joker know about it in no uncertain terms.

The call of salt water led him to buy a 21 feet half-decked centre-board gaff-rigged sloop *Freya* which he could sail single-handed. Wastle helped him once to step the mast alongside a jetty while fitting out. He probably sailed *Freya*, for parts of four seasons, 1917,18,19 and 20, but this is uncertain. Jim Tindal talked of spending a night in "the open yacht at Port Bannatyne". Presumably the open yacht was *Freya*.

In the south Sandy again felt the call of the sea and owned and sailed an open boat on the Solent. The author distinctly remembers sailing in this dinghy in his third year of age. Sandy and his family, on a sailing picnic, landed on the Isle of Wight and began to light a fire of dry driftwood below high water mark. They were promptly instructed by a ranger to depart. Sandy thought he was entitled to be there, but as it was a Royal Estate, the beach picnic had forthwith to come to an end. The Crown owns the bottom of the sea.

Although Sandy was to become one of the 'Old Salts' of the Hebrides, he never owned another vessel after that dinghy in the Solent.

For decades Sandy chartered yachts of various displacement through brokers like Blair and Binnie. This is no place to detail ships and cruises and crews, but in 1925 the charter from Roseneath was to begin on a Saturday afternoon. The previous charterer brought the yacht, *White Heather*, to Roseneath twenty four hours late. Sandy and his crew of five spent the night on the beach. It was, fortunately, a good spell of weather. The calms had held back the other skipper and as frequently happened, the auxiliary was, to say the least of it, not running well.

Sandy sailed hard on his cruises. He felt that two or three weeks afloat 'cured' him for the rest of the year. He never had 'adventures' however, always planning prudently ahead and reducing sail in time. He was never embayed on a lee shore. He taught his crews well, instilling into their minds the motto 'One hand for the Ship, one for Yourself'. He taught weather lore for the North Atlantic which he had learned before the days of radio forecasts — "First rise after low often brings a stronger blow", and how to forecast if a Backing Wind (against the clock) or a Veering Wind (with the clock) was being logged. Often it is wise to put to sea in order to make a safer anchorage. He was always conscious of the "weather".

In September 1945 he and Jim Wilson sailed with Sam Strang and Walter Strang in the Clyde Cruising Club's yacht *Rosemary* for a long weekend. It was their first cruise since 1939. Sam Strang owned a '1924' yacht *Robina* in the middle 1920s (19 feet on the water line and 24 feet overall). An excellent helmsman, Sam started to win races with *Robina* immediately. He taught Walter and Fulton the same sport. As schoolboys they would travel to the Holy Loch, take *Robina* to sea in a gale, sail up and down the starting line, really challenging older crews to race, but nobody would come out and the boys went back to their mooring. After one hard race Sam's crew found a gold watch which had slid down from behind the slats lining the cabin. The yacht had been sailed so hard that the watch, lost by an unknown person years before, had worked loose and come to light.

Sam was full of yachting lore which he passed on to Sandy. He was also full of his wartime experiences and talked at great length about them, so much so that his son Walter, who saw Naval Service in the Mediterranean in the next war, never told his father anything of his adventures between Spain, North Africa and Vichy France. Meantime Sam was on the water patrol on the Upper Clyde, policing the river. He managed to be bombed, was in the water, took pneumonia and recovered to tell the tale. After the war he asked Sandy to listen carefully whenever Walter was talking and to pass on any snippets of information.

Sam sold his yacht *Robina* before 1930 at an excellent profit (after all she had won many races) but rumour had it that the new sportsman found out that he himself was not the helmsman he thought he was.

Sandy was not a racing man — he liked plenty of sea room and felt embarrassed by the close proximity of yachts on the starting line, while rounding marker buoys, etc. He had, however, raced enough with Sam to know how to get the very best out of his ship from wind, sea and tide. In fact, while racing home from Belfast with Sam, Sandy's seamanship and aerodynamics came to the fore. *Torridon* and a gaff-rigged cutter were ghosting along neck and neck before a light southerly breeze, with spinnakers set. Sandy got Sam's permission to set a jib below the boom of the mainsail, pulling it out by an ingenious arrangement of light line available, without hauling *Torridon*'s boom in-board. Had the light wind been spilled from the mainsail the other vessel would have gained several lengths. The outcome was that *Torridon* was first to cross the finishing line at Hunter's Quay, but next year a new rule came out — "No Water Sails Allowed". Sandy claimed he had altered yacht racing rules that year!

For many years the Clyde Cruising Club published *Sailing Directions for the West of Scotland*, a very useful volume. Thom loved exploring new and unreported anchorages and one of his hobbies was to send in plans of such havens. This meant several hours of careful checking in each place. After a tracing had been taken from the 6-inch scale OS survey plans available in libraries, he would write up a report. He kept in touch with the editors of the *Sailing Directions* (one of them was RG Mowat).

In these days yachts were not fitted with echo-sounders. Instead excursions in the dinghy were necessary in order to sound the whole harbour effectively.

Many times while sailing into or out of Loch Crinan, we saw the summer residence of the family of Professor Jenkin, the first Professor of Engineering Science at Oxford. His establishment was reached by boat from Crinan harbour. The house, on the point of the mainland, had no access road.

Sandy loved the Crinan canal. His colleague William MacGregor, whom he had taught as a student, was brought up in Ardrishaig. Many a yarn came Sandy's way via MacGregor. A Mr Sidney MacEwan gave a broadcast over the BBC radio, which moved Sandy to write the following letter on 12th March, 1977 —

Dear Mr MacEwan,
My son and I just missed your broadcast but we understand that you referred to Swallow. I remember one night many, many years ago taking a boat into the sea lock at Ardrishaig. I did not know how to work the gates or the lights and I was standing somewhat hesitantly in the dark on the bridge when two figures slunk along the other side of the road. Just as they passed a voice came, "Ach, its yourself, Doctor". A voice much relieved. The two were Swallow and Mr MacGregor returning from an expedition. Many years later MacGregor's son William explained to me he was worried about his father because by that time he (WG as he initialled himself) was in a responsible position and did not want an arrest of his father to appear in the papers. The next time I met him he said, "I've made an honest man of my father. I've bought him a river." After a month or two I asked him how his father was enjoying his river and he said, "Fine, he is out every night." And then he admitted that his father had told him, "Ach, the fun's out of it now." I remember, later on still, going in to see the old man on his death bed. He thought I was Swallow. This I consider to be one of the greatest compliments that was ever paid to me. I suppose my voice had drifted into the slight Highland twang which I acquired in my youth.

Did you know MacGregor?
Alexander Thom

Until the advent of butane gas, paraffin Primus stoves were used for cooking. While cruising Sandy invariably made breakfast before taking his ship to sea. He had discovered that if it was left to others, it always took twice as long and he wanted to cruise, not lie at anchor eating. He frequently cooked other meals — on one cruise he had been sailing so hard that no trips ashore had been possible to replenish stores, such as fresh bread. He made pancakes by the dozen. The crew ate them as quickly as he could cook them. He made steamed dumplings frequently. His philosophy as cook was always to attempt to make a little less than enough. The crew then rose from meals with feelings of pleased satisfaction. He boasted about 'setting a jelly' while sailing across the Minch one August night.

In the summers of the 1930s Sandy often sailed *Torridon* from Fairlie Roads during the week, thus introducing many people to sailing. He was a first class seaman and never in all the time that the author sailed with him did he have a misadventure at sea. I never saw him seasick, but he was not immune. He instilled into all of the crews who sailed under him the importance of never having adventures. He always reduced sail in time and took great care of his ships and crews. He taught us all to be good foredeck men, and to be especially careful with the anchor. He told us of the man who went to the bottom with his anchor, and of the man who stood in a coil of chain as the anchor plunged to the bottom tearing off his foot. He taught us never to throw an anchor from the foredeck. "Always keep a good look-out, never become embayed, and keep one hand for the ship and one hand for yourself."

The Fastnet race disasters moved him to write the following letter, a carbon copy of which is in his 1979 file, undated and unsigned —


The Editor,
    The Daily Telegraph
    Sir, It is a well known phenomenon that a shallow patch in the ocean bed acts as a lens and brings the waves to a focus behind it.
    In the Fastnet race the waves were possibly 2,000 feet long and so were running at a speed of about 100 feet per second in deep water. But in a depth of 50 fathoms speed would be reduced to something less than this. It follows that at the edges of the shallow patch the waves would bend

inwards and so would meet behind the patch, thus
producing a very violent sea. I do not have to hand a chart
of the area but I see from an ordinary atlas that there are one
or two patches of this nature in a direct line from Land's End
to Fastnet. Did the navigators realise how important it was
to keep well clear of these patches?

AT

A highlight in his sailing experience was his seven day non-stop
voyage bringing Andrew Tindal's 12-metre yacht *Cerigo* from Brixham
to the Clyde. *Cerigo* had no auxiliary.

*Bloodhound*, then a Royal Yacht, passed Sandy in a light breeze in
the Sea of the Hebrides like a stately Spanish Galleon. The sighting
stirred him to write to Buckingham Palace pointing out that the Queen
and the Duke of Edinburgh and their entourage in the Royal Yacht
were missing the real atmosphere of the Hebrides by being taken into
busy open roads to anchor. He supplied a list of suitable quiet sheltered
bays and landlocked anchorages, of which there are hundreds. The
Duke's equerry acknowledged the letter.

Sandy was very aware of the depopulation of the West Highlands. In
1932, sailing through Kyle Rona, between Raasay and South Rona,
we became aware of a boy watching us navigate through the channel.
He ran from one vantage point to the next, the longer to see us. His
home was visible, the only house on Eilean Tigh (House Island). In
other years a woman would wave a towel at us from the house.
Nowadays the house is practically invisible, its ruins having merged
into the overgrown landscape. We often anchored in Acarsaig Mhor,
the beautiful land-locked 'Big Harbour' on the west coast of South
Rona and visited the one inhabited house, the home of the MacRaes,
two brothers and a sister. There were no other inhabitants on the island
except the lighthouse keeper at the north end. A village had existed
at Acarsaid Thioram, the 'Dry Harbour', but it was by that time
derelict. Pupils' books could still be seen through the windows of the
school.

On one visit to South Rona, when my mother was not with him,
the MacRaes asked for the 'red woman'. They remembered her ruddy
complexion. The MacRaes aged and became too frail to work their

croft. We were told that they developed scurvy and had to go to an Old Folks' Home on Skye. Since then their home has been unoccupied, except on occasion by visiting shepherds who come to dip their sheep.

Whenever Sandy boarded a yacht he saw to it that as soon as possible the deviation chart for the ship's compass was checked, or a new one made. Yacht owners are often incapable of making the table or graph required. It is simply a matter of measuring, for each of say twenty courses or directions of the ship's head, the difference between the magnetic bearing of the course as taken from the Admiralty chart or read from a good hand-held compass some distance from the cockpit, and the bearing given by the ship's own compass. Depending upon the magnetic field surrounding the yacht engine and propeller shaft, this deviation can be dangerously large. Engine installations are frequently and of necessity near to the compass. Heeling angle has an effect as well. Sandy liked to know all about the compass so that he could navigate in safety on a course of, say fifty miles, in the dark or in fog, across the Sea of the Hebrides and make a sure and safe landfall. He insisted that anchors (which can be magnets) were always stowed in exactly the same position on board. He was making sure that the 'adventure' of being embayed in a gale, for example, would never happen.

Navigating through the Crinan Canal was always interesting. Modern chartered yachts usually had engines, some of them with a reverse, but Sandy had been introduced to sailing in the days of no auxiliaries. A horse and its rider were hired to tow the ships through. Sandy knew the canal drill well. It was customary to have a bucket on the counter tied to the yacht with a 2-fathom length of rope. As a lock was approached the bucket was kicked over by the skipper to act as a drogue, effectively to take way off the ship. One time Sandy kicked the bucket over. To his dismay it was not made fast to the ship and sank immediately. His face was a study. He had lost a good bucket; but his ship had too much way and instant attention was needed to get a line ashore. That yarn was told often at his expense.

He enjoyed chatting with fishermen in the canal basins. Once, telling them where he had been two nights ago, he had remarked that he had come out from the anchorage in the Treshnish Isles through the north passage by the Irishman, a distinct rectangular rock. "If we had seen you we'd have said you were acquant," said one of the fishermen.

139

Sailing small ships is a strenuous sport. Age and infirmity overtook Sandy at last. He had to stop cruising on his beloved west coast. His last cruise to the Outer Hebrides was on *Aline* in 1974 when he was eighty. David Austin took him on a weekend sail on *Kerry Mist* in 1975. His final "sail", in October, 1978, was on the Crinan canal on David's ship. Beryl drove him to the canal, his beloved canal. He boarded the yacht at Bellanoch and really enjoyed himself. In one of the locks while tending the ropes, a callow youth on an accompanying yacht alongside was chatting politely, "Have you been through the canal before, Sir?"

"Yes, fifty seven times." A fitting remark from the Argyllshire man that he was. He wrote to Sandy Prain about that day —

I had a little sail on the canal last Saturday. Beryl took me
there to come through part of the way with David's boat
which was coming home. He suggested that I should go on
to Inverkip with them but I knew there was a gale coming
up and in fact they were down to bare poles before the wind
and still going fast.

Thom was a hard sailor, achieving long passages between dawn and dusk by setting sail before breakfast, a habit not entirely enjoyed by some members of his crews. A memorable sail in one daylight was from Isle Oronsay, Skye, to Crinan, a distance of some ninety six miles, under sail all the way. The Clyde Cruising Club had a cup which could be won by a log written up for a fourteen day cruise. With a six-man crew, hard sailing Thom once wrote up his log and won the Ogg Cup easily.

Alexander was an excellent conversationalist. He told countless yarns in the cabins of his yachts after excellent meals. He reminisced frequently, passing on the lore of the coast —

Sheltered anchorages attract large numbers of yachtsmen.
Young bloods used up some of their excess energies at night
by slipping quietly aboard a neighbouring yacht after dark.
Burgee halyards were carefully cast off, a light line attached
to the end and taken back on board their own ship. An
hour's rhythmic pulling on the long line to the masthead of

the victim's ship rocked the boat steadily from side to side. The operation was put into reverse. Remarks bandied between the two yachts next morning can be imagined; 'stormy night outside'; 'rollers coming round the point'; 'we never noticed it', etc.

A cruel trick was to drift downwind on to a yacht with sleeping crew. The bowsprit was then butted one mighty blow with a sweep. The culprits disappeared downwind into the darkness.

At one time the Cock of Arran was a large upright boulder shaped like a rooster. Legend has it that this landmark was destroyed by naval gunners using it as a target. There is no bird-like rock there now.

Love of small ships dies hard. Once upon a time there was an elderly Greenock yachtsman whose wife extracted a promise from him not to replace his yacht but simply to do small repairs and maintenance work on it. An unexpected storm broke the yacht up at her moorings and the yachtsman was combing the beach in disconsolate frame of mind. His eyes lit up when he found her hatch-cover with name painted on it. He wrapped the cover up in brown paper and took it to his friend Mr Fyfe the yacht builder in Fairlie, who knew about the promise to the wife. Said the yachtsman; "Willie, would you mend that?"

Mention of Fyfe brings to memory the skill demanded by him from his craftsmen — the screw nails had to finish up with slots parallel to hinges etc. A sacrilegious story of the next generation is as follows. The screw nails were driven in by hammer (Birmingham screw driver) and the tradesman was being ticked off by the boss for not having the slots right. The boss said what do you think the slots are for ? The man replied, For taking the screw nails out.

Alexander had made himself a sextant in his student days. Graduating the arc had been difficult for him. He bought a wooden one, which was probably made about 1810 — unfortunately the nameplate has fallen out of its housing. He presented it to his Alma Mater, in its sextant-shaped original wooden box.

After the 1939–45 war he bought several ex-RAF integrating bubble-sextants for five shillings each, one of which he adapted for use from the deck of a yacht for finding 'distance offshore from terrestrial altitude.

He wrote a memo on the problem, using some simple mathematics and his knowledge of earth's curvature and refraction. In his own words, "the method, by measuring the altitude of the object on land above the shore line is in many cases rapid and easy. But the matter is complicated when the shore line is much nearer than the object or the shore line is 'hull down'." (The author is indebted to Mrs Ruth Dare who sent the original memo and two graphs which were among her late husband Victor Dare's papers.)

Sandy Prain gave him a brass sextant. Let the Skipper describe it in his own words —

> The sextant in this wooden box was given to me by Brigadier A Prain, ARTC. He got it from his uncle, a sea captain who used it last century to navigate back and forward from Montrose to the Baltic ports. He died in 1912. I made the wooden box and used the sextant on the west coast of Scotland, principally for getting distances off the coast.
>
> I remember one night leaving Barra Head in the late evening. In the dawn we were off Gunna Sound between Coll and Tiree. There is a rock to watch. I tried to get the distance off by measuring the height of two hills on Tiree, but my eyesight had gone and so I was faced with the problem of teaching a member of the crew (Douglas Gibson) how to use a Vernier. But we got through OK although the wind did come away later.

The above incident took place on SY *Molita* the morning after our epic visit to Barra head Lighthouse when the Keeper reported she was the first yacht he had seen at anchor there in seven years. Sandy was a careful navigator. He was worrying about the cross tide off Gunna Sound in the light breeze at the time. Douglas can still read a vernier.

My father's sense of humour was highly developed, waggish and palky. His repertoire of stories was large and varied. Their quality will indicate the kind of humour Sandy possessed —

> At a county dinner, a young lady had spilt plum juice on a new white frock and exclaimed, "Dae ploom stanes come

oot Willie?"

"Och dinna worry lassie, I've swallow'd yin mony a time!"

In his aircraft industry days, one of the drawing office cracks was — Why did the rudder lever? Because it saw her pylon stays!

The shape of City of Glasgow tram car body work at one time made it possible for boys to travel unseen by the conductor. The City fathers decided to stop the practice by displaying a printed notice for all to read "No boy with pride ever steels a ride". Soon grafiti appeared below, "No girl with pluck ever sees him stuck!" Overnight the notices were removed.

Sandy's sense of humour was enjoyed by all. He knew of course when to use it and when not to overdo it. One of his stories he told about himself has no end. He asked one of his departmental secretaries a simple question, "Will you answer Yes or No to my question?" The lady fell for it and so Sandy merely asked, "Are you still sleeping with the same man?"

Sandy could tell a story against himself. The winter of 1939–40 was severe. He had to cycle some four miles from his home in Fleet to 'The Factory'. On a bitter morning he passed a platoon of marching soldiers. A loud remark coming from the wit, "Are you ill, or do you always look like that?" amused him (and later, of course, his family) greatly. He probably was ill, as he had a bad bout of 'flu' that winter.

A customer desirous of knowing if his footwear had been repaired by the Dunlop shoemaker, Are ma bits din Matha? They were din afore ye brought them in!

One farmer at market to another, Did you know that your son has put my daughter in the family way? Has he. The clumsy bugger — and he broke a spade last week.

Scene: At aperitif time before dinner at William and Helen's home in West Kilbride, Helen excused herself saying she had a tart to cover in the kitchen. Quick as knife, Sandy saw his chance, "I think I'd make a better job of that than you, Helen."

A farmer was in serious trouble with the factor, so serious that he decided to ask the minister's advice. After listening to the woes of the parishioner, the minister responded, "Take it to the Lord in prayer."

Two days later the pair of them met in the street. "Minister! God's the Boy! The factor's dead!"

Animal tracks in the snow are always of interest. Sandy could trick children into thinking they were seeing tracks of a very strange animal by leaving a trail of impressions made by his knuckles.

My mother had a great sense of humour too. She said once, when a new war had broken out somewhere, "Whose side are we on?" She was once returning home from Beith to Dunlop in the last bus. It stopped when a notorious inebriated gentleman called Rab Gillan rose to stagger along the bus to the exit. As Rab descended the steps the whole bus was told,

"See this parcel? It's a lamp globe! If I can get this hame withoot breakin' it, Ah can say tae ma wife Ahm sober!" Rab wisnae fu', he jist had plenty.

Sandy loved the Para Handy stories. With crew of Skipper, Engineer and cabin Boy, the Puffer was charging full speed at Inveraray pier while Para patiently gave the official order by voice tube to the engineer,

"Stoap her Dougie. Just when ye'r ready!"

He frequently told this one. The Vital Spark was lying this Saturday night beached by a jetty. Para asked the mate, returning from getting the messages, What did you get? Six bottles of whisky and two loaves. Och Man! What for did you get all that bread?

Sandy insisted that the following rendering of a nursery rhyme is correct in spite of editors of children's books —

> Dickory dickory dock,
> The mouse ran up the clock!
> The clock struck wan,
> Doon the moose ran!
> Dickory Dickory Dock!

In the same vein the rhyme reputedly running —
> Kyle for a Man,
> Carrick for a coo,
> Cunningham for butter and cheese, Gallowa' for 'oo.

should run —

*Carrick for a man,*
*Kyle for a coo,*
*Cunningham for butter and cheese, Gallowa' for 'oo.*

Sir William Wallace raised his Carrick Spearmen against the English before Bruce's time. Kylie was the old name for an Ayrshire cow. Milk from the cows of hilly Carrick was not as creamy as milk from Kylies.

Many were the sayings that echo down the years from my childhood from the lips of my parents — It's one thing having afternoon tea but it's a different thing eating tatties!

My mother had a saying, 'I've a thirst I wouldn't sell!'

My father described a dark night at sea as being, "Black as a Wolf's throat." He also used "Black as the Earl of Hell's riding Breeches."

The Professor was visiting an elderly friend. Upon the remark that the weather was cold, the host said, 'Yes I'm wearing a chair to keep warm today'.

An east coast woman in a fishing village was asked, where's your husband? She replied, "Plain Mary." Is this a remnant of French from Mary Queen of Scots' time? *En pleine mer* means on the high seas?

A fa'in' stook is a winnin' stook. In windy weather the sheaves were drying quickly.

A faur awa' brugh (halo round the moon) foretells a near haun' storm.

Use of the word 'steerage' at table referred to the possible less polite table manners in the 'steerage' class in ships and Clyde steamers. Pass me a slice of bread please by hand was 'pass it steerage'. In bigger ships, cabins near the rudder and steering gear were less expensive because of the constant yet intermittent noises from the mechanisms and the propellers.

A rumour started at the top of the village as a feather and by the time it got to the toun foot it was a Hen !

There were two churches in Dunlop. Sunday services began at noon. One of the ministers almost always let his congregation out sooner than the other. On the occasions when the two congregations met in the street en route home, it was said to be "a sign of rain".

Snow is referred to as Poor Man's Manure. The grass always seems greener after snow. Is there more nitrogen in it than in rain?

When the Renfrewshire hills are exceptionally clear it is a sign of rain. The sun has legs this evening — a sign of rain.

A story was told about programme dances by the late Hugh Colquhoun, husband of Janet Kirwood. At a dance, each person had a programme supplied with a small pencil with which he or she noted his or her partner for each listed dance. When names were known, it was easy, but on occasion the person booking the dance could forget the name of his partner to be. During the interval one of Hugh's friends asked why Hugh had written 'dt' for the girl's name. Hugh explained, 'She had dirty teeth!' Hugh's brother Norman was to become a dentist.

Miss Peg Guthrie in Dunlop kept the newspaper shop for a while. Gossip in such shops can be superb. A couple, Mr and Mrs John Mitchell, who had married fairly late in life, were being discussed, not maliciously, it must be said, but in a kindly neighbourly fashion because they were both liked and respected. Peg was reported as saying, "It's strange, Nettie is aye that perjink (prim) and John aye lucks as if he had jist pit oan his cla'es wi' the tangs (tongs)." It was true. She was a school teacher, he was the village plumber.

In the pub on the eve of the second world war, an old soldier was asked what he thought of it now. "Och it's a' richt. Jist keep your heed doon and volunteer for bugger a'."

A quotation which AT used often was, "He that complies against his will is of his own opinion still."

Throughout his life, in a sense, Alexander's work was his hobby, especially his research work and his archaeoastronomy. He always had a wide range of interests. As a boy about 1908–1909 Alexander tried his hand at book binding the 1861 *Gazetteer of Scotland*, but did not progress very far. The pile of monthly issues probably came from Finnock Bog Farm.

Sandy's mother played the piano well. His father sang. Wastle played the flute. Someone had left a guitar and a concertina in the Bungalow. There was a pedal-driven harmonium which finally succumbed to the ravages of woodworm. Sandy had a good ear and learned to play the violin. I remember him playing it last about 1925.

He climbed on the Arran ridges, Chir Mhor, the Castles and A'Chir. In the mid-1930s he took a party of students climbing on The Cobbler, at Arrochar. Sandy Crane remembers him saying that a real climber was always recognisable on his way home "He just looks as though he has been out for a Sunday afternoon walk."

He loved church architecture. From Westminster Hall to Kirkwall Cathedral, from Italian Prisoner of War chapel in Orkney to small English village churches, he visited all sorts and kinds. Salisbury Cathedral fascinated him. Perhaps he realised that such triumphs of architecture were designed and built by men who lived in an age when there was nothing else for intelligent people to do but build cathedrals.

When 'wireless' came in, Sandy very soon began to use the crystal sets of the day. A very high aerial was strung up beside Thalassa, between two high poles about eighty feet apart. A suitable earthing switch was arranged for protection against a lightning strike when the set was not in use. The 'earth' consisted of a scrap negative plate from one of the big lead acid cells of the Bungalow house lighting battery. He began by building crystal sets which required no electrical power input. A delicate wire called a cat's whisker was brought into contact with a crystal detector to rectify the current and produce audibility. He built a crystal set for his aunts in Wemyss Bay and they used it. If a good point had been found on the crystal with the cat's whisker, the ear phones could be placed in a china dish and more than one person could hear the news.

He soon graduated to valve sets. They needed a two-volt lead-acid accumulator and a separate 90 volt high tension battery. The two-volt cell was of course charged by the water wheel generating plant on the farm. The high tension expendable dry battery had to be purchased.

The romance of listening to voices from afar caught his imagination. It was the done thing to sit up late at night to "receive America". He heard a programme from a broadcasting station in eastern USA, noted the content and the time, wrote to the 'Voice from Away Down East' and received a certificate (No 4966 dated Oct 15,1923) that he had heard, on his two-valve receiver, their programme broadcast at the time claimed. By return there arrived a twelve page advertising brochure from the Radio Broadcasting Station WMAF of Round Hills Radio Corporation, South Dartmouth, Mass. The pamphlet still makes interesting reading.

Radio buffs in these days built all of their own apparatus from scratch. Sandy was no exception. He made coils by weaving and winding them on bobbins bristling with nails. After extracting the nails the coil was carefully sewn together and stiffened by dipping in hot paraffin wax. Placed on a block of wood, the coil was then movable axially on the ebonite top of the set, its position relative to its neighbour being adjusted for best amplification. He also built up his own adjustable condensers (capacitors) for tuning. One of them had a ten inch wooden lever for reducing capacitance caused by his hand. Reception was sometimes impossible and it was always better at night. To receive a different broadcasting station or wavelength the coils had to be changed by hand. Daventry was the station which covered Britain in the early days.

He had a certificate (No 529 dated 21st April, fee ten shillings annually) from the Postmaster General saying that, "pending the issue of a formal licence, he authorises you to install and use a station for receiving wireless signals for experimental purposes." In the file I see a letter from the Manager of The Radio Corporation WKAQ of Porto Rico, dated November 28, 1923, enclosing a programme for their broadcast on November 30th. At that time they were broadcasting every Tuesday and Friday from 9 to 10.30pm and Wednesdays from 8 to 9pm for experimental purposes. There is no record of Alexander having received WKAQ, nor can I remember him talking about it.

Wireless enthusiasts read specialist magazines, visited each other's homes and shared their expertise. A new industry was burgeoning rapidly.

He did not look at television much, but in her last years Jeanie loved it all — a window on the world. Sandy's opinions of some programmes was, "What a misuse of a marvellous invention". In his last years, with failing eyesight, Sandy really enjoyed watching snooker. He could see the coloured balls easily.

Before the Kaiser's War he had been in the same first year class at the Royal Technical College as Baird of television fame. Baird, born in 1888, had to work as a baker to live, and often fell asleep during morning lectures. Sandy remembered that his classmates would take carbon copies of relevant notes for Baird. Class attendances were taken in each lecture. Baird's attempt to make money by selling his special socks was also remembered by Sandy. Sandy is mentioned twice in *Secret Life of John Logie Baird*.

Photography was a hobby enjoyed from boyhood onward. Emulsions were slow, needing long exposures. He used an exposure meter. A special dark room was constructed in the loft for his use. As colour plates came on the market he enjoyed using these in the mid 1920s; 4"x4" transparencies, they had good entertainment value. Rolled film, of the 16mm size used in cinematography became cheap. In 1938 he attempted to make a coloured quarter-plate paper print of a Greek temple which he had photographed in Athens. The process took about a day. He tried it once only. In due course he acquired a stereoscopic camera and surprised us all with its effects in colour. He used some of the retirement cash collected at Oxford to treat himself to a stereo-projector. Viewers had to wear special spectacles.

Sandy's father's foot-driven lathe was used once for re-winding the field coils on the water-driven 30 volt dynamo. He obtained an old machinist's lathe about 1936 and in 1950 a new Myford lathe, both of which machines could be made to cut all sorts of screw threads.

Sandy delighted in making furniture of home grown timber, in the form of stools, tables, table lamps, ornaments, etc. With an ample supply of seasoned cherrywood he used his lathes to advantage, turning bowls, a goblet, a hollow sphere with two hemispheres screwing together, table mats, a dodecahedron, lamp standards with threaded screws, etc. He made a cherry-wood replica of the hardwood till used in the the Carradale dairy by his parents. One can imagine it rimming full (reemin' fu') of the coins of that time — farthings, halfpennies, pennies, silver threepenny pieces, silver sixpences etc, the cash earned from the sale of fresh milk, cream and butter.

When he was a schoolboy he cut a wooden chain out of a solid rod of red pine. He carved out a wooden jewel box for Margaret with her name embossed on the lid. In his last few years at Oxford he built himself a fold-away table 3'9" x 2'6" using chestnut planks from home. It was suitably wired for a shaded table lamp. He loved to take the months of time needed to build up layers of oxidised linseed oil on his articles of natural wood.

Bricks fascinated him and he relaxed for hours making a series of hardwood bricks for children to build with. Meticulously made to inch sizes, generations of children have enjoyed them.

Sandy loved skating. He skated on Kay Park at lunch time when he was at Kilmarnock Academy. He skated at Fulwood, the local curlers' club pond in existence as early as 1879. Dunlop had a curling pond, which, when dammed in winter, flooded over into a few square yards of The Hill Farm. Sandy got a free ticket to skate here, in company with the other village youths, including Jeanie Kirkwood, his brother Bill and cousin Jim Tindal. Later he was to construct the small skating pond — The Cement — at Thalassa. Filled from the 'tub', it froze in one night, while the local ponds needed two nights' frost. In keen frost Loch Libo and Lochwinnoch were used as well. The whole Thalassa family skated. In the winter of 1926/27 Jeanie took baby Beryl, who was ten weeks old at the time, to Loch Libo for the afternoon's skating. The baby was fed, wrapped up and put to sleep on the ice at the edge of the loch among the bull-rushes.

Coming home from one of the last skating outings on the FN at Loch Libo, with two boys and Baby Beryl only ten weeks old, the FN engine was started by heating the induction manifold with a paraffin blowlamp, itself difficult to light in the cold, because the methylated spirit used for preheating had to be carefully warmed first by the flaming match. The acetyline lamps lit easily in the cold. The pungent aroma of the acetylene is with me to this day.

On these skating evenings we often met (Professor) Adam Thomson of RT College who lived in the vicinity. Adam admired AT's skating. On occasion we collected bull-rushes and had a blazing bonfire. Great bubbles of marsh gas collected below the ice after a few days. By breaking a hole with the heel of a skate, the gas was allowed to well out. It burned for long enough.

A rope was always taken to the ice. A group of skaters in echelon could give a huge and fast catapulting swing to the one on the outer end. The person on the inner end did the controlling. The ringing noise of the curlers' stones was delightful when heard at a distance through air and ice.

Winters were much harder that decade. They were harder fifty years before, too. It is on record that in 1879 John Dunlop Reid of Borland skated for miles on the Glazert, the local stream.

Sandy possessed a fine pair of roller skates (with rubber mounted ball bearing spindles) but I doubt if he used them very much on rinks.

Sandy saw the 5:1 bevil-shaft-drive gearing of his dismantled FN motorcycle. He made and rigged up a three feet diameter windmill-driven crank to drive a cross-cut saw, but it would not work; at the low speed the teeth of the saw jammed with sawdust. The idea was to load a log into the saw-bench and go away, leaving it to work away steadily by itself. Ideas are two-a-penny but making them work is different!

150

AT made a roller to be pulled by tractor. He took an old thirty gallon water cylinder, filled it with concrete which when set, held a dozen four-inch radial steel spikes projecting from the circumference, like a sheep's-foot roller. The idea was to aerate the heavy clay soil. The idea worked, but tore up the turf too much.

A keen cyclist from his boyhood days, a motor cyclist for ten years, Sandy was interested in bicycle design. Speed-wobble killed many motor cyclists until vibrations were understood. The slope of the 'head' or bracket holding the bearings for the forks was critical and I can remember seeing him doing some demonstration experiments with the slopes and curvature of forks about 1924. This interest stayed with him all of his life. He and Stuart Wilson published their paper on the efficiency of 3-speed bicycle gears in 1956.

His experience of a chain drive with his father's windmill, where the chain-wheel shafts were not horizontal — with the result that excessive chain and tooth wear occurred — had led him to dislike de-raileur gears on bicycles. Yet they were more efficient than hub gears. In 1934 he had advised me to use a 'trivelox' gear where the chain was kept always in one plane. This was not a great success, because the triple-sprocket sideway movement wore badly too, and the freewheel arrangement was of poor design.

At Oxford he tried unsuccessfully to make the rear sprocket variable in size. At first sight this appears to be impossible. He began by sawing a twenty-sprocket cog-wheel into four equal quarters, each having five sprockets. The idea was to expand the sectors radially so that the circumference of the fresh gat-toothed cog-wheel would have exactly twenty four sprockets. The resulting wheel was basically to be a square with rounded corners and four single link spaces each spanned by the chain. The problems of the 'nuts and bolts' of the design were time-consuming and he gave it up. He had had his fun out of the idea however.

Alexander Thom's contribution to mathematics
His pioneer work on numerical solutions

Squaring
     About 1933 Thom became interested in standing stones although at the time he was working on his book *Standard Tables and Formulae for setting out Road Spirals*. Following this, in 1939 he published a paper on Zodiacal light. When work on this latter article was finished his attention turned to what was later to be called archaeoastronomy, the study of astronomy in prehistoric times. Before this, however, with his pioneer work on numerical solutions called the method of "squaring", he had made his contribution to applied mathematics.

     In aeronautics, in spite of the vast amounts spent on building fighters, bombers, seaplanes, and flying boats, Thom maintained that the Great War hindered theoretical development. At Glasgow University, here was his chance — the field was wide open for original research. He had a searching mind and he began to apply it. He built his wind tunnel, did much experimental work with it, beginning in the late 1920s to work on the arithmetical solution of problems in steady two-dimensional flow (for example ideal flow of fluid between parallel plates or in shallow water). His publications indicate that he was an expert in this branch of applied mathematics, and mathematicians agree that his contribution to applied mathematics was significant. His researches into fluid flow led him to develop what he called "squaring", a numerical method for solving partial differential equations.

     Some confusion has existed, in the minds of students, between Thom's "squaring" and Southwell's "Relaxation", and the author records here the dates of published work and extant letters from Southwell to Thom. The methods used by the two men differed. They developed along different lines. Thom's initial publications (1928) appear to precede by some seven years those of Southwell (1935).

The author has a distinct memory of more than a slight 'intellectual atmosphere' caused by Southwell never acknowledging that in January 1937, Thom had sent Southwell, upon request, off-prints of all his work on squaring up to date.

By chance in March 1987 the author met Professor Ian Sneddon (Glasgow University, Simson Chair of Mathematics). Sneddon remarked pointedly that a biography should state that Thom invented 'Relaxation', the name given to Southwell's method.

In 1928 Thom was investigating flow past cylinders. His DSc thesis was on the stocks. PJ Roache, in 1972, refers to the pioneering work of Thom (1938, 1933) in *Computational Fluid Dynamics*. Some of the background is shown by the following letter from an ex-colleague Dr JW MacColl, a Glasgow 1924 graduate in mechanical engineering. (In February 1926, Mr MacColl had read a short paper to Glasgow University Engineering society on Principles of Fluid Motion.)

> Royal College of Science, SW7,
> Wed, January 25, 1928.
> Dear Thom,
>
> Thanks for your letter received last Friday. I'm sorry I have not managed to write earlier but I have not had the opportunity to visit the Science Library until now. I've got the volume that contains Prandtl's 1904 contribution by me. It is not at all what I was led to expect and I don't see that it will interfere with your work in the least. He appears to deal generally with the flat plate and cylinder and the generation of the vortices from them. Hence there appears to be no need to worry over this paper. There are some diagrams illustrating, I think, the generation of the vortex by the breaking up of the layer of discontinuity. However that does not come into your problem yet.
>
> The book containing the paper is *Verhandlung des III Internationalen Mathematiker Kongresses in Heidelberg 1904*. Prandtl does seem to indicate how back flow sets in.
>
> Have you seen Fage's three recent papers in the Phil Trans Roy. Soc? His paper to the Aero Soc three weeks ago was a discussion of all that work and is quite interesting. He deals with the motion of the stagnation point of an aerofoil and with the discontinuous regions behind cylinders, aerofoils, etc. If you'd care for a look at the advance proof of the lecture I can send it on. It will likely be a month or so

before it is in the journal.

MacDonald will find the paper on *Stability of Cycle* in the *Messenger of Mathematics* for about 1898 — at least I think that is where it is but the date may be in error by a few years. It is 18— at any rate. . .

Did you know that Stevenson had been with Saunders, East Cowes, IOW, for the past few months?

Must hurry off now. Excuse scribble. Hope you are well.

Yours sincerely,

JW MacColl.

PS LB says that he will welcome any work you do on cylinders if it will throw any light on the phenomenon and allows them to know something of what happens. He says there is not any likelihood of clashing with his work and that the R Soc would publish any work up to their usual standard.

By the way the range of $vD/\hat{\imath}$ he is working at in his analysis is from 12 to 100 or so. Over 100 eddies came off (See Relf).

I only asked LB casually what he thought of the projected paper so all he knows is that you have been making investigations over the front of the cylinder and he does not require to know further if you have decided to send it to Lamb. JWM

The MacDonald referred to above would be George G, 1928 graduate in Mechanical Engineering; JC Stevenson was an ex-aero student of Thom's; MacColl and Stevenson helped Thom to build his wind tunnel; MacColl experimented on it later using a rotating sphere. Thom was to meet Prandtl and other aerodynamicists at Aachen in 1929; LB was Bairstow. It was at this time that Thom decided to learn German rather than ask others like MacColl to hunt out German references for him. He wanted to obtain his material first hand.

Macoll's next letter, still discussing compressible fluids, was from the External Ballistic Department, Royal Arsenal, Woolwich.

The following letter to Professor JD Cormack from L Bairstow gives some more background to the work done in Glasgow University at that time —

From L Bairstow,
Ardengair, Home Park Road,
Wimbledon,
June 22nd, 1928
Dear Professor Cormack,

I have now had time to look through Thom's paper on 'the Boundary Layer on the front part of a cylinder'.

From recent experience of the Royal Society I should judge that there would be little likelihood of acceptance by that body. It would almost certainly be suggested that the paper is more appropriate to the Aeronautical Research Committee.

Turning to the material of the paper I find myself critical both of the observations and of the mathematical treatment. At the speeds at which Thom is working the boundary layer is so thin that his pitot tube could not accurately measure the structure of the layer. We have so far failed to discover any method that is accurate enough for use on an 18" aerofoil.

I am not here referring to the point made by Dr Thom that a pitot tube changes the form of its calibration at low values of VL.

This point has been dealt with by GI Taylor and Miss Barber and also by Sir T Stanton in papers to the Royal Society, papers of which Thom appears to be unaware.

On the mathematical side we have found that the Prandtl boundary layer theory does not sufficiently account for the facts round an aerofoil and I suspect that similar discrepancies would have shown in Thom's results had the accuracy been sufficient. The method of averaging which he adopts is probably responsible for the degree of agreement between experiment and calculation which Thom finds.

I think it would be useful for him to send his paper to the ARC since work of a similar nature is being carried out at the NPL under the general direction of that body.

I again apologise for my slowness.
Yours very truly,
L Bairstow

The types of problem Professor Thom was most concerned with were those aerodynamic problems which give rise to simultaneous partial differential equations. Such equations appear in many branches of mathematical physics, eg in cosmology where such field equations can be used to describe the evolution of the universe.[2]

In 1928 when Thom was developing and publishing his methods described above, he referred to them among his research associates by the name "Squares" and this name has remained in the literature of the subject.

James Orr, a Glasgow graduate of 1925, and by this time a junior member of staff, published in September 1930, R & M 1393, ('Several cases of non-circular torsion solved by analysis and direct test'.) He acknowledged indebtedness to Dr Thom, whose squaring method of analysis formed the basis of the paper, for his assistance in its application to the problem.

In December, 1930, a joint paper by Thom and Orr was published in the Proceedings of the Royal Society referring to a 1928 paper of Thom's using squares (R & M 1194). This paper was communicated to the Royal Society by RV Southwell.

In December 1990, in a private communication, Dr DK Brown, who knew James Orr well, wrote that later James never used the term 'Methods of Squaring', but referred to 'Finite Difference Methods.'

In 1940 Southwell published his book *Relaxation Methods in Engineering Science.*

Thom believed that 'Squaring' was the fastest and most convenient method available for the arithmetical solution, by desk computation, of certain classes of problem involving partial differential equations.

On 14th January,1937, Thom received the following letter from Southwell —

> Dear Dr Thom,
> Could you conveniently spare me separate copies of all your published papers which deal with the numerical solution of differential equations involving two variables? I find that I only have R&M 1475, (published by you in 1932), and since I am working in this field, separate copies would be a great convenience.
>
> Yours sincerely,
> RV Southwell

Thom once remarked to me that he had sent Southwell all of his useful material and it was not acknowledged publicly at any time or in any place.

One other letter exists from Southwell, dated 30th November, 1938 —

> Dear Dr Thom,
> It was very kind of you to write to me at such length about the paper I sent you, and I was very much pleased to learn that you found the presentation clear. *I felt a certain diffidence in intruding on a field which you had made your own,* (the italics are mine, AST) but I do feel that we have made some advance in applying our relaxation ideas, because the continual recalculation of mean values round different points is a process which I found laborious and liable to error, whereas the liquidation of 'forces' by the simple rule of "add 6 and at the same time subtract 1 from each surrounding point" is relatively simple and unlikely to be done incorrectly: moreover, the device of block relaxations can be used, and errors which have crept into one net are detected at once on an advance to a finer net. If it had not been for the simplification introduced by "liquidation of forces" I think that I should hardly have thought it worth while, on balance, to use the triangular net, despite its better approximation: as it is, I fancy it will be best to choose a net to suit the given boundary.
> I wonder whether Dr Orr could spare me a copy of his R&M 1393 (published in 1930) which I do not seem to have in separate form?
> I hope before very long that we may have an opportunity to meet for a talk about these approximate methods: possibly next year's meeting of the British Association may provide one? As I see the position, a few of us are discontented with the restrictions that encumber orthodox mathematics, and are content to yield a little accuracy for the sake of greater generality: naturally we differ in our approach, but we are united in a common point of view, and I fancy that the effects may be appreciable before very long.
> With kindest regards,
> Yours sincerely,
> RV Southwell

(To the best of the author's knowledge, the two men never met.)

Southwell, in his book *Relaxation Methods in Theoretical Physics*, 1946, refers once to Thom's paper published in 1928. He refers once in the same book to the work of Thom and Orr, 1931, and briefly to that of Hardy Cross, 1924, this time only in a footnote, but see under GFJ Temple below.

I record the following polite protest by Dr David K Brown of Glasgow University, who, while a Visiting Professor at University of Rhode Island, RI, spotted an article in *American Scientist*. Brown wrote —

> The Editors,
> American Scientist,
> 28th February, 1975
> Dear Sirs,
> May I thank Professor Birkhoff for his informative article on *Mathematics and Computer Science*. I notice he attributes the development of the 'relaxation' iterative procedure to Sir Richard V Southwell. Whereas it is true that Southwell did much to perfect and apply the technique to more complex problems, the origins of the procedure go back further. Professor Alexander Thom did much work in the 1930s in solving the torsion problem with Poisson's Equation using the numerical technique. Reference can be made to this work in *The solution of the Torsion Problem for Circular Shafts of varying Radius* to be found in the proceedings of the Royal Society, Vol 131-A. This paper was written by Professor Thom and the late Dr James Orr and published in 1931. Indeed this paper was communicated to the Royal Society in London by Sir Richard V Southwell.
>
> Yours faithfully,
> David K Brown,
> Visiting Professor of Mech Eng and Appl Mech

Professor Birkhoff (Harvard University Department of Mathematics) replied via *American Scientist* on March 30th, 1975.

> Dear Sirs,
> It is interesting to learn that Southwell may have gotten

the idea of using relaxation methods from Thom and Orr as early as 1931, since Hardy Cross is often cited as having anticipated Southwell in 1935. However it is very hard to be sure just who was the first to use a given numerical method; even Gauss solved linear systems by iterative techniques that might properly be termed 'relaxation' methods. My statement was that Southwell developed relaxation methods. This I think he did, to a level and on a scale that had not been achieved earlier.

Yours truly,
Garret Birkhoff

Although Squaring was developed for desk computation it proves to be very suitable for programming for use with modern digital computers; larger fields can be tackled. The 'large molecule' type of formula was developed independently by several workers but the application to non-linear equations was first demonstrated by Thom in 1934.

Professor Hans Motz, in a personal appreciation of Professor Alexander Thom, wrote the following, (see *RIS* 1988 p14) —

Southwell had developed numerical methods for the solution of problems of Mechanics and Elasticity. They are known as Southwell's Relaxation method. The term is somewhat misleading, because it involved weeks and months of tedious work turning the handle of a mechanical calculator, an occupation which was not exactly relaxing. I know it because I became a member of the team but was lucky enough to acquire an assistant, (Dr Laura Klanfer, an able and patient lady paid by the Admiralty) who helped me with my research on Radar. I had adapted Southwell's ideas to the solution of problems of electromagnetism, in particular microwave problems in Radar research.

Professor Thom was the independent originator of another method of dealing with the same class of problem. In solving partial differential equations according to both methods, values of the function were calculated at the points of a discrete net of squares. Partial differential equations approximately valid at these points were used. Starting from arbitrary values, the errors at every point were calculated and successively removed. In the relaxation method this was done by intelligent and purposeful actions by the operator;

in Thom's method it was achieved by a process which could eventually be automated. This is why, with the advent of digital electronic computers, the Thom method was used and is still employed to this day. Professor Thom may therefore be regarded as a pioneer of modern computing methods. His contributions are by no means confined to this field. He did important work in fluid dynamics.

For his computations the Professor used a gadget (a Curta Calculator) looking like a cross between a Tibetan Prayer wheel and a Turkish coffee grinder with a rotating handle.

Hans Motz

In 1985 the editor of *The Brazen Nose*, a Brasenose College magazine, printed the following tribute —

In 1928 Thom published a paper describing a numerical method for solving partial differential equations which was the forerunner of much later work. At Oxford he continued work on the development and application of numerical methods of analysis to the mathematics of fluid flow. This culminated in the publication in 1961 of the book *Field Computations in Engineering and Physics* written in collaboration with CJ Apelt, a former student of his.

Apelt is now Professor of Civil Engineering at Brisbane University. The dust cover claimed the book gave "A faster, More versatile Squaring Method of obtaining numerical Solutions to partial differential Equations in two dimensions — ideally suitable to digital computation.

GFJ Temple, Sedleian Professor of Natural Philosophy, Mathematical Institute, University of Oxford, in the Foreword to the above book, had written the following —

Mathematics has the reputation of being a deductive science but in fact progress in applied mathematics is often achieved by induction from numerical solutions of particular problems. Even when general theorems can be formulated and proved it is often most difficult to apply them fruitfully to concrete problems.

In these circumstances special interest and importance

attaches to any systematic method of calculating numerical solutions of problems in applied mathematics, above all when this method can be carried out either with the modest equipment of a hand or desk machine, or can be programmed for use with an electronic digital computer. Professor Thom was, I believe, the first to apply such a method to a substantial problem, and his early researches in 1928 on the non linear fourth order equations of viscous flow are still of considerable interest, of fundamental value and a monument to Thom's untiring patience.

The 'squares' method employed by Thom is basically a systematic method of iteration, to which experience in computing had added a number of special techniques to accelerate convergence to the accurate solution.

A similar method for the solution of large blocks of simultaneous equations is that invented by Hardy Cross in 1932 and subsequently (from 1932 onwards) developed very extensively by Sir Richard Southwell as the 'relaxation' method. Whereas the 'squares' concentrates attention on the successive approximation to the functions to be calculated, the 'relaxation' method focuses attention on the 'residuals' at each stage of the calculation, ie on what may roughly be called the errors produced in the individual equations of the system by substituting the current approximation.

It is clear that it is far more difficult to programme a relaxation method than a squares method. The latter is a routine iteration, the former demands judgement at each step. L F Richardson described the squaring solution as a 'jury' problem in which the value of the unknown function at a lattice point is settled by the united efforts of the jury consisting of its values at a number of neighbouring points, which successively deliberate and give provisional, approximate verdicts, which are improved on appeal during the next round of computation.

The publication of this book marks, in a sense, the end of an epoch in research using this type of calculation. It is the end of what might be called 'steam' calculation, carried out with considerable labour by dedicated individual computers aided only by desk machines. In the coming epoch these methods, which have proved their value, will be programmed for rapid calculation on automatic digital computers. But the pioneer work carried out by Thom and his fellow workers will always remain as a monument of

patience and industry which has given the world of
mathematics, physics and engineering a splendid series of
exact numerical solutions of various outstanding problems
of great interest and significance.

In the above book *Field Computation in Engineering and
Physics* Thom and Apelt referred to Southwell's Relaxation
method, saying that Thom's method, that of squaring by
differences was so much quicker. They gave a page of
description of relaxation so that readers could, by making a
comparison, understand that the "two methods are quite
distinct from the beginning and have accordingly developed
along different lines." ... "The method of squaring can be
made quite routine without losing much of its speed and
this renders it much more apt for use with high speed
electronic digital computers than Southwell's method of
relaxing the results."

Calculating
Squaring manual calculator

Before the advent of calculating with electronic machines,
everything had to be done manually. I well remember AT working
away in his study in Thalassa when I was a schoolboy. He was then
using a Brunsvega mechanical machine which speeded up
proceedings greatly. Later the university obtained for him the next
Brunsvega model, a big improvement. At one stage, after he had been
working for months on a particular problem, I remember him saying
that he would work for another three weeks on this field before giving
up, as it was not settling. He worked on, and it settled.

I can remember to this day the mechanical noise of these
Brunsvegas, turned by hand of course. Lighting in Thalassa was by a
large paraffin lamp, hung by four chains from the ceiling at his left
side to illuminate the machine. I still have that lamp.

Time was saved by using the short cuts he had discovered but
he wanted to speed up the process yet more and so he developed a
manual calculator for squaring. Exactly when he made it I can not
say — probably it was between 1930 and 1933. The instruction
template on it gave an indication of what he had been attempting to
do. I found this manual calculator mouldering in the stable, and since
then have carefully cleaned and oiled it where necessary. It had been
forgotten for decades and was not in good order but there was enough

162

of it left for the experts to glean its purpose. Dr Peter Swinbank has it in the Department of the History of Science at the University of Glasgow.

Had AT been pleased with the Squaring Manual Calculator he would have carried on with it. He must have spent much energy on its design — the wooden case was probably made in the joiner's shop of the Master of Works — to me the case does not have the look of AT's handiwork about it. The metal work would have been made in the Engineering Department.

The author does not remember seeing him using the device at home.

Later, before the advent of the modern electronic machine, he used Curta pocket calculators. He had seen many changes in calculating machines, having used ten-inch slide rules, twenty-inch slide rules, eight-figure log tables, cylindrical drum devices, digital calculators, two Brunsviga machines, two Curta pocket calculators. Finally he used pocket electronic machines. He had a set of ten Napier's bones in his study, but I never saw him use them. Called Napier's bones because they were often made of ivory, they were invented by Lord Napier to facilitate long multiplication and division. Navigators found them very useful. They were superseded by tables of logarithms, another of Napier's inventions.

Thom's squaring activities diminished in the early 30s, but he did teach the late Drs James Orr and William MacGregor how to use the method successfully. Later, at the Royal Aircraft Establishment, Farnborough, he used the method and got others to help. At Oxford, he worked at the method with Dr Laura Klanfer and in 1961 with Colin Apelt, published the book (see above).

Rain Gauge

Each day from 1954 onwards Sandy's grandson Alasdair measured and recorded the daily rainfall for the Meteorological Office, Edinburgh. Some thirteen years later Alasdair was to be awarded PhD for the first post graduate degree in meteorology to be given in Scotland. The standard 5-inch funnel-gauge with its sharp-edged brass rim drew the grandfather's attention. He could see the problem immediately — the difficulty of catching rain as it falls diagonally across the funnel at an angle varying with wind strength. Rain gauges on ships and on mountain slopes are notoriously inaccurate.

After thinking about the problem the grandfather came up with a fresh idea. He applied his squaring methods to calculate the theoretical lenticular shape of a collecting device. His calculations showed that the collecting funnel would be shaped like a rubber deck-quoit with a membrane across its base, something like a miniature ship's life raft. He wanted the air-flow across the top to have parallel stream-lines, unlike the extremely turbulent flow over the standard gauge, the height of which is twelve inches above ground, placed of necessity in a more or less open space.

This device could be fixed at any reasonable height above the collecting dish, on land or on board ship, with the collected water draining through a pipe to the storage vessel. Its exposed central circular aperture could be of standard diameter; cylindrical anti-splash rings could be fitted; it could be self-checking, if desired, by measuring separately, the rain collected in one or more of the outer annular areas, each having the same area as the central circular aperture, but a separate drain tube.

From April 1960 until September 1964, Sandy made and attempted to run an automatic recording rain gauge which showed the hourly rainfall. It was supposed to be read once every ten days or so. The apparatus was fixed up in Violet's Hut in Thalassa compound. Rain collected in a funnel on the finial of the Hut ridge was led by a pipe to a tipping device which when filled, tipped itself, at the same time as triggering the release of a millimetre steel ball which defined a quantum. The ball rolled down a channel into one of twenty four compartments on a clock-driven table. The idea was to find the pattern of hourly distribution at various times of the season. Each morning the balls were counted (quite easily) in each compartment for each hour, and returned to the reservoir above. The device was not very successful. He soon tired of looking after it. He had taken up the gauntlet as it were, and needed to do no more. Surface tension kept some rain drops in the pipe, but the apparatus worked.

Astronomical calculations

In 1916 some photographs of a comet, taken in December 1916 at Winchester, Mass, USA attracted Thom's attention. He began to calculate the orbit. I have a file of his figures with a letter dated August 8th 1919, addressed to Professor Becker of the department of Astronomy in the University of Glasgow.

The young enthusiast almost certainly completed the calculations between April and August 1919 in the interval between two jobs. He always found something at which to work.

Professor Becker, who had taught him Astronomy in 1914–15, had been interned in the UK during hostilities. He returned to Germany some time later. A mutual regard existed between them. Professor Becker wrote him a testimonial in 1936, when Thom applied for the Chair of Civil Engineering at Edinburgh University.

Thom's Contribution to Statistics

Later in life, the Professor made no claims to being a statistician. His contribution to the subject consisted in the questions he asked of practitioners. He gave them occasion to work on a completely new set of data. The author can do no more than report on the history of analysis of the survey plans of megalithic remains. Suffice it to say that in Glasgow University, in the final examination paper for Mathematics on the Honours standard, a 25-line question appeared in 1970 on least squares used in analysing stone spaces in megalithic yards in alignments.

Photo-electric theodolite diaphragm

In 1958 he became interested in developing a theodolite diaphragm with three vertical slots for use with a photo-electric cell device for timing the meridian passage of a bright star. With GN Roger of Oxford University he made it work and passed on the idea to the Department of Surveying.

Servomechanism

By the end of the Kaiser War pilots were finding that forces on elevators, rudders and ailerons were becoming too much for them to handle for hours on end. While an aircraft designer in Sussex, Thom had realised that pilots were having difficulty in delicately controlling these forces. He thought about it and finally, at Glasgow University, designed and made a servo-mechanism which was essentially today's 'power-assisted steering'. He had invented a pneumatic device for controlling rudders and aileron surfaces, yet still leaving the pilot with the feel of the aircraft's responses to their guidance. He realised that power-assisted steering was needed. The device lay at The Hill for about twenty years. When he got to Farnborough in 1939 the twin-piston affair was soon surrendered into the hands of the control boffins. Compressed air was its working fluid.

Platonic solids

The mysterious prehistoric carved stone balls intrigued him. No satisfactory explanation of their purpose has ever been put forward by prehistorians. He firmly believed that the makers knew about solid geometry and about the platonic solids. He reckoned that visualisation of the sphericity of the earth and the movements of sun and moon was an easy concept for men whose brain power allowed them to make such artifacts. He made a six inch diameter dodecahedron box of cherry wood, each side, 10mm thick, being an exact pentagon carefully dovetailed into its neighbours — a masterly demonstration of a platonic solid.

Uniform sub-division of the sphere

The Professor had become deeply interested in 'geodetic' framework used in the construction of Lancaster bombers and spent much time in trying to determine the shape of a standard refractory brick for making hemispherical domed furnaces. The problem exists also in the construction of dome-shaped buildings which are less expensive to make if all cladding units are similar. His 1954 file of calculations with diagrams and photogrtaphs of models makes excellent reading. Headed *Uniform Subdivision of the Sphere*, a six page draft article begins —

> The problem is to find a shape which, repeated many times, will build up a spherical surface. The Greeks showed that there are only five possible solutions (the Platonic Solids) if the shapes are to be regular. The five are the tetrahedron, cube, octahedron, dodecahedron and icosahedron. Where only a few (4 to 20) surfaces or shapes

166

*the mind of an engineer! — Alexander Thom had a reputation for being a prodigious doodler in meetings. The offerings above and overpage are the work of scientist as artist . . .*

167

will suffice one of these can be chosen. But for a variety of practical cases we need a much smaller unit than, say, the face of the icosahedron, etc.

He was off to a good start!

Slide Rules

My father had a 10-inch slide rule (Faber, Bavaria) which he used for years. It would be the one he used in his student days. In my youth I saw him using a cylindrical slide rule, the equivalent of a 60-inch straight rule. He treated himself to a 10-inch log-log rule with trigonometric functions. In the mid-30s he acquired a 20" rule with prize money presented for winning the Clyde Cruising Club Ogg Cup for a fortnight's cruise in the West Highlands. In 1973, just before the advent of pocket electronic calculators he was given a gift of a very good rule (Aristo, Germany) by Harry Clough in recognition of his testing Harry's freshly ground and polished 24-inch telescope mirror. At that time this was the be-all and end-all of slide rules.

The arrival of the pocket calculator in the 1970s sounded the death-knell of the slide-rule, invented in 1630 by a mathematician Edmund Wingate, since when it has been used by generations of scientists, engineers and mathematicians. John Napier of Merchiston, Edinburgh, had invented logarithms some twenty years before. Basically, a slide rule uses the principle of logarithms. The golden age of slide rules was from about 1850 until 1970, around the time that Clive Sinclair, the British inventor, mass-produced his first pocket calculator.

The Professor owned, consecutively, two mechanical pocket Curta calculating machines, made in Lichtenstein. He used them to advantage. Long after his retirement he took advice from his friends and in 1973 purchased a Hewlitt Packard 25 which, at the age of seventy nine, he soon learned to programme. Later he used an HP 34C and an HP 11C with programme memory. These were of course exceedingly useful to him. His programme book of 1982 lists all of the astronomical types of programme he needed, along with perimeters of megalithic eggs and ellipses and probability levels.

He possessed a set of Napier's Bones.

Health

Sandy was not considered 'strong'. He had his ups and downs. At one stage in his youth he was exceedingly ill with pneumonia. He described being ill in the small bedroom immediately above the front door in the steading. That must have been before The Bungalow was built. At one time the family doctor for some reason snipped off his uvula with scissors. Sandy never forgave him!

A doctor once told him he had a weak heart. He played on this a bit at times, when he was feeling off colour, but weak heart or not, it lasted him well. He did not over exert himself and probably learned early in life to stop heavy activity before he got tired.

His sight remained normal for a long-sighted person until he reached about seventy five, when he gave up his hobby of telescope building because he said his eyes were failing. Cataracts began to develop. His specialist postponed operation until finally both eyes were done about 1981. He began to have retina trouble and lost the sight in one eye about midsummer 1982. Registered as a blind person for about two years before he died, he made good use of the talking book service. An electronic screen display device was obtained to enable him to read books, but by that time he was not physically strong enough to handle the books placed horizontally below the apparatus.

About 1927 I can remember Mr Kelly, a young assistant lecturer, travelling out to Dunlop to be tutored in Sandy's lectures, because Sandy was incapacitated by rheumatism and Kelly had to take all of his lectures for several weeks. Andrew Howie made a pair of crutches for him with which he used to struggle to the station and travel to take his classes.

This bad bout made him realise that he had to pay much more attention to his health and to the eating of a balanced diet. For several years indeed, he was a strict vegetarian. His health improved and he forged ahead. He received a certain amount of criticism for his views on health food at this time. Let it be said that he outlived most of his critics by many years and enjoyed good food. He knew how to cook well. One of his tenets was not to eat too much. Overeating he said was like adding fuel to a smoking fire! He added All Bran to his porridge to increase his intake of roughage as it once was called.

A note on the back page of his mother's handwritten cookbook indicates that Alex broke his arm on 20th July 1920. It happened on one of the water-wheel driven shafts in the byre loft. Luckily his arm was not torn off.

A second note told of Alex breaking his leg on 11th July, 1921. A motor bicycle was involved. He used one crutch.

While building Thalassa he had cut his big toe very badly with a wood chisel. I remember being shocked by seeing how the toecap of his laced motorcycle calf-length boots had to be cut wide open to accommodate the bandaged toe. He decided to have a holiday and took his family camping to Carsaig on his Precision motor cycle and side car. His Uncle Sam had invited him to join the Strangs at camp at Carsaig, where they had established a fairly big well-organised camp, with their friends, including Dr and Mrs Alex Fraser with son John.

It was 1922. The road surfaces were not good and many were the steep hills for the machine to climb. En route, at the top of the 'Little Rest' a steep hill some miles before the summit at the 'Rest and be Thankful' stone, we met Sandy's teacher, Mr Archibald Brown, headmaster of Dunlop School. Mr Brown was out for a walk with his camera and stand. He was on holiday in the district, and had almost certainly arrived at Arrochar/Tarbet by rail.

The author was four years old at the time. I can still remember three sections of the road between Dunlop and Carsaig Bay, some one hundred and twenty miles in all. At one stage on the journey the sidecar chassis broke and had to be lashed together temporarily. After dark, a small voice was reported as saying "Mum. Is this camping?" Much later the combination arrived safely at the camp, to the west of Tayvallich. The writer can remember being very sleepy and seeing from afar the white canvas tents glowing with the bright lanterns inside.

A cracked rib self-inflicted while using a large pair of long-handled pruning snips incapacitated Sandy once for a few days. He was pruning a fruit tree branch above his head, with one handle of the shears against his chest while he pulled the other handle towards himself with the strength of two arms. He heard his rib break.

171

In 1938 while turning over his Bentley engine by starting handle, something slipped and he broke his nose on one of the huge head lamps. The doctor did nothing to it, saying that he had successfully squeezed it back into correct shape himself!

Sandy had an exasperating habit of sneezing very loudly. He shouted his sneeze. Jeanie used to complain vehemently when this happened all of a sudden with no warning. One quiet summer's evening in Tobermory he was cooking in *Torridon's* fo'c'sle. Most of the crew were ashore. They heard his sneeze reverberating round the harbour! During the last twenty five years of his life, whenever he took a cold, it took him many days to throw it. He retired to bed and let it take its course. One particular infection about 1978 laid him low, his balance mechanism failed, he did not relish shaving and thenceforth he grew a beard like his father, who had never shaved.

Jim Tindal's anecdote about him and Wastle celebrating Sandy's wedding in 1917 by smoking 333 cigarettes indicated that Sandy smoked then. He was a moderate pipe smoker, sometimes puffing a cigar. He had a pipe-rack in the study at Thalassa, where a Meerschaum hung with some others. On the Austrian holiday he bought a huge Austrian pipe and smoked it frequently in Thalassa. While at Farnborough he stopped smoking "until Hitler died." Thereafter he smoked about an ounce of tobacco per week. He never smoked cigarettes.

He fell in January 1982, breaking his femur. He was, at the time, recuperating from the double cataract operation. Unfortunately he did not have usable spectacles while he lay in hospital. He could not read, nor could he distinguish objects across the room.

When Thalassa was built in 1922 the water supply came from a collecting chamber 1,000 feet across the Mid Park behind. Sandy made an oblong storage tank of planking fixed at a level suitable for the simple plumbing initially installed. The water flowed continually through this service reservoir, making a pleasant noise. When the extension was built in 1926, the higher framework to support the existing reservoir needed to be more robust and Sandy obtained a 40-gallon used whisky barrel from Johnnie Walker's. This was easily supported at its higher level. It was now natural to use the discarded wooden box to receive the overflow, and this was dubbed 'the tub'. In hot summer weather a plunge in the tub was pleasant. In colder weather, the plunge took about two seconds, the Archimedean overflow going in all directions.

Thus began the cold plunge. The wooden tub rotted, leaked, and was finally replaced by an old enamelled cast iron bath. In winter the ice had to be broken. But a habit is a habit, ice or no ice, and Sandy and Jeanie had developed the habit. In England, both at Fleet and Oxford, they continued, in the bathroom — to me a much 'colder' activity, for obvious reasons.

At Oxford Sandy met a colleague who had the same habit. This man once explained that one morning he had had 'a temperature', but also had to attend a most important meeting in London. He knew, if he did not take the morning plunge, that his wife would suspect something and would not even let him go to London. He took his cold bath as usual, went to London, and survived. Sandy asked if it had had any bad effects, but the cold plunge and brisk rub down after had toned him up as usual.

Jeanie continued with the habit until twelve days before she died at seventy eight. She took the plunge after her afternoon rest, laterally returning to bed to rest again. Sandy continued with the habit until his eighty sixth year.

Sandy told me once that he had a recurring dream. By holding his breath, he could feel as though he was flying along. I know that he frequently slept with his head below the blankets.


The Beginnings of Thom's Archaeoastronomical work

The family were on holiday in North Glen Sannox on the Island of Arran in the Inner Hebrides, about 1931 or 1932, and it was there that the author recalls first hearing his father talking about a "standing stone". Until then the only standing stones I knew about were the six upright 'rubbing stones' in the fields on the farm at The Hill.

In South Glen Sannox, Sandy theorised while standing at the nine feet high stone, explaining how it might be possible that prehistoric people watched the sun setting on the high mountain ridge above the Punch Bowl to the south west, while viewing from the big stone. He was thinking then of what he was later to call a 'back sight'. He surveyed the Sannox stone many years later and discovered that from the stone, at Martinmas and Candlemas, the sun set behind the mountain ridge and reappeared momentarily an hour later in the col. It was, right enough, a calendrical site, one of the alignments which showed up the division of the year into sixteen epochs or months of about twenty three days each.

In the mid-1930s Dr James Orr and his mother camped frequently. James had a small tent and Mrs Orr slept in their car. Thom and Orr at that time were research workers together in applied mathematics. Thom sowed the idea in James' mind that it would be feasible to use the car-camping procedure in summer time to survey the standing stones in Mull. Thom had taught James field surveying some ten years before and it was natural for James to go ahead in Mull, at the same time as giving his mother the open air holiday. The result was that in March, 1937, Orr published a paper in the Transactions of the Glasgow Archaeological Society, *Standing Stones and other relics in Mull* (Vol IX, Part II, pp128–134).

In one of Thom's first field notebooks there is a remark written in by James Orr about an object which appeared to be a megalith, 'aus holz gemacht' (wooden). James had been booking for Thom. From the instrument the vertical object had appeared to be a menhir. A bearing of it had been taken.

The following was written by Alexander Thom many years later, but it serves to illustrate here for the interested reader of this biography what Thom's standing stone work was about, and how it overlapped his first career —

Megalithic astronomers evidently marked or noted the position of the heavenly bodies at their rising or setting. Let us look first at the sun at equinoxes and solstices. Of these the setting or rising positions of the sun at the solstices have a special importance. Since the obliquity of the ecliptic alters with time, a measurement of these points can give us the approximate date of the observation.

An examination of my published books and papers shows that there is an enormous amount of work still to be done.

There are plenty of clues if we are but able to recognize them. In this connection it must be remembered that the culture probably existed over centuries, and fashions and beliefs must have changed as time advanced. It will be a very big task to find out about the development of the subject as the centuries advanced.

The following was written by him for the preface to a book written, printed, bound and published by Neil L Thomas of Melbourne, Australia in 1985.

> Each summer for over sixty years, I have cruised in the waters of the Hebrides, exploring out-of-the-way places, many of them normally inaccessible by public transport. In the year 1933 I cruised in the sailing yacht *Hadassah*, a Bermudan sloop of some 11 tons, with my son Archie and four friends. We left the Sound of Harris and after a long day's sail in the North Atlantic we arrived in the twilight at East Loch Roag, that beautiful secluded inlet to the north-west of the Island of Lewis. I was seeking a quiet anchorage for the night and navigating with care between rocky islets and promontories. I finally made up my mind where to anchor, as far up East Loch Roag as my chart allowed me to go with safety. We stowed sail after dropping anchor, and as we looked up, there was the rising moon with the stones of Callanish silhouetted on it. That evening I had been concentrating on the navigation as darkness was approaching, and I did not know how near we were to the main site of the Callanish megalithic monument, the Stonehenge of Scotland. After dinner we went ashore to explore. I saw by looking at the Pole star that a north-south line existed in the complex. This fascinated me, as I knew that when the site was built no star of any magnitude had been at, or near the celestial pole. Precession had not yet brought Polaris as near to the celestial pole as it is now. I wondered whether the alignment was a chance occurrence or whether it had been deliberately built that way. If it had been deliberate it would probably be found at other megalithic sites. I had of course known about the complex of stones and menhirs at Callanish since 1912 when Admiral Somerville's paper had greatly intrigued me.

> The Outer Hebrides have a charm all of their own, not the least being their remoteness. To realise that megalithic builders had lived and worked there as well as on the mainland of Britain aroused my interest in the working of their minds.

He was to write later —

> My interest having been aroused; I started carrying a

theodolite and making detailed surveys of all the sites I could find. Thus, although it was the astronomical side of the subject which first attracted my attention, it was not long before I became deeply involved in the geometrical side.

Gradually he began to realise that many rings were D-shaped, egg-shaped, etc. He analysed the diameters and ended up with the megalithic yard. Many egg-shaped circles were built using radii from the corners of Pythagorean triangles having sides of integral numbers of the unit.

Thom claimed that the more important rings of megaliths were designed on geometric principles. The plan shape of some was circular, others were egg-shaped and some had flattened sides. Some were elliptical. By statistical analysis of his plans he found evidence to show the use of a standard unit of length, the megalithic yard, used at sites in the Shetlands, the Hebrides, at Avebury, at Stonehenge, in Wales, Ireland and Brittany.

He wrote —

Having made a little collection of good surveys the first thing that struck me was that upon removal of the pure circles, the remainder practically all possessed a symmetry about one axis. Belonging to this group are the flattened circles. It was not very long before I noticed that they fell into two types, A and B, and I found that the calculated ratio of minor axis to major axis was for type A, 0.911(4) and for type B, 0.860(4). A little work showed the geometry on which the two types are based and this was the first real breakthrough.

By this time I was really interested and proceeded to survey every circle/ring I could find. I soon found another group, the egg-shaped rings, but these did not have constant ratio of minor to major axis. I proceeded to find for each, the centres of curvature of the various arcs.

Very soon it became apparent that these lay on the apices of right angled triangles. By this time I had a strong suspicion based on my surveys of true circles together with the major axes of the flattened circles, that there was a constant geometric measurement; and so I examined the sides of right angled triangles in terms of megalithic yards. All along I had been very careful to make sure that I had not been imposing my ideas on the surveys.

176

Thom was claiming that the more important rings of megaliths were designed on geometric principles. By statistical analysis of his plans, using radii and circumferences, he found evidence to show that the builders had used a standard unit of length, which he called the megalithic yard, with a unit for circumferences, of two and a half times this, the megalithic rod.

His first publication on the above was in 1955, the next two in 1961. The fourth one was in 1962, when in addition to stone rings he brought in the distances between stones in stone rows.

In 1964 he first published information obtained from the ellipse at Sands of Forvie. Dr AE Roy et al had demonstrated in 1963 the use of the ellipse in megalithic times. Their plans include the first known example of a stone ellipse, at Tormore, Isle of Arran. Integral numbers of megalithic yards were used for major and minor axes and distances between foci, with integral numbers of megalithic yards for circumferences.

All of the above 'Thom' geometry he discovered later was evident in cup and ring markings, but with a unit exactly one fortieth of a megalithic yard (one hundredth of a megalithic rod). He maintained that this allowed him to date the cup and ring markings as being contemporaneous with megalithic rings.

Some of his field notes made in 1938 are extant. On 30th August at Glasserton and Drumtroddan he was using only a prismatic compass. He was at Dalarran on 1st September,1938. Here he noted a moon and a sun bearing by compass at a booked watch time. Compass variation was worked for several places. He worked out a solar declination of -23°54' and stated "1600BC midwinter Sunrise" for the line between two circles at Cambret Moor, East Group, Cauldside. He returned here in 1939 to survey the site properly. He surveyed Temple Wood in 1939.

He continued to survey until his final expedition in August 1977, in his eighty fourth year, by which time he had measured up megaliths from the Hebrides, Orkney and Shetland, to Wales, Cornwall and Brittany.

He soon realised that menhirs were being removed at an alarming rate. Soon there would be none left. He was spurred on by a sense of urgency to survey as many sites as possible.

He wrote in this vein about the site in the narrows at Barragloam, Bernera, Lewis, a site recently surveyed and partly excavated by the Curtises —

> Years later, on the sailing Yacht *Torridon*, but before the bridge across to Great Bernera Loch Roag was built at Barragloam, we made a quick survey of the surrounding sites including the three stones at the north end of the bridge. On this visit we noticed that a small menhir stood where I think the south end of the bridge now lands. Unfortunately we did not have time to note its position carefully. It seems likely that it is now gone.

What exactly is Archaeoastronomy?

As a lead in to archaeoastronomy for the interested reader of biographies, I give here the bones of the introduction to the BAR book *Stone Rows and Standing Stones* by Thom, Thom and Burl. This volume was not published until 1990, some five years after the senior author died.

It has to be understood that the material presented in this volume can in no way give anything like complete details of what Thom did in archaeoastronomy and the geometry of megalithic rings, etc. Diagrams are given but it is not possible to explain each one in detail. This is an attempt to show the lay reader what Thom did to arouse the interest of research workers worldwide.

Introduction to *Stone Rows and Standing Stones*

In our previous BAR book, *Megalithic Rings* (1980a), we give details for all rings for which we hold accurate surveys. In this book we shall deal in a similar way with alignments. In so far as an alignment is a row of menhirs arranged to show a definite point on the horizon at which the Sun or Moon rose or set, it could well be replaced by a flat-sided slab provided the faces are true enough and large enough to give an accurate azimuth, or by an outlier to a circle or by the line joining two circles, by a track or a ridge on the ground or by a line of mounds, and so surveys of slabs, circles, tracks and mounds have been included in this book.

Our terminology depends on the assumption that alignments were astronomical, and so we define a foresight as a distant object or mark on the horizon on which the observer at the backsight can see the Sun or Moon rise or set, and we define a backsight as a marker showing the position from which the foresight should be viewed. If there is an indication at the backsight of the direction to the foresight, then the foresight becomes an indicated foresight.

In some cases it is not necessary to have the foresight indicated; in many the Sun or Moon will do this itself as the turning point approaches at the solstice or at the standstill; day after day it would get nearer and nearer the final position and the rate of approach would decrease.

It is, of course, quite impossible for a small group of surveyors to survey all the stones in the British Isles. In fact, it would be difficult even to visit them all. Here we give particulars of those we have visited and surveyed. Some of these are in difficult country and we did not always find it possible to carry a heavy theodolite.

An *azimuth* of a line (its bearing from true North) has usually been calculated from a timed observation of the Sun. Today we normally carry a Tavistock theodolite and an electronic watch. Many of the earlier surveys were done, however, with a small theodolite that we have specially lightened by milling, turning, drilling and filing. Azimuths surveyed using this small theodolite may be in error by a minute or two.

When measuring up a *large slab* the best method is to sight along one of the flat sides, pick a point on the horizon and measure the azimuth of this with the theodolite; then turn and look along the same side in the opposite direction, pick another point and measure the azimuth. These azimuths are expected to differ, of course, by 180°; if not, take the average. If it is an important slab the same procedure can be carried out on the other face of the slab.

Arrangement of stones at megalithic sites may be different today from what it was originally and a short alignment would be more liable to disturbance than a circle. The following points should be noted —

1. Stones may have been taken away by farmers, builders and contractors.

2. Stones may have fallen due to natural causes. We personally know of two which are reported to have been blown over in recent years.

3. Movement of the ground. It is said that boulder clay can slide downhill when the slope is as flat as $1^0$.

4. Lack of drainage at the base of stones may cause the stones to fall.

5. The continual thawing and freezing of ground may move a stone.

6. Trees, of which there are now no signs, may have been growing on the site at some intermediate date. We have seen a menhir lifted bodily in the roots of a tree blown down in a gale. When such a tree rots away the stone is peculiarly out of place.

7. Systematic destruction carried out on the instructions of religious authorities; for example in Skye, where we are told the Church instructed that all stones be removed.

8. The growth of peat may have completely covered the smaller stones and at least one site which we know is now almost submerged in swamp.

9. Rising level of the sea in recent centuries has submerged some rings, eg in Brittany. In Eday in the Orkneys the weathering back of a cliff by wave action has eroded a foresight.

In view of the above it is surprising that we have as many sites as in fact remain, but the destruction is going on more rapidly under modern civilisation, eg during the construction of highways the contractors actually removed two stone rings (at Moncrieffe and near Inverness) and built them in another place. This kind of thing is particularly misleading. One hesitates to estimate how many single stones have been moved in the same way.

A ring of stones has perhaps a greater chance of survival than one or two stones. A farmer will often remove an outlier but leave the circle untouched. Fallen long stones are sometimes set up on end, but perhaps on the wrong end. When a stone falls the top may sink deeper than the bottom because the bottom end is supported by the small stones that had been packed round the base by the original erectors.

We do not know and perhaps can never know how many sites have been removed completely without trace.

Our surveys show only what appears on the surface except in one or two cases where we used a bayonet to prod. In a great many cases much more could be discovered by careful excavation by experienced archaeologists.

The above points should be kept in mind when examining our surveys.

We find it impossible to study these monuments carefully without being convinced about the astronomical significance of many of the stones and alignments. This is not to say that all are astronomical. After all, there are many modern buildings in this country which are not observatories. Accordingly, where we find an astronomical significance we describe it.

When a large slab is standing with its faces arranged north and south then it is said to be in the meridian and when the Sun grazes across the faces it is local apparent noon. We have on various occasions tried this out with existing menhirs and found the time of midday to a minute or two. Apart from using the midday Sun, megalithic observers appear, as far as we know, to have used only observations made on the horizon, that is when the Sun, Moon or star rose or set.

When we find a line which we think is astronomical we must calculate a declination. To do this we need the azimuth of the line, its latitude and the altitude of the horizon; the latter must be corrected for refraction and parallax. The refraction we can take from the tables provided by the Nautical Almanac. Suitable values for the parallax and the perturbation can be found in the standard astronomical textbooks or, better, in LV Morrison's paper. The solution of the spherical triangles is then carried out by using standard trigonometrical formulae. Thus we find the declination corresponding to each sight line. Many of these declinations turn out to be that of the Sun at the solstice or equinox.

Where the alignment, be it a stone row, outlier or slab, indicates a definite mark on the horizon, the mark, of course, becomes an indicated foresight and we are entitled to measure it up and calculate the corresponding declination but where there is no mark on the horizon we are on less secure ground and must be guided by what we find, for example Glen Prosen [P/31] and Kell Burn [G9/13] called Kingside. (Site numbering system is detailed in the references). We consider that if an accurate alignment indicates a significant declination, even without a foresight, it must be retained.

In Thom (1967, fig. 8.1) we show a histogram of declinations for most of our measured lines. It will be seen that there are 16 calendar dates definitely marked (see also Thom, 1955; and Thom, 1982).

A few first magnitude stars are also marked, but these

181

are, however, of less importance than the lunar lines on which we have recently concentrated. In the text the intermediate calendar dates are sometimes referred to as numbered epochs of which there are sixteen. Many alignments show the declination of the Moon at its turning points (or standstills).

There is a peculiar wobble or perturbation $\Delta\iota$, of the Moon's orbit amounting to about $\pm$ 9 arc minutes. At the standstills the Moon's declination is very close to one of the values $\pm(\varepsilon + i)$ or $\pm(\varepsilon - i)$, where $\varepsilon$ and $i$ are respectively the obliquity of the ecliptic and the inclination of the Moon's orbit to the ecliptic ($5^{0}08'.7$). But the wobble we have just described means that we may find declinations between 8 and 10 arc minutes greater or less than these values. Quite apart from this there is the fact that we have found large clumps of values close to $\pm(\varepsilon \pm i)$ with or without the semi-diameter (see, Thom, 1980). If no semi-diameter is involved then megalithic man must have employed two observers, one for the upper limb and one for the lower; he then took the middle position on the ground on a line perpendicular to the line of sight. He must have dealt with $\Delta i$ in the same way; at the equinox the Moon's declination at the major standstill is $\pm(\varepsilon + i + \Delta i)$ and at the solstice it is $\pm(\varepsilon + i - \Delta i)$. So if megalithic man marked these two positions on the ground, the mid position gave him $\pm(\varepsilon + i)$.

Finally we apply the parallax, 56'.4 at the equinoxes and 57'4 at the solstices. We thus obtain the geocentric altitude for each line.

From the mean geocentric altitude we find the declination by the usual spherical trigonometrical formula.

The azimuth at many of our sites depends on measurements made on one day. They should all be checked. An azimuth can only be considered to be completely checked when an independent determination is made either by a second observer, or when it is done on a different day. Only a few sites completely fulfil this condition.

Some rows, for example Dervaig B and C, have definite astronomical significance but there are many for which this is not true. One of the best alignments is the row of stones at Nine Maidens, S1/9. How straight and accurate it is can be seen in our survey and yet the only suggestion we have for its use is that it indicated a first magnitude star.

It is hoped that this collection will be of use to future

182

workers in archaeoastronomy, showing them some places where they can profitably work, but it is hoped it will also be useful to others.

The greater number of these sites are simply waiting to be resurveyed by an independent surveyor, and there are many other sites for which no survey exists. The observer, however, must be fully qualified to use a theodolite in such a manner that all instrumental errors are eliminated. To obtain azimuths we ourselves do not in general use Ordnance Survey co-ordinates of points on the ground.

Many of the sites described in this book were surveyed before we realised their importance and so we did not take the same care with these as we would today. We sincerely hope that some fully qualified person will check all our surveys and survey the remaining sites.

A strong philosophical argument for the astronomical significance is that at a number of sites we find marked positions for an observer whose duty it was to warn the people that the Sun or the Moon was about to emerge. Examples of these will be found in the present work.

Royal Aircraft Establishment Farnborough

During the early summer of 1939 the Government arranged for a number of scientists and engineers to spend two or three weeks at defence research establishments to which they might be sent if war started, so that they could become familiar with activities and be ready to start useful work immediately in the event of war.

Dr Thom received a circular from the Air Ministry asking for volunteers to go to the Royal Aircraft Establishment, Farnborough for a month to become acquainted with the wind tunnel research procedure. By this time Sandy was well known for his abilities both theoretical and experimental, through the work he had done in his own tunnel. His visit was arranged for the middle of August. War broke out while he was there.

He rented a furnished house in Fleet, expecting to be there for only two or three weeks. He never went back to work in Glasgow and it became a joke that he "came for a fortnight and stayed for six years".

The High Speed Wind Tunnel (HST) at the RAE had been designed by WGA Perring with assistance from AA Hall and others. The design work started in 1937, but about the end of July, 1940, Perring was appointed as Superintendent of Scientific Research under AA Hall, Chief Superintendent. Perring later became one of the two Deputy Directors under Director WS Farren.

Thom worked in the low-speed tunnels from August 1939 onwards. About the beginning of August 1940 he was appointed as the man in charge of the High Speed Tunnel. He used to meet Hall from time to time for discussion of matters concerning the construction of the HST. The task given to Thom was the job of getting the tunnel and all its ancillary equipment and the enclosing buildings completed and in use as soon as possible. With his wide experience in many fields of engineering he was exceptionally well qualified for this task.

In a private communication, Austyn Mair has written —

184

The ancillary equipment included the balance and all the instrumentation for the control room and also the refrigeration plant for keeping the tunnel cool. This plant used ammonia compressors to cool calcium chloride brine which was stored in two large tanks and then pumped through jackets in the tunnel walls. Settlement of the tanks caused worry. AT was out on the site each morning with his theodolite, checking the latest position of the tanks, which settled fairly quickly into permanent position with no further movement.

The fan was of course a vital part of the tunnel; it and its lining up caused us some headaches.

The HST designed by Perring was a well designed pressure and vacuum vessel but it was poor aerodynamically, with seriously unsteady flow. Thom and Mair spent a considerable time inside the tunnel while it was running. Here Thom's sailing and climbing experience was useful — they were always well secured by ropes to make sure that they did not fall down the steep slope of the contraction or get blown downstream.

A way of improving the unsteady flow was devised by AT — mixing vanes were fitted in the return duct. This was very successful. It showed his remarkable ability in design, based on a mixture of intuition and long experience of flow observations. Austyn Mair cannot think of anyone else at the RAE at that time who could have cured the severe unsteadiness so successfully.

The tunnel working section was 10ft x 7ft, horse power 4,000, minimum pressure 1/6 atmosphere absolute, maximum 4 atmospheres absolute, maximum wind speed 600mph. Four 65hp ammonia compressors cooled the unit. Total air compressor 880hp. Lift balance 1,200lb.

The HST Building, comprising Spray Cooling Pond, Air Compressors, Automatic Balance, etc, was completed by October 1942. Sixty nine men were in the photograph at the opening ceremony.

Mair wrote —

Preliminary experiments with the HST
In 1942 when the HST was ready to run, the first jobs to be done, before mounting any model, were to calibrate the tunnel and determine the tare drag of the struts which were

185

to be used to support the model on the balance. The calibration involves measurement of the velocity distribution in the working section. Problems of choking and uncertain blockage were evident.

A Spitfire was the first to be tested, including the Vampire and the Meteor in several of its Marks. All the aircraft models used were of wood, usually laminated teak as proposed by AT. They had adequate strength and stiffness.

In addition to the HST, Thom was in charge of two other major wind tunnel construction schemes which had been started by Perring.

One was a reasonably straightforward low speed tunnel with 4,000hp drive. Thom supervised the design and construction of the reinforced concrete shell and the balance and other instrumentation. Mair designed the corner vanes and the fan, etc, helped by numerous discussions with Thom.

The other construction project was a tunnel for the study of icing and de-icing of aircraft. The problems of the first design were formidable and Thom and Mair resolved that it would not be built. They reasoned that the best scheme would be an open-return tunnel running in a cold environment. AT wrote the author to ask what he thought about restoring the old observatory on the top of Ben Nevis and building a small wind tunnel in that. The author pointed out a number of difficulties, especially the problem of access with relatively heavy equipment. They abandoned the Ben Nevis idea and started to think about putting a small open-return tunnel in a refrigerated room. AT's contact with JK Hardy led him to a refrigerated room at Ditton Laboratory, East Malling, Kent, where Hardy had been in charge of research in the storage of fruit before the war. The room had been used for experiments on the storage of apples. A small tunnel and then a larger one were successfully used for the study of icing and de-icing until the end of the war. One of Hardy's staff, KC Hales, carried out the studies at Ditton.

The intensive use of the HST from 1942 to 1945 led to greatly improved understanding of the problems of high-speed flight, such as the importance of thin wings, the causes of longitudinal trim changes at high Mach numbers, the redesign of jet-engine nacelles.

Mair has written —

Everyone who knew AT and his work realised that he had been the ideal man to get the HST running as early as possible and that his drive and enthusiasm would ensure that the most effective use would be made of the tunnel after its completion. When he started work at the RAE in 1939 he was graded as a Senior Scientific Officer (SSO), but after about two or three years he was promoted to Principal Scientific Officer (PSO) in recognition of his achievements in a very wide field. (It should be noted that the grades that were introduced in the Scientific Civil Service after the war used these same names for posts that were at a lower level. Thus the grades in which AT was employed cannot be compared directly with the post-war grades having the same names.)

With his move to Farnborough, Alexander Thom was somewhat apprehensive when he realised that he had become a civil servant, even if only a temporary one. This was something he had never previously contemplated and he consulted one of his colleagues who was a career civil servant about what would be expected of him. The advice given to him was, "Know all the rules and know when and how to break them." Thom didn't know all the rules by any means, but he soon broke plenty.

Fanny Bradfield, a colleague, told a yarn about Douglas, Head of the Aerodynamics Department. He had a wooden leg, having lost his own one in the first world war. Miss Bradfield used to relate how he surprised them all, when he first came to the RAE, by using a drawing pin to pin his notes to his leg.

The 'Factory' as it was still called, mainly by the old hands, especially in the workshops, had in its beginning during the 1914–18 war been the Royal Aircraft Factory.

While at Farnborough Thom frequently lunched at the Clockhouse, a local eating house where he met with other staff members. Some names which come to mind are JK Hardy (of Isle of Man), NI Bullen, Arnold A Hall, John Adamson, Jim Gordon, R Smelt. Later Sandy was to take Adamson and Hardy cruising. Hardy came from agricultural research, concerned with fruit, particularly apples. He had been drafted into Farnborough to turn his attention to more war-like things, which he did to valuable effect. His father was a famous zoologist and oceanographer. Adamson was a mathematician.

187

Daniel Martin, of Glasgow University Mathematics Department, and Mr Caldwell, Lecturer in Aeronautics at the Royal Technical College were both at RAE. Sandy also met Professor Orkney of RTC there, who later referred to 'that brilliant young man in charge of wind tunnels'.

Dr Dan Martin was asked to do some mathematics for Sandy who was of course deeply involved in wind tunnel work. Dan spent some days on the problem and was impressed when one morning, off his bike, Sandy said, "Was the answer Ä (Pi) squared ?" It was. Sandy had a flair for 'thinking it out.'

Experiments of all kind were under way and Will Gray had the idea of painting parts of an aircraft with a sensitive chemical. The aircraft was then flown through a chemically reactive smoke made to billow from the Factory chimney when the stoker had banked his fire with the chemical. The technique was devised for detecting transition from laminar to turbulent flow in the boundary layer, indicated by the stains fixed on the aircraft. Results were successful but injection of chlorine into the chimney was not popular with the authorities.

Jim Gordon, a yachtsman and naval architect, was later appointed to a chair in engineering materials. In his book *Structures* he illustrated one of his points on engineering design while discussing Efficiency and Aesthetics —

Whatever we make and whatever we do nearly always leaves upon the thing or upon the action the imprint of our personalities, written in a code which can only be read at the subconscious level.

For instance our voices, our handwriting and our manner of walking are quite characteristic and are usually difficult to disguise or imitate. But this sort of thing extends much further than these familiar examples. One dark evening I was in a yacht anchored in a remote Scottish loch. Round the corner of the land, three or four miles away, there came another sailing yacht which I had never seen before and of which I had no knowledge. Though it was quite impossible to recognise her name or her crew I said to my wife, "That boat is being sailed by Professor Thom." And so she was — for the way in which a man sails a ship to windward is quite as individual as his voice or his writing, and, once seen, can hardly be forgotten. In the same way one can tell which of ones's friends is flying a light aircraft . . ."

I was on board my father's yacht that evening, in August 1954, as we made Loch na Beiste, Skye. We visited Jim Gordon on his yacht *Jessie Jane* when he told us about his recognitive ability.

Sandy had met Barnes Wallis, inventor of the 'spinning bomb.' There was no discussion at RAE about Sandy's pre-war work on spinning cylinders, but Austyn Mair remembers "a day when a man from the Armaments Department of the RAE came to see AT and asked him about the work he had done at Glasgow on flow past cylinders and whether he had worked on spheres. I think he also asked about the effects of rotation but I am not sure of this. After the news came about the raid on the dams AT realised what had been the reason for the enquiry."

An enemy air raid shook things up — one nervous local lady who had peeped out of her air raid shelter described the 'Messershit' opening its bomb doors or whatever. After that raid until the end of the war it was arranged that there were always two of the experimental flying test pilots nominated each week as Duty Defence Pilots and two Spitfires were kept ready for their use. Whenever there was a warning of enemy aircraft approaching at least one of these two Spitfires was in the air over the RAE and its airfield. The pilots were highly skilled and many of them had served with operational fighter squadrons.

Sandy became acquainted with (Sir) Arnold Hall, about whom the following anecdote is related. Hall had invented a new gyro gunsight for use in fighter aircraft. With this gunsight a pilot would manoeuvre his aircraft so that the crosswires were on the target aircraft, which would in general be moving across his field of view, and fire his guns. The Hall gunsight, with its gyro-stabilised platform, would then allow automatically for the transverse component. The gunsight was in service in time for the invasion of France in 1944 and made the allied fighter aircraft much more effective.

Pressure and urgency of all their work can be illustrated by the following story told by GF Midwood to Austyn Mair about a journey with AT in his car, an Austin coupé. There were three of them, on their way back from visiting a firm, probably one of the HST contractors. Midwood was in the back of the car. About 4pm AT called out to Midwood, "What about some tea?" Then from Midwood, "Yes, good idea, when are you going to stop?" AT immediately replied, "We don't need to stop, you've got a Primus stove and a kettle in the back!" Midwood told Austyn that he did actually succeed in making some tea in the moving car. AT was no man-driver, but he "had a way with him."

Austyn wrote —

> AT and I shared an office. We had a phone each, with the two phones connected to a common line. When the phone rang, either of us would answer it, usually AT if he was there. I remember well the afternoon when the news came through about the crashed Hudson. The phone rang, AT answered it and I think he said very little. He put the phone down, walked the two or three paces to my desk and said, "There's been a crash and they think Alan's in it." I was too shocked to say anything much and AT walked slowly out of the room, in silence. I learned later that he went immediately to see GP Douglas, who had lost his son in a canoeing accident when the boy was about 16. AT stayed with Douglas until it was confirmed that Alan had been indeed in the aircraft. I think it was about 20 minutes after the first phone call. AT must then have gone home to break the news to your mother. The thoughts of all of us were with him.
>
> During the next few days AT spent a lot of time with Douglas, who had been through a similar trauma himself and was a great source of strength.

The Oxford Chair

In 1936, after the death of Professor JD Cormack, Sandy and another member of staff at Glasgow had both applied for the Regius Chair of Civil Engineering and Mechanics in Glasgow University. Neither of them was appointed.

When at the Royal Aircraft Establishment Sandy had applied for the Chair of Civil Engineering at Edinburgh University, but was unsuccessful. He was told that the Edinburgh University Court was going to wait until the end of the war before making an appointment.

The Deputy Director of RAE was WGA Perring. In May 1944 the Director, WS Farren, suggested that Sandy apply for the Oxford University Chair in Engineering Science. The advertised closing date for applying had already passed. Sandy did not think he would get it, but Farren advised him to try.

Sandy forthwith took his two previous applications for engineering chairs, pinned them together, typed a covering letter and sent in the lot. There was no carefully edited or printed curriculum vitae this time. His testimonials printed for the application for the Rankine Chair in Glasgow in 1936 make interesting reading.

He was interviewed, wearing a blue suit which before the war was so old that he used it while yachting. Jeanie had repaired and cleaned it. Sandy was offered the position, on the understanding that the chair would be kept vacant for him until the end of the war. As the chair was attached to a College, he knew before the interview that the new incumbent would be a Fellow of Brasenose College. It had become evident to Sandy that wining and dining in College was important — he had made it his business to read a book called *The Butler of Brasenose*.

During the interview he was asked by an elderly man, "Do you drink too much?" Sandy did not know what to say but came out with, "I haven't signed the pledge, but I don't overindulge." Later the questioner, who turned out to be Stallybras, Principal of Brasenose College, told Sandy that he thought it was a great answer. Stallybras, the lawyer, was delighted with the way Sandy had wriggled out of the question.

Immediately after the war stopped in western Europe the allied powers began to strip Germany of useful equipment in any way superior to their own. German scientists with their equipment and knowledge of how to work it were offered living quarters in the west. Von Braun and his rocketry team, for instance, accepted American offers. Allied military personnel were detailed to find out as much of the Germans' technical knowledge as possible. Backroom boys, civilians of many disciplines were sent over, nominally being looked after by the military personnel. Sandy was in a Royal Air Force party detailed to investigate as much as possible of the up-to-date aerodynamic discoveries. For convenience Sandy was completely kitted out in RAF uniform. There was no time to issue him with plain buttons and so Jeanie had to sew little cloth covers on all of his uniform buttons.

In the company of Dr George Douglas, who had lost a leg in the 1914–18 war, Sandy was taken round the German wind tunnels. He helped to prepare a report. My impression was that the team felt that German technology would have ended up far superior to that of the British, but that there was so much inter-departmental rivalry and jealousy that even given five years they would not have succeeded.

Many of the problems involved in supersonic flight were known to both sides.

Sandy was appalled to see the horrendous bomb damage to the German cities. He did not really talk much about his fortnight in Germany. Jeanie was worried stiff about him flying to Germany. Alan's very recent death in the Lockheed disaster near Woodstock was too fresh in her mind.

### Alexander Thom at Oxford

Upon appointment in May 1944 to the chair of Engineering Science in Oxford University, Sandy, like his two engineering predecessors, was elected a Fellow of Brasenose College.

When the University was founded, Fellows lived in the Colleges, using them as their homes. Sandy, the new Fellow, was soon, in a symbolic ceremony, "given the keys of The Cellars" of Brasenose. He frequently used the College facilities, but more so after he retired, when he was visiting in the South. If AT had occasion to spend a night in Cambridge he used the facilities of Caius College, as a reciprocal arrangement exists between these two colleges for visiting Fellows.

The most junior Fellow in Brasenose common room had to be the "snuff boy", whose duty it was to hand round the snuff, clockwise with the sun, after dinner. This was Sandy's first task and he was snuff boy until the next Fellow was elected. It would be in the common room that Sandy observed how to decant wine, holding the bottle with forefinger on top, pointing in the direction of pouring. He himself was very particular about this display of etiquette.

Jim McKie, a Don, who had been a Fellow of Brasenose since 1927, soon befriended Sandy, initiating him in the ways of the common room. Jim had been on military service and had returned to Brasenose in 1946. A philosopher, he needed the stimulus of dialogue and the cut and thrust of two-sided debate, and he soon realised that Sandy might have the benefit over the philosophers, lawyers and classicists in having the engineer's three-dimensional view of things. Many of the fellows did not have this three-dimensional approach. They were literate, Sandy was numerate. Perhaps in the beginning, Sandy the new boy doing his best to find his feet in his new Engineering Laboratory, might have been having difficulties in the common room, at times finding little to discuss. Jimmy McKie probably realised this, befriended him immediately, and so began a life-long friendship.

Jim had won a Brasenose Scholarship in the mid 1920s and had spent his four years abroad. When he returned to the UK he taught in Aberdeen University for a term. His old tutor in Brasenose met with a fatal climbing accident in Snowdonia. Jim was forthwith appointed a don and returned to Brasenose College in 1929.

At that time College rules did not allow dons to marry for five years after election. The idea was to bind the don to his College, in a sense shutting him off from the outside world, as though in a religious order. In 1946 the system had sufficiently relaxed to require Sandy to live within three miles of College during term time. In 1933 Jim had applied to Brasenose College for permission to marry Trude, his Berlin fiancée and naturally he had to leave the meeting of Fellows during the discussion about his application. They forgot to recall Jim who spent a worried period wondering what was happening, thinking that a great argument was under way. Permission was of course given and Jim and Trude married forthwith.

College rules did not allow Fellows to take in their own wives to dinner. They could, however, take in the wife of another Fellow.

I visited Trude at her home in Largs in June 1989 and January 1990, and she supplied me with many details.

In Oxford at that time, lectures in Arts were attended only voluntarily. Classes and laboratory were always compulsory in Engineering however, a custom with which Sandy, from Glasgow University, thoroughly agreed. For many years after the war a class attendance register was taken at the beginning of each lecture. Typically there would be two lectures each morning followed by two hours of laboratory or drawing office. The afternoons were free but later there might be early evening lectures or drawing office work. Lectures and laboratories were taken on Saturday mornings.

The arrival of a new Fellow in the common room at Brasenose College led later to a short discussion between two members. "Our new Fellow has a pawky sense of humour!" This remark sprang from an incident during a meal when there was a pause in the conversation. Peas had been served. Sandy said quietly to his neighbour in a steady level tone of voice, "You know. I always eat my peas with honey."

The Fellow fell for it, "Really?"

"Yes", said Sandy. "I've done it all my life."

To which the Fellow could only say, "Oh?"

Sandy went on quietly with a straight face, "I know it sounds a trifle funny, but it keeps them on the knife!"

Like his mother before him, Alexander was an excellent conversationalist. Discussions in the Brasenose College common room, where the port still circulates with the Sun, must have broadened and stretched his mind just as they had Jim McKie's and others'. It is certain that Sandy would be defending his theories on British prehistoric man's engineering, geometry and astronomy, against arguments from classicists and classical mathematicians.

To the sceptics he would say, "Look. You have no right to criticise me for showing that mathematics of this type was known in Britain about 2,500BC because it takes the same type of brain to think out mathematically the movements of Sun, Moon and stars as it does to develop Greek and Latin grammar. You are unable to say who developed these grammars, whereas I can show where this type of applied mathematics existed. Do you know who the Etruscans were, who made up their grammar, or who developed mathematics?"

He would point out that the brain power of men two hundred generations ago would be equal to, if not better than, modern man's brain power.

Oxford University does not acknowledge degrees of other universities and so bestowed on Sandy the honorary degree of MA on his appointment in 1945 to the Chair of Engineering. In 1961 he was elected Emeritus Fellow of Brasenose College.

For seventeen years, under his guidance, both the teaching of undergraduates and postgraduate research work flourished. To begin with the annual grant of £9,000 per annum had to suffice for salaries for staff and mechanics and for expenses, but not for the building. He did not pay the Donald Pollock Reader (later to be Hans Motz). The commencing salary for a staff member was about £450. Sandy was told by an elderly member of the workshop staff (Mr Canning) that when the Laboratory was opened, Professor Jenkin and Mrs Jenkin had prepared personally the departmental accounts for auditing. From a tiny group his department grew into a thriving organisation comprising an academic staff of fifteen, and more than one hundred and fifty undergraduates and research students.

More students had graduated in engineering during Professor Thom's tenure of office than during the whole of the previous years.

An increasing number of research students had passed through and several members of staff had been elected to chairs elsewhere.

While believing that his primary responsibility was teaching undergraduates, he maintained the research work of his department at as high a level as possible. His staff was of a high standard and the technicians were good. The quality of the students was high.

The main feature of the early post-war years was the small size of the department, as regards student numbers and buildings. They were all jammed for room in lecture-room, drawing office and laboratory space. As the years passed, its deficiencies became more and more obvious. Conditions were aggravated by the fact that half of the drawing office and the yard had been used during the war by Ricardo & Co, the internal combustion engine research team from Shoreham. A big compressor had been installed in the yard.

Most of the students were ex-service men, some older than the staff. The small number of research students were mostly Rhodes Scholars, largely from Australia, South Africa and New Zealand. Subsequently most of them did very well. Gradually the numbers in the department increased and accommodation became a problem. Deficiences in the building became more and more obvious. In 1955 the problem was temporarily solved by adding a floor above the Parks Road or Southwell wing. Soon after this the university appointed a committee under chairman Sir Alan Wilson to advise on the future of Engineering Science at Oxford. The choice was clear cut, either close it down or expand it greatly. Sandy wanted to double the intake of students. It was touch and go, since two powerful members of the committee were Lord Cherwell and Sir Francis Symon. Both physicists, they were in favour of turning the Department into one for Applied Physics. Fortunately there were other members from industry who maintained that the department was turning out the sort of people needed in industry, so the day was won. Money from the University Grants Committee for the new building followed immediately after the choice was made.

Sandy asked a small internal team to advise on the design of the new building — Peter Lund (Electrical), Dr Joe Todd (Structures and Materials) and Stuart Wilson (Heat Engines and Hydraulics). These three did a mini-tour of universities including Glasgow, Edinburgh and Newcastle. Thanks to years of their unremitting work on the design, the new building turned out to be successful. It proved difficult to get the architect to study their needs properly, as he was mainly concerned with the external appearance, the team with function. The small site necessitated a tall building and the nature of the ground a hole thirty feet deep, which allowed for a basement and semi-basement with eight floors above. The fifty ton test machine weighing five tons determined the floor strength and this gave flexibility in later planning and re-planning. Sandy specified, and was given, lecturers' rooms larger than those normally allowed. He reasoned that as lecturers were expected to teach and research, they needed more than the normal amount of floor area. The building is a success, despite some criticism of its appearance.

Although Sandy retired before the building was completed and opened, many decisions had to be made earlier about equipment which affected the detailed design and services. He insisted on having a Pater Noster continuously moving lift to save congestion at lift doors. The architect had not even heard about this type of lift. Stairways on the 'Two-start' thread principle were built into the tower-like structure. In particular the staff had to decide what, if any, laboratory items to transfer and what major new items to order. All this was done under Sandy.

The laboratory extension was finally built and named, in his honour, the Thom Building.

Normal retirement age was sixty seven. Several dons discussed making an appeal so that Sandy could continue beyond this age because he would then have the chance of occupying his new building. Eventually it was decided against because the grounds were largely sentimental. Sandy appreciated the thought but was really quite glad to go. The new building was well under way. He was having to make decisions which were going to affect future actions of staff and students, and he felt that detailed decisions were for a new holder of the chair to make.

There were other compensations. Trude McKie remembered Jim remarking that Sandy sometimes took a longer way home from the laboratory, cycling along a street where someone occasionally burned peat. The smell evoked memories of the north and west. He was always homesick for Scotland, where he invariably spent Christmas, Easter and summer vacations. He had gone south from Sir William Arrol's in Glasgow to work in the aircraft industry in 1917. After two weeks he came north, married Jeanie Kirkwood and they had lived for most of the next four years in Hants. When they came back to Scotland in 1921, it marked in a sense for them the end of the Kaiser's war. In August 1939, before Hitler's war began, they went south again 'for the duration', this time in the Royal Aircraft Establishment Farnborough. After the war he enjoyed seventeen years at Oxford, by the end of which period he and Jeanie had spent a further twenty two years in the south. Near the end of this period one of them had remarked, "It's been a hell of a long war this time!" Perhaps in some respects Oxford was more of a war than Farnborough. The war had been long enough!

Besides, he was realising that his second career was well under way. Before retirement he had published sixty five times. As it turned out, sixty four more publications were to come.

# PART III

## INDIAN SUMMER

# Third Three Decades
# 1954-1983

"I just go right on — reporting what I find."
Alexander Thom

The Second Career

Alexander Thom's second career really began about twenty four years before he retired from Oxford in 1961. He had read Admiral Somerville's paper on Callanish in 1912 and had remembered its content in 1933 on that memorable moonlight visit.

After a long day's sail in the North Atlantic he had arrived in the twilight at the secluded inlet of East Loch Roag to the north-west of the Island of Lewis. Deciding to anchor as far up East Loch Roag as possible, as he looked up, there was the rising moon with the stones of Callanish silhouetted on it. After dinner he went ashore to explore the Stonehenge of Scotland and was fascinated to discover that by looking at the Pole star that a north-south line existed in the complex. Thom's mind was immediately set to wonder whether the alignment was a chance occurrence or whether it had been deliberately built that way. And if deliberate would this pattern be found at other megalithic sites?

But he did no surveying of standing stone sites until the late 1930s. Thereafter, weather permitting, he surveyed sites in Scotland and England on every possible occasion at weekends and during vacations.

After Thom realised that the megalith builders had an intelligence equal to his own, he began to reason out how they thought by placing himself in their situation. He referred to this process as "wearing their mocassins". Ancient peoples lived most of their lives in the open air, observed the skies by day and night, and the rising and setting positions of the heavenly bodies on east and west horizons. He reasoned that they kept a record, memorised it and passed it on by word of mouth. The positions of the astronomical megaliths were their permanent recording of their calendar, both solar and lunar. At observatories each astronomer would know what to expect each season — his students would be well instructed.

As Thom worked, the subject was developing in his mind, and

by 1954 he was ready to commence publishing. By this time he was aged sixty, when most of us begin to slow down. But Alexander Thom had still to make his contribution to archaeoastronomy, a contribution which has led to worldwide recognition. He still had, however, seven more years of work to do at Oxford Engineering Laboratory before officially retiring.

Thom claimed that the more important rings of megaliths were designed on geometric principles. The plan shape of some was circular, others were egg-shaped and some had flattened sides; some were elliptical. By statistical analysis of his plans he found evidence to show the use of a standard unit of length, the megalithic yard, used at sites in the Shetlands, the Hebrides, at Avebury, at Stonehenge, in Wales, Ireland and Brittany.

Part of an undated letter signed 'John' epitomises his second career —

"I have thought many times how extraordinary it is that what started as a simple hobby, your interest in megaliths, should have developed into something of major importance which may well lead to a more enduring reputation than anything you may have achieved in the engineering line. What a pleasant and fruitful way to spend your old age!"

The writer could have been none other than John K Hardy, his friend of the Royal Aircraft Establishment days.

Thom's first publication on archaeoastronomy was in 1955. In another early paper in1962, in addition to stone rings he brought in the distances between stones in stone rows. In 1964 he first published information obtained from the ellipse at Sands of Forvie. Dr Archie Roy and others had demonstrated in 1963 the use of the ellipse in megalithic times. Their plans include the first known example of a stone ellipse, at Tormore, Isle of Arran.

In a 1965 publication in *Vistas in Astronomy* (Vol 7), Thom referred frequently to 'the extreme positions' of the moon. In *Vistas* in 1969 (Vol 11) he used 'lunar solstices' and 'mean lowest declination'. It was not until *Megalithic Lunar Observatories* (MLO) was published in 1967 (written afer the Vistas paper) that he used the words 'major and minor standstills' to describe concisely the maximum and minimum points in lunar movements. I well remember long discussions in his study as to the merits of various groups of words. 'Lunistice' was one way of describing the phenomenon, being parallel with 'solstice', but he decided finally on 'standstill'. Many years later he invented the phrase 'lunar band'.

Rolf Sinclair wrote in December 1987 pointing out that the following note appeared in *The Washington Post's* Science Notebook on December 7th, 1987 and saying, "It looks as if the term 'standstill', and interest in it, has become a part of public notice." The cutting from the *Washington Post* reads —

"The Moon is at an 18.6-year High.

Now — the few days on either side of last Saturday's full Moon — is the time of the Major Lunar Standstill, which is the occasion every 18.6 years when the moon reaches the highest point in the sky it ever attains — 80 degrees above the horizon, as calculated at Washington's latitude. Ninety degrees is directly overhead.

The event was apparently significant to the builders of Stonehenge, whose prehistoric 'observatory' seems to have been aligned to sight the moon at this point in its path, but it is little noticed today. In fact, its name is a misnomer. The moon of course does not stand still. It will, however, be at very nearly the same high position around the time of January's full moon."

From the biographer's point of view, letters are important. I start off on one tack with scant information and later discover a very relevant letter hidden in a file of calculations and, 'Hey Presto', the field opens up!

One letter survives to shed light on the Professor's initial work on the statistical analysis of his megalithic rings. He must have been asking for advice or discussing his problem with J M Hammersley who held the Readership in the Design and Analysis of Scientific Experiment in the University of Oxford. Hammersley wrote on 15th November 1954 explaining procedure recommended for calculating lack of randomness.

S R Broadbent, in *Biometrika*, Vol. 42, 1955, in a paper on 'Quantum Hypotheses', quoted Hammersley & Morton's (1954) Druid Circle problem and gave in his references, A Thom's 1955 (JRSS paper in the press), *A statistical examination of the megalithic sites in Britain.* Broadbent, in *Biometrika*, Vol. 43, 1956, in his paper *Examination of a quantum hypothesis based on a single set of data* refers again to Thom's same 1955 paper and 'the division by Professor Thom of Druid Circles into English and Scottish circles' . . . as being . . . a "difficulty of this treatment of data."

Evidently the statisticians were more than interested in Thom's 'Druid Circle' problem with his 'single set of Data'. It was only after the publication of the 1955 paper that people other than astronomers began to take interest in the work.

In the discussion on the above JRSS paper of Thom's, Professor DG Kendall said —

"I move the vote of thanks with great pleasure. We always give a special welcome to the application of statistical methods to a new field and Professor Thom has provided us with a paper which is not only of great intrinsic interest but raises some fresh problems for the theoretical statistician. One must admire the immense amount of field work which lies behind the paper as well as the moderate and careful way in which the conclusions are stated. . . "

In seconding the vote of thanks Mr Hammersley was glad to pay tribute to Professor Thom's work. What impressed him most was Thom's breadth of scholarship and the wide range of talents necessary to execute his work. "With archaeological work of this character," said Hammersley, "it is not enough to be a mere archaeologist. One must also be a local historian, a surveyor, an astronomer, an engineer, a statistician, a yachtsman, and a hiker all rolled into one.

"In these days when we are apt to pay too much lip-service to narrow specialisation and routine research by battalions of doctors of philosophy, it is pleasant to recollect that savants are not yet an extinct species and that those who prospect the no-man's-land between two or more branches of science are very often the real instigators of progress. Not only do such people raise new problems; but they raise them in refreshingly unorthodox ways, which cause us to re-examine in a fresh and critical light the existing foundations of the orthodox structure."

By 1956 Thom was able to write that any lingering doubts he may have had were completely removed by his measurements of the diameters of circles. He writes of "some sixty new values."

Alexander Thom had always been interested in statistics and its teaching to Civil Engineers. He was always attempting to have his statistical approach correctly stated and explained. He wrote in February, 1979 to his friend of the Oxford days, Professor A N Black. The reply, in amongst a page of mathematics, amounted to the old problem —the size of the sample — ie not enough lunar lines!

In June 1972 the Professor had written to Dr Hammersley enclosing the draft of a paper on the Theorem of Pythagoras. Hammersley replied instantly. One paragraph of his reply stated that the discrepancies listed in Table 1 were all sufficiently small to support the contention that integral measurements were used. That, I think, is a fair statistical conclusion. But to argue from that towards Pythagoras Theorem is to go outside the realm of statistics, and to enter the field of inferential philosophy.

Having had enough material on his researches into standing stones to begin publishing in 1954,. exactly when Sandy gave his first public lecture on the subject is uncertain. But as the years passed, various learned societies gradually took notice and invited him to talk. Each time that he lectured he attempted to give something new — a new site, a fresh idea, a new discovery. He was working steadily and developing his subject almost daily, and such procedure was natural.

He kept no record of the societies to which he delivered his lectures. I know that among many others he lectured to the archaeologists in Ulster, to a small group of workers in Campbeltown, and to an audience of four hundred invited by the Faculty of Engineering in the University of Glasgow.

At the age of seventy six he was beginning to feel the need of making a list of his appointments. One such list exists. It was made in June 1970, before the Carnac surveys began.

He had left the main arrangements for the first expedition to Carnac to the author, while he himself planned his astronomical work ahead and arranged to borrow theodolites, etc. The list is a measure, if nothing else, of the interest in Thom's work. It also says something about the man's energy.

Between 8th June 1970 and 23rd February 1971 he visited

Churchill College, Cambridge and later had lunch with Bruce Wilcock of Clarendon Press in Oxford; had a guest for dinner at Oxford; visited Shrewsbury, Llangollen, travelled back to Glasgow; was interviewed by Magnus Magnusson at Dunlop; travelled to Carnac; supervised the first Carnac survey; had a fortnight's sail on *Aline* in the Hebrides; visited Dorset; was interviewed by Southern Television; sailed for two days on *Aline* for filming a beach scene; travelled with a BBC film crew to Callanish; was interviewed by Magnus Magnusson on film in the Cabin at The Hill; plotted hundreds of stones on the Carnac survey; analysed the layouts of the stones; gave lectures in Queen's University Belfast, in Edinburgh University, at Newcastle, Reading University and at Oxford. He also gave a talk in the Department of Extra-Mural Studies in Sheffield.

A two-day symposium was arranged jointly in London in 1972 by the Royal Society and the British Academy. Fourteen men read papers on *The place of Astronomy in the Ancient World*. Sandy was one of them. His paper, number ten on the list, was on Astronomical Significance of Prehistoric Monuments in Western Europe, and he referred to his publications from 1967 onwards. D G Kendall, of the Statistical Laboratory, University of Cambridge gave his paper last, on Hunting Quanta. It was quite a strain on Sandy, having to wait until the end of the symposium to hear Kendall's verdict on the existence of the megalithic yard, and knowing that there would be no chance to defend himself from his own podium. Members of the audience were sitting on the edges of their chairs intently listening to Kendall.

It was eighteen years since Sandy had discussed his statistical analysis of megalithic rings with Hammersley and Broadbent. This is not the place to report the final discussions, but I do remember AAJ Hogg saying after it was all over, "Well, Thom, you win the day!"

A year before, Hogg had been critical of Sandy during the BBC television programme *Cracking the Stone Age Code*. Unconvinced, Hogg had at that time put the question, "How much of the prehistoric Einstein's calculations had been put in by Professor Thom inadvertently?" . . . and he claimed that . . . "the fact that something could have been set out in a particular way was no proof that it was so set out." Quite a victory for Thom this time!

In October 1973 Sandy was invited to lecture at a symposium in the University of Cagliari, Sardinia. Beryl went with him (he was seventy nine years of age). His eighteen-page paper was published in English in Cagliari. (In 1990 at the Oxford 3 International Conference on Archaeoastronomy at St Andrews, Professor Edoardo Proverbio, who had been an active participant at Cagliari, presented the author with a copy of his 1989 book on Archaeoastromomy, as a memento of Alexander Thom, to whom he referred forty one times in the book).

During the flight to Cagliari, Beryl and her father were 'ashore' at Rome airport. Purely by chance they met Graham Ritchie who remembers the meeting well. The Skipper was in a bad temper because his open razor had been removed from his nightbag by the security staff using electronic scanning devices! Naturally he wondered if he would ever see his razor again.

Lecture rooms have distinct auras and Sandy really enjoyed delivering the Thomson Lecture to the Institute of Measurement and Control in the historic Faraday Room in the Royal Institution, London. This was in October 1977 and the author accompanied him, prepared to give the talk if Sandy had felt unable to do it. Sandy rose to the occasion. En route home we visited his old haunts in Oxford.

After another lecturing occasion in London we took the chance of visiting the *Cutty Sark* and the Greenwich Museum. Glasgow University's Dean of the Faculty of Engineering invited him to lecture. A large audience turned out. The Royal Philosophical Society of Glasgow followed suit.

Standing Stone material and Archaeoastronomy

By the 1950s Thom's field work on standing stones was far enough advanced for him to realise that he had to know more about horizontal refraction, the bending of a ray of light by the earth's atmosphere near the horizon. He forthwith did much experimental work on refraction and so his first paper on this, *Some Refraction Measurements at low Altitudes* was published in 1954 in the Journal of The Institute of Navigation. (Twenty nine years later he was still to be found working and publishing his discoveries on horizontal refraction.) His second paper on archaeoastronomy, *The Solar Observatories of Megalithic Man* appeared in 1954 in the Journal of the British Astronomical Association.

The statistical examination of megalithic sites in Britain appeared next in 1955 in the Journal of the Royal Statistical Society. By this time he had developed a punched card system for storing information about each standing stone site.

Thom had offered his material to editors of archaeological journals but with no success. He tried America, but had to wait for six months for a reply. The established American archaeologists had sent the material to their British colleagues, the ones who had already refused to publish. And so it continued, until 1967, by which time Thom had published sixteen times in all, but not once in any archaeological journal.

In 1967 he published his own book, *Megalithic Sites in Britain*. By 1971 he had published *Megalithic Lunar Observatories*. He carefully hand-printed the manuscript for this in ink. It is very readable and the publisher's instructions to the printer are on each page.

Finally, in 1990, his last book was published posthumously.

His cousin Jack Mclay once asked him, after a broadcast aimed at the general rather than the specialised public, if he had published any form of 'Child's Guide' to the whole thing. His answer was that he had published one book but confirmed he thought there were not more than five people in the world who would understand it! He added that he had had a number of letters asking the same question after the BBC broadcast. He was trying to do something of the kind but so far as it had gone he was rather afraid that there might be no more than twenty five people who might understand it.

He drafted about four papers for the Belgian learned journal *Kadath* which were thought to be "not for their readers".

Several years before he died he had been invited to write a 'popular' book on Archaeoastronomy, but as I was helping him with every publication by this time, I knew that he still had much to contribute to the subject and I advised him to use his energies on productive thinking and writing.

Before he ceased working hard he made the decision to give all of his survey plans to the Royal Commission on the Ancient and Historical Monuments of Scotland (RCAHM), and I saw to it that these plans and copies of his books with offprints of his published papers went to Edinburgh.

Among his papers I found a hand printed manuscript of a book, and also six out of twelve typewritten chapters of another. The file for this latter book he had given me in 1978 and on it was my note that he had remarked that it was 'childish'. This I cannot judge.

*Knockrome, Isle of Jura  (photo Chris Jennings)*
*Starting from his awakened interest at Callanish, Alexander Thom*
*surveyed megalithic sites extensively over Scotland, England, Wales and*
*France*

"Many times as I approached a site . . . I felt a sense of anticipation. I needed every site I could find to add to the material in the statistical analysis. But there was much more than that. Where there were several stones upright, I quickened my pace and got beside them, I suppose in an unconscious attempt to get in touch with these mysterious people . . ."                                        Alexander Thom

*a lunar line  (photo Chris Jennings)*
*Dun Skeig, West Loch Tarbert*

*Loch Stornaway, Knapdale (photo Chris Jennings)*

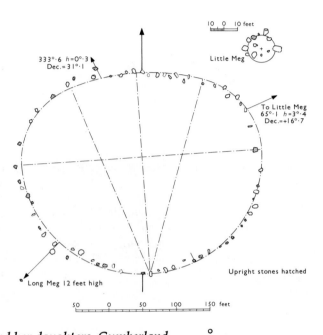

333°·6  $h=0°·3$
Dec.=31°·1

10  0  10 feet

Little Meg

To Little Meg
65°·1  $h=3°·4$
Dec.=+16°·7

Upright stones hatched

Long Meg 12 feet high

50    0    50    100    150 feet

*Long Meg and her daughters, Cumberland*

212

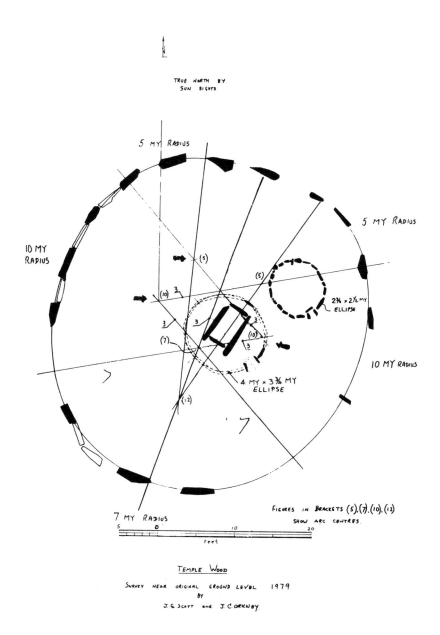

TRUE NORTH BY
SUN SIGHTS

5 MY RADIUS

5 MY RADIUS

10 MY
RADIUS

(5)

(5)

2¾ × 2½ MY
ELLIPSE

(10) 3

3

3

(10)

3

(7)

10 MY RADIUS

4 MY × 3¾ MY
ELLIPSE

(12)

FIGURES IN BRACKETS (5),(7),(10),(12)
SHOW ARC CENTRES.

7 MY RADIUS

5    0         10        20

Feet

TEMPLE WOOD

SURVEY NEAR ORIGINAL GROUND LEVEL  1979
BY
J. G. SCOTT and J. C. ORKNEY.

*Temple Wood, Argyll*

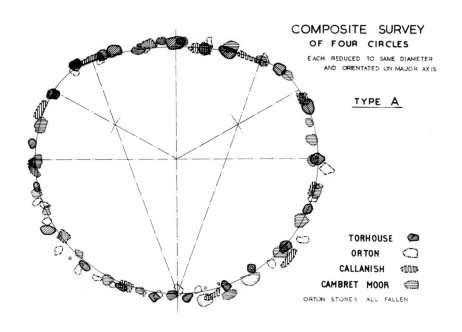

*a composite survey of four circles*
*Torhouse, Wigtonshire; Orton Westmorland; Callanish, Lewis and*
*Cambret Moor, Kirkcudbright*

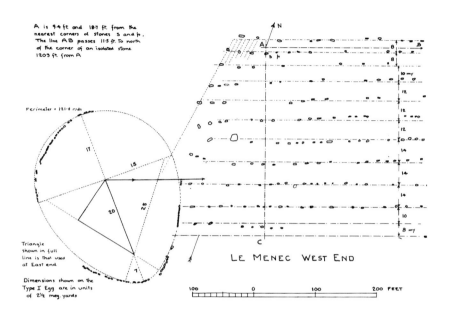

A is 9·4 ft and 18·7 ft. from the
nearest corners of stones 5 and 6.
The line AB passes 11·5 ft. To north
of the corner of an isolated stone
1203 ft. from A

Perimeter = 121·8 rods

Triangle
shown in full
line is that used
at East end

Dimensions shown on the
Type I Egg are in units
of 2½ meg. yards

LE MENEC WEST END

100    0    100    200 FEET

*Le Menec, Brittany*

215

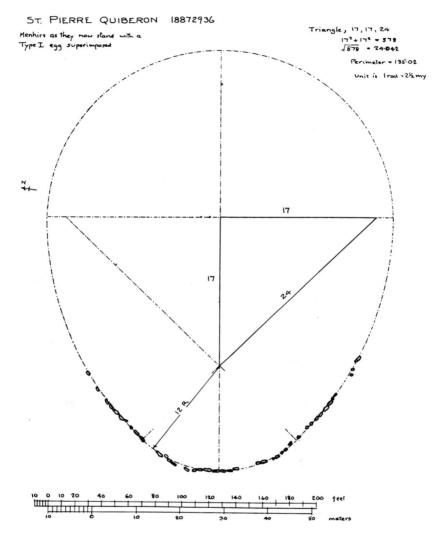

*St Pierre Quiberon, Brittany*

Perhaps twenty seven years after he wrote it he was thinking that the subject and the writing about it was undeveloped.

I quote most of the preface, which includes some more of his memories of his first visit to Callanish in 1933. At that time not many yachtsmen sailed these waters.

To be titled a Statistical Examination of the Standing Stones on the West Coast of Scotland, Thom begins —

"I am not an archaeologist and can lay no claim to a knowledge of archaeology. I had of course, known since 1913 about the complex of stones and menhirs at Callanish. Somerville's paper (1912) had intrigued me greatly when I read it."

Here the Professor wrote about his cruise outside of the Hebrides in 1933, as described previously.

"The Sound of Harris is the only passage to the Atlantic in the 100 miles chain of the Outer Hebrides, and after a hard sail from the Sound we put in to West Loch Roag, in north western Lewis. Passing through the Barragloam Narrows we proceeded in the gloaming up East Loch Roag as far as my chart allowed me to go with safety. I was navigating with care; finally the anchor went over and the sails came down. As we stowed sail, we looked up and saw the rising moon. Silhouetted on the moon's disc like great fingers were the stones of Tursachan Callanish. That evening, since I had been concentrating on navigation as darkness was approaching, I did not know how near we were to the main Callanish site.

"After dinner we went ashore and explored the avenue formed by the two main lines. We saw the other alignments, the circle and the cist. Being night time it was possible, by standing on the terminal rock to the south, to see in the moonlight how the North/South alignment appeared to run straight to the Pole Star.

"I never forgot that visit to the site in the moonlight. The long days of buffeting in the Atlantic made one ready to appreciate the quiet and perfect anchorage. At the site one could not but be affected by the surroundings — the mystery of the unknown terrain — the loch lying quiet

217

below and above all the towering stones of the most unspoilt monolithic structure in Britain.

"My interest in the workings of the minds of the megalith builders was stirred. I began to carry surveying gear and to make detailed surveys of all the sites that I could find.

"I have now such a mass of data that it is becoming difficult to handle. The present monograph is an attempt to put on record the conclusions I have reached. The interest of the results will be many times enhanced when someone can find time to examine thoroughly another district. I believe that Somerville left many unpublished surveys and it would be interesting to analyse these."

The contents list indicated the areas dealt with were Callanish and other sites in the Hebrides, sites in and near Mull, in and near Argyll, and in and near Galloway. A form of histogram was developed for statistical examination of declination of all kinds and he described making four small gaussian templates for building up his main illustrations. He dealt with rising and setting declinations and star magnitudes and gave reasons for the solar and stellar concentrations. He had a chapter on seasons as determined by stellar risings and finished with a statistical examination of average dates.

Exactly when this book was drafted is not known. No date appears on it other than a pencil note in Chapter Nine reading "observed up to 1950". No mention appears of the basic unit of length used on the rings and the author has to assume the book was written before the paper to the Royal Statistical Society in 1955 where units of length and declinations were discussed.

It would appear that he drafted it about 1951 before he published *The solar observatories of Megalithic Man* in 1954. In Chapter One he wrote "some fourteen years ago I set myself the vacation task of visiting and surveying as many sites as possible in the chosen region." By the author's knowledge of what happened, this fits well with the date 1936/1937.

Little did he know then that he was embarking on his second career!

Whatever the reservations of the archaeological and astronomer communities up to that point, undoubtedly the BBC film *Cracking the Stone Age Code*, broadcast in 1970, made publicity for the professor's archaeoastronomy. After this, Dr Michael Hoskin, Editor of JHA began to take articles from Sandy for publication from 1971 onwards.

Professor Owen Gingerich of Harvard College Observatory wrote that in 1970 he had spent several months in Cambridge, and during that time had heard Thom describe the Crucuno site on BBC television. He mentioned this the following morning to Michael Hoskin, suggesting that it might make a nice paper for his new journal. Gingerich is credited by Michael with having brought Thom as an author into the JHA, which is particularly ironical since the report on Crucuno was published eventually in *Current Anthropology* rather than in *Journal for the History of Astronomy*!

In all, by 1978, Michael Hoskin had published nineteen papers from Thom and these were a catalyst for the rise of archaeoastronomy as a recognised field of enquiry in its own right. The Archaeo-astronomy Supplement to the *Journal for the History of Astronomy* was created and seven more Thom articles duly appeared. According to Ruggles in *Records in Stone* the Supplement "owes its existence to AT."

The BBC documentary in the *Chronicle* series, produced in the autumn of 1969, serves as a sterling monument to the power of television to bring complex subjects to a wide cross section of the population. Thom had been at a meeting of archaeologists in Cambridge and during the discussion Glyn Daniel indicated that although Professor Thom did not yet know about it, he, Daniel, was intimating that Thom would be going to Brittany in 1970. Evidently Daniel had been arranging things with the BBC. That was the first Thom heard about the possibility of an expedition to Carnac. The *Chronicle* programme invited him to go, and arrangements were soon begun.

Thom wrote to the French Authorities in Rennes and in due course authorisation for survey work was received, provided no excavation, no felling and no marking of the megaliths took place.

Magnus Magnusson was to be the presenter and interviewer. The programme was produced and broadcast in the autumn of 1970.

This expedition, the first of many to Brittany, consisted of a party of fourteen assisting Thom, plus of course, Magnusson and Daniel and the television crew, the latter body of people staying only a few days.

Because it does give a good guide to the general reader into the whole archaeoastonomical field, the transcript of the dialogue between Magnusson and Thom is included. This dialogue also indicates how Thom actually spoke. Some words of Daniel, RJC Atkinson and EW MacKie are included. The reader is politely asked to realise that at most places the background is screen action of views, sites, etc.

M Magnusson
"Up and down the country in England Wales and Scotland there are hundreds of prehistoric sites; in mist and heather as remote and incomprehensible as the men who put them there with a vast extent of toil 4,000 years ago or more.

"Stones and circles, stones standing in strictly straight lines, marching nowhere, doing nothing. What were they for? Why should a primitive people scratching a living from the land go to such trouble to build these seemingly pointless monuments in the middle of nowhere? Was it for ritual or ceremonial purposes?

"One man claims to have found in the stones a reality about our ancestors more fascinating than any fiction. This man has devoted all his spare time to tracking down his prehistoric cuounterparts. He is seventy six years old now. Alexander Thom, a Scot, one time professor of Engineeering Science at Oxford University. By studying hundreds of these half-forgotten sites he produced a theory which may force us to modify our preconceived ideas. To him stone age people were not just simple primitives. They could be intelligent and sophisticated mathematicians and astronomers to whom time was an exercise in science, using stones as calendars and clocks; men who could measure and survey with the accuracy of a modern theodolite.

A Thom "It is intensely interesting. I get a tremendous thrill when I come over the top of a hill and see a circle lying amongst the heather, and I realise this is a new one and it may be that anything will come out of it."

M "And therefore you are not content until you've cracked it?"

T "Well, in some places you can't get anything because there may only be one or two stones left; the site's incomplete. In others cases, well, it took me twenty years to crack the most important of all, but it was worth cracking."

Glyn Daniel "All professional archaeologists are beset by the lunatic fringe. Professor Thom is not part of this."

M "At his home at Dunlop, Ayrshire, Thom buries himself every day in a converted hen house; to process the patient surveys which have set the world of conventional archaeology by the ears.

He has established to his own satisfaction that stone age man used a standard unit of length for all his work, a megalithic yard of 2.73 ft precisely, that was consistent throughout Britain, implying an organised society with an agreed yard stick. His theories about megalithic geometry and astronomy have been described as putting a time bomb under archaeologists. Take Avebury ring for instance. To him that is just a prehistoric temple, a stupendous exercise in Stone Age geometry made by mathematicians and astronomers. And this is the nub: Thom has found dozens of alignments between individual stones and the setting and rising positions of the sun 4,000 years ago. He subjected all these observations to statistical analysis. On a chart it emerges that these alignments fall into groups which correspond with remarkable accuracy to the major solar events of the year, winter and summer solstice, spring and autumn equinox and so on, to form a stone age calendar of sixteen months and one that could be synchronised throughout Britain perhaps by beacons of which Mayday and Midsummer bonfires are an ancient memory. It's heavy stuff, suggesting a race of prehistoric Einsteins. But not all archaeologists are wholly convinced, to say the least.

GD "What Thom has done is he has emphasised by studying not only the grand monuments like Stonehenge but all the stone circles in the north of Britain. He studied these things and made us appreciate again, all of us, that there was was an accurate body of engineering and mathematical knowlege in times so very long ago."

M "RJC Atkinson is one of the few archaeologists with the knowledge to evaluate the mathematics of it."

RJCA "I think that this has to be taken very seriously

indeed. No-one I am sure is going to question the accuracy or the comprehensiveness of the evidence which Professor Thom has put before us. Where people are going to have difficulty is with the implications made. If we accept the implications we are going to accept something which to us as archaeologists sounds pretty improbable but I still think we have got to take it seriously simply because if we reject it we are in fact flying in the face of a great deal of evidence which can not be explained away simply as the result of chance or accident."

M "Unruffled by controversy Alexander Thom works on, getting closer and closer to the megalith builders he has come to respect and know so intimately that he calls them now 'The Boys'."

T "The problems they solved without pen and pencil and without logarithmic tables and so on were remarkable. I think they were, as far as brain power is concerned, my superiors."

M "He has set himself an enormous task. For the megalithic culture is found all over Europe. The 'boys' were astonishingly assiduous in their building and liked to do it in style. The scale is sometimes breathtaking. At Carnac in Brittany the most spectacular megalithic site in Europe, thousands of massive stones stand there in great battallions, line upon line striding across the countryside for miles on end. The standing stones have survived because of their sheer weight. Many of their tombs are roofed with great slabs of stones some now stripped of their covering of soil, exposed to the light. Others are in the form of covered passage graves and in these passage graves we find their mysterious art carved on the massive stones.

Carnac is not the only place where stone alignments have survived. In the avenue of stones at Avebury for instance, but on a much smaller scale; on Dartmoor we find similar lines of stones. Unlike the Carnac lines they don't stride over the country-side, they trudge on aimlessly for miles but they are recognisably part of the megalithic culture, for megalith is simply the Greek for big stone. But apart from these alignments Britain and particularly the west of Britain is littered with circular structures, rings of stones that Alexander Thom has studied so minutely, many of them almost lost in the heather and in ruinous condition. But

222

some have tremendous power and magnitude like the great monument of Avebury with its enormous ring of standing stones.

A place of mystery and magic for thousands of summer visitors rivalled only by the sheer grandeur of Britain's most celebrated prehistoric monument, Stonehenge itself. The ancient Greek historians may have known it as the great circular temple of Apollo they described in the islands of the Hyperboreans north of France. These Hyperboreans they said were field astronomers who visited the Greeks in turn, what's more and taught philosophy to Pythagoras and his followers. And as for the astronomy according to Professor Thom the megalith builders were using Pythagorean geometry to design their circles almost 2,000 years before Pythagoras was born."


On a sandy beach now in Argyllshire —

Production of a balanced television presentation required that AT explain the ring geometry which he had discovered. As he had spent fifty years of his life explaining his lectures using chalk and a blackboard, he volunteered immediately to draw it all out for the cameras. Instantly Magnus demurred — in his experience that would turn viewers off right away. Sandy had for long enough felt that 'The Boys' as he affectionately called them, had initially worked out their designs on sand, and so he suggested that the team use a suitable beach.

Sandy knew authoress Marion Campbell of Kilberry Castle, Argyll. She led the team to nearby Cretshengan Bay with a large standing stone in the background. The tide was coming in; one cameraman was standing in the sea; he suddenly took off his pants without explaining first that underneath he was wearing bathing shorts. A canoeist in the background was complicating things. Producer David Collison used his camera team to good effect, making them dance round Sandy and Magnus, the "willing helper" and questioner. With Sandy scribing on the sand, Magnus holding the end of the string, the salty waves the while lapping at their backs. The whole effect was marvellous. It was much better than on a blackboard, and it later convinced many viewers that Sandy was right. The crew had made a first class film.

M "On a sandy shore in the west of Scotland, Alexander
Thom treated me to a Hyperborean seminar, a prehistoric
tutorial in engineering, demonstrating with pegs and
knotted string how these stone age designers had used
Pythagorean triangles, right angled triangles whose three
sides are all whole numbers, as a basis for their circular
designs. Many of the stone rings are not true circles but
subtle variations of a circle. Any fool it seems can draw a
circle with a stick and a piece of string but that didn't satisfy
these stone age Einsteins. At first glance rings of standing
stones look like circles but Thom's meticulous surveys have
revealed that frequently they are not, like the ring at
Penmaen-Mawr in north Wales. It's actually an ellipse or
oval, the easiest modified circle there is to draw, once you
know how."

T "It is called mathematically an ellipse. You notice that
it's drawn to two centres. Now this again gave them a
certain choice in the size. This choice was to enable them to
make all these resulting measurements integral whole
numbers based on a Pythagorean triangle, measured in a
standard unit of length, a megalithic yard.

The ring at Meini Hirion is an ellipse drawn from two
centres with a long loop of rope designed expressly to make
the circumference an exact number of megalithic yards.
There are ten of them in Scotland, three in the west country
and two in Wales. The next way of modifying a circle is to
stretch one end of it into an egg-shape based again on the
Pythagorean triangle whose integral sides ensure that all
your measurements stay integral apart from the
circumference, and you'd have to experiment for years to get
that integral as well. And this seems to have been one of
their chief intellectual occupations.

The Druid temple near Inverness is based on a classic
Pythagorean triangle with sides precisely 3, 4 and 5
megalithic yards. There are 6 of these egg-shaped rings in
Scotland and the timber ring at Woodhenge in Wilts is also
an egg not a circle.

It has its significance for geometry. They were storing
away the fact that they knew that it was a 3, 4, 5 triangle. But
there is another point — the circles and rings were all made
so that the circumference was an integral number of units
and if you are using eggs you have far greater freedom to

adjust matters because having put down the basic triangles you can start off with any set of radii you like provided they are based on the triangle. If one of them is integral the other two will also be integral.

The cult was of the whole number or of dogged determination to impose their will on the obstinate stones. Sometimes instead of making an egg shape, they 'clipped' pieces out of the circle. There are twenty of these in Scotland, fourteen in England, eg Castlerigg and Long Meg in the Lake District. Some compound rings were extraordinarily intricate as if the designer had gone berserk. At Moel Ty Ucha in Wales there is a five sided ring with a whole series of interlocking arcs in some structures. If that's complex, what about Avebury, based on a massive Pythagorean triangle, the megalithic yard being used in units of ten which seems to have some sort of mystical significance."

M "This is pure mathematics — it appears only for its own sake then?"

T "Well it might have been geometry for its own sake. These people were, well they were researching into geometry. All the time they were controlled by this convention that they had to have it in whole numbers."

M "I suppose the definition of pure research is that it hasn't really any functional purpose. They didn't require to make the stone circles in this shape?'

T 'Well that's true. They could just have drawn any old circle, and said there's a circle, boys, but they didn't. They wanted the thing perhaps to have this hidden significance. The man in the street — the ordinary man who helped them to set it out — wouldn't have any idea what was hidden or involved in this thing. The experts, the priests or whatever you call them, they knew what was in it. This hidden information that was stored away in this construction."

M "Looking out toward the island of Jura nineteen miles off the west coast of Scotland at a place called Ballochroy there are three stones standing close together on the hillside. From them on a good day you can see Ben Corra, one of the Paps of Jura, and it was here thirty years ago that Thom first realised that the stones could have been markers for making truly accurate observations for the summer solstice.

Magnusson continued, "The seminar turned to prehistoric astronomy." Here in the film, an animated scene was constructed showing
the sun setting behind Ben Corra, the north eastern slope of which
had the same slope as the path of the sun. A close-up of AT at
Ballochroy adjusting his theodolite was also screened.

T "Well the solstice was midsummer day and thus it was a
calendar date that gave them a fixed point on the calendar."

M "It wasn't all that important to farmers for instance to
know when midsummer was. They would count according
to the season and harvest governed the season.'

T "Well, you see, if the observer was interested in some
astronomical event such as an eclipse it was necsessary to
have a calendar. You can't make predictions without a
calendar."

M "Why should they want to predict eclipses?"

T "Well that I don't know. It was obviously very
important. You know the story about the two Chinese
astronomers who got their heads chopped off because they
failed to predict an eclipse? Probably these chaps were just
as anxious."

M "In 1970 the megalithic summer solstice no longer
works because of something which astronomers call the shift
in the obliquity of the ecliptic. The earth's axis is tilting,
which means that the midsummer sun is setting a little
further south each year. The difference can be calculated and
allowed for and Thom has worked out that in 1800BC an
astronomer at the stone would have seen the setting sun just
twinkling down.

T "The sun was coming up, getting a little further to the
north every night as it set. Eventually when it was near the
solstice it was very near the slope of Ben Corra, and the
observer would have to move along here, notice right along
the line of the stones, until he was somewhere out here and
he would move along here until he got the edge of the sun
just twinkling down the slope of Ben Corra. He would mark
it. The next night he would find it moved along a little,
getting to the same position. He would mark it again. By the
time he got to the stone he knew that the sun had reached its

extreme position and it was the solstice."

M "Is this a case such as they had with their geometry, that they simply wanted to know about time dates and astronomy as knowledge for its own sake or was it all put to some use?

T "Well I think eclipse prediction was one of the things, but also there is the fact that just as today our astronomers like to produce a time and a calendar which is exact, to a fraction of a second if you like, these people were working to a fraction of a day. And they wanted to be accurate, just the same as our scientists today want to be accurate. They wouldn't have been scientists if they hadn't tried to be accurate."

M "Now what is it that you do with your theodolite that stone age man was doing without his theodolite ? What are you doing when you keek through it?'

T "When I keek through the theodolite I'm determining the exact azimuth or the exact bearing of the various points along the hilltops and I must get these exact to a minute part of a degree so that I can do the calculations and see exactly what the declination was and so I know that it was the edge of the sun coming down Ben Corra."

M "Let's have a look and see what happens when you keek through it. Do you take a bearing on the stone?

T "No. I don't touch the stone. I have previously, from the sun, determined the bearing of a reference point by sighting on the sun and using my watch so I know the exact bearing of some reference point — so I get on to the reference point like this, set it on exactly, and note this is now set. I clamp up and can turn on to Ben Corra. I can do as many points along the slope of Ben Corra as I like, one after the other."

M "So this is how you can tell precisely how the sun was setting in what, 1800BC?'

T "Exactly. I can only use a theodolite because I can't look at it in 1800BC. They could but I can't. The present position today would be away up there somewhere because of the change in the obliquity of the ecliptic. The sun's not coming so far up in the summer or so far south in the winter."

M "The Paps of Jura could apparently be used as an astronomical foresight to observe the winter solstice as well, from a place on the mainland called Kintraw, thirty miles away.

The site here consists of a standing stone, a large ruined cairn, a deep gully and on the far side of the gully, twenty feet further up, a large boulder on a ledge like a platform. No-one had paid it any heed until Thom went clambering up that tricky slope in search of a prehistoric observation platform.'

T "Because I couldn't see how these boys had got the position without getting up and obviously if you go over there you can get up as high as you like and I thought, well, the obvious thing is to go over there and see if I can get a good view. I took the theodolite over there, and found myself on the platform."

M "Now this ledge was being excavated by a team from the Hunterian Museum of Glasgow University, led by Euan MacKie, to see if there was any evidence that it had once been man made.

Had the stone age astronomer priests deliberately constructed this site, formed to help them in their astronomical observations on a December day some 4,000 years ago? Which is the platform itself?"

T "Well we're on it now. There is the wooded top which hides the Paps when you are down at a lower level but they come in just over the trees there when you are in the neighbourhood of this stone. That was how I spotted this bit that you can actually dodge back and forward on, to get yourself into alignment."

M "Come and show me what a stone age man would have been doing standing on this platform."

T "This I reckon is where he actually made his first observation of the winter solstitial sun setting in the Paps of Jura, behind Ben Shianti. Now from here the sun goes into the notch; goes in behind Ben Shianti and then appears momentarily in the notch. The notch is just over the knoll above where the standing stone appears from here. Now the sun at the winter solstice setting went behind Ben Shianti completely, out of sight and then it reappeared momentarily in the gap. The problem for the megalithic observer here was to get himself into such a position that it just twinkled in the gap, in the vee. By very careful observation I have established that that happened just here about 1800BC. To get into the correct position he had to move along here very rapidly because he had only a few seconds while it was showing. He could get into the position where it would just twinkle and no more. Now that was a dangerous operation — this hillside came straight down. He could have tripped when he was doing the side movement and therefore I reckon he used this platform. The whole point is that here is a platform which is in exactly the right position, exactly the position that megalithic man wanted for making his observations over there and it seems . . . Well I am perfectly certain, he did use it. Whether it was natural or not, I don't know. I suggest that's a parapet to prevent him falling over."

M "What are the chances that it was man made, Euan?"
Euan MacKie "I'd say about 50:50."
M "What would have proved it one way or another?"
EM "Well, some concrete sign of human activity like potsherds or a post hole or stone socket. Perhaps a piece of charred timber: something like that. We haven't had any of those."

M "So the excavation was inconclusive but a significant thing is not so much that no material evidence was found on this occasion to corroborate the theory, but that for the first time a professional archaeologist has given time and attention to looking for it."

EM "I think the evidence that Professor Thom has given us makes it overwhelmingly probable that astronomy could have been practised. It seems to me that it's up to us the archaeologists to make an all out effort to investigate at as many sites as we can whether in fact neolithic man did do the things that Professor Thom has shown could be done."

M "A serious simple solar observatory — it isn't too hard to accept that but at a site called Temple Wood in Argyll, Thom takes things much further. At Temple Wood there is a small stone circle but it's not the circle that interests him; it's a group of five standing stones a couple of hundred yards away across the field. A large centre stone has a special significance to Alexander Thom, and for the stone age astromomer priest he thinks erected it."

T "This stone is at the centre of what in my opinion is the most important lunar observatory in Britain. It has nothing to do with the sun. It is lunar. Standing at this stone and looking up to the notch it shows the extreme position of the moon when it is at its furthest north. When the lower edge of the moon just comes down through that notch it's in its extreme position as it sets in the northwest."

M "Once every nineteen years the moon makes its greatest sweep of the night sky from its rising point in the northeast to its setting point in the northwest. It's called the major standstill of the moon in the north, and here at Temple Wood prehistoric man could capture that vital moment. Now why was it so important for them to get this particular moment in time?"

T "I think the whole object of the thing was to predict eclipses. By using this stone and its neighbours one is enabled to detect a slight movement of the moon in addition to the normal nineteen year cycle and it is this additional movement of the moon which is connected with eclipses and when this wobble is at its maximum then one is in the middle of a danger period for eclipses which can then happen every 173 days thereafter."

M "And once you've got this day you said, right, in 173 days' time there's going to be an eclipse? And this might have been the secret of the power of the astronomer priests, the power of knowledge?"

T "Quite possibly. If he could say that at the next time the moon comes to the full it will be eclipsed, he was obviously in a strong position."

M "How long would it have taken them to work out a site as precise, as exact, as this one was?"

T "Well I think possibly something of the order of fifty to a hundred years, because they could only get the observations made here along this line every nineteen years and if they missed it they had to wait."

M "Now this stone is clearly pretty important. It's got stones all round it . . ."

T "And it's got cup and ring markings and it's also got

four stones, little stones, around about it."

M "These cup and ring markings look as if impressed by a big thumb."

T "Of course there are thousands of these scattered throughout Britain but this is the only stone in this alignment that is marked with cup and rings and I suspect that these carry a message if we could read it telling us what the stone was for."

M "Was this the high point of their development as astronomers?"

T "Yes I think so. The precision with which these positions are placed — showing exactly where you have to stand — the precision of that is almost unbelievable; it splits a minute of arc. That is doing better than an ordinary surveying theodolite."

M "What about the observatory in Caithness?"

T "Well the observatories in Caithness show a little more. I don't say they are more accurate but they contain the information which enabled me to discover the geometric construction which was used to, as it were, compute the results once they had got them. Without this method of computing you can't really use it."

M "The few people who know about this scatter of boulders near John O' Groats called it The Hill of Many Stanes. But to Thom they are like a sort of megalithic graph paper — vital equipment to the stone age scientist. They must once have existed at all the great lunar observatories like Temple Wood if the astronomers were really to know what they were doing."

T "They knew what they were doing all right. This thing was not set out without endless headaches and trials and worry and calculation if you like but the only calculation was done on the ground geometrically. If you put me here in megalithic times I could have worked this thing, knowing what I know now."

M "One site in Scotland on the island of Lewis embodies all the elemental mysteries of megalithic sites — Callanish, the Stonehenge of the north. It's a magical, haunting place. It's to Callanish that Professor Thom comes back again and again to refresh his sense of intimate connection with his prehistoric fellow scientists. For Callanish, exactly aligned on the north south axis embodies so many features of megalithic astronomy — circle and alignment, solar observatory and lunar observatory being combined. It was Callanish that inspired him many years ago to try to crack the stone age code."

T "Well I've sailed this coast since 1912. One year we had gone out through the sound of Harris. Well, you know what that's like and you know what it's like on the outside — it is always blowing. The gale frequency up there is about three times what it is at Tiree. A filthy coast too, exposed and open, and so when we had done about forty miles from the Sound of Harris up to the mouth of Loch Roag, round Gallan Head, the great seas pounding away on the islands there, I thought well we had better go up into Loch Roag. We sailed up Loch Roag as far up as you can go until there was a little bay there and as the light was going I thought we'd better anchor here: put the pick over and dinner came on. We got the mainsail down and when we looked up the moon was rising and silhouetted on the moon were the Callanish stones, sticking up like fingers on the moon."

M "On the island skyline of Lewis the cruciform shape of Callanish draws him like a magnet still. The big stone inside the circle, aligned exactly north south could have been put to many uses — a multipurpose pointer for detecting or observing the wheeling of the stars across the meridian — and there is an alignment exactly to the west which shows the equinoctial sunset."

"Chronicle invited Alexander Thom to Brittany, to Carnac, the Mecca of the megalithic world. The three alignments of le Menec, Kermario and Kerlescan dominate the whole region and bring tourists flocking in their thousands, so Alexander Thom with his prolific family and friends from America and Australia descended on Carnac in search of further mathematical facts. What does he expect to achieve there?"

Glyn Daniel "I think three things. First of all we shall have for the first time an accurate survey of these astonishing alignments with their many thousands of stones.

Secondly we shall know about the things that happen at the ends of these rows. What people miss is that they are broken up into several series and at the end of each series of rows there is a half ellipse or an ellipse or nearly a circle. We shall find out if they are of the same kind of geometrical systems as the circles in Britain. And the third thing is that he will be able to apply his astronomical ideas and answer the question, do these alignments point to any significant place in the heavens?

There are interesting outliers — do they point to other places so that we shall be able to see whether in this area of northwest France, perhaps the most important area of megalith building in the whole world, that they may have some astronomical significance too? and that will be very intriguing."

M "For three and a half weeks they toiled in the sun, surveying, measuring and plotting these monstrous alignments and the other extraordinary monuments of Carnac. Then Thom came home to work on his bulging note books. When I went to see him in his den in Dunlop, after several weeks of processing and analysing the data, the preliminary results more than lived up to everything he had hoped to find."

T "Well probably the biggest job we did was the alignment that runs through here at Le Menec."

M "The first accurate survey of Carnac ever made was now on paper. Only one of the lines appeared to be straight. It is now being checked for astronomical alignment and the use of the megalithic yard. And at the end this strange enclosure of standing stones, half submerged amongst the farm buildings is now surveyed. Only half a dozen of the stones have not been moved out of place by mediaeval farmers, but these original stones fitted precisely with the menhir geometries found in Britain. The design was based on the equally familiar Pythagorean triangle with integral sides and this is exactly as you determined in Britain."

T "I found many of them, a dozen of them, like this in Britain, built on different triangles sometimes on the 3, 4, 5 triangle, sometimes on the 5, 12, 13; but here it is based on the 12, 16, 20."

M "Professor Thom had also been busy nearby at

Crucuno where there is an extremely unusual arrangement of stones, apparently a square. You'd be inclined to ignore it first as an aberration but survey it he did and found that there was more to it than met the eye — a perfect rectangle precisely aligned to the north. A diagonal divides it into two Pythagorean triangles, classic 3, 4, 5 triangles measured in British megalithic yards multiplied by that mystic factor of ten, and a diagonal aligned precisely on the midsummer sunrise."

T "Only in this latitude of Crucuno would the midsummer sun rise on that bearing, In fact it is within a few miles of where it should be. By the time you get up to Scotland this thing becomes a square."

M "There is one other monument near Carnac that always intrigued and staggered scholars and visitors alike. It stands or stood at the edge of the sea looking out to the Atlantic. Alexander Thom could not resist it either. It is simply enormous. It must be the biggest lump of manmade stone anywhere in the world you feel. And as you walk in its shadow you feel dwarfed and puny even though it's lying on its side in bits. The French call it Le Grand Menhir Brisé, the great broken stone and if you imagine it vertical as it once was it would be just about as high as Cleopatra's needle, or about sixty eight feet, but it's twice as fat as Cleopatra's needle and its weight overall would be something like three hundred and thirty tons.'

T "People have puzzled for long enough as to how it got into its position, how they ever got it up, what brought it down and why it broke the way it did? I find that actually it was put there as a universal lunar foresight."

M "From five crucial points on the compass up to fifteen miles away the Grand Menhir Brisé could be used as a foresight for critical observation of the moon. A stone at the tip of the Quiberon Peninsula gave a sighting line for the major standstill of the moon as it rose above the tip of the standing Grand Menhir Brisé every nineteen years. All in all the visit to Carnac was a vindication of all Thom's theories, to his own satisfaction at least. Pouring over the figures every evening he sees the same patterns emerge in Brittany as he'd found in Britain. They implied an intellectual common market 4,000 years ago in which the megalithic yard-stick, the wand of power in knowledge, held sway.

Alexander Thom is not the first man to try to prove that megalithic monuments might have been used once as astronomical observatories. Norman Lockyer had suggested it many years ago and others including Gerald Hawkins of America and Fred Hoyle have interpreted Stonehenge as an eclipse predicter.

But now it has been taken much much further. In the peaceful surroundings of Carnac Alexander Thom and his determinedly Scottish clan of helpers has vastly extended the vision of the intellectual capacity of our prehistoric ancestors.

From now on just the belief of the simple nomadic primitive will no longer do.

But for Alexander Thom the stone age code isn't fully cracked yet."

T "I have an idea that is entirely nebulous at the moment that the cup and ring markings were a method of recording, of writing, and that they may indicate, once we can read them, what a particular stone was for. We have seen the cup and ring markings on the stone at Temple Wood and that's on the main stone but we can't interpret them, yet.

M "Your theories about Stone Age Einsteins have got up the back of some archaeologists. The idea that the cup and ring marks were used as writing has got up the backs of a lot more. Does it worry you?"

T "Not in the slightest," he laughed, "I just go right on . . . recording what I find."

This last remark shows his resilience. It resonates with the Moorish saying, "The dogs bark but the caravan goes on."

After the BBC film was broadcast, Sandy was a celebrity for a time. Southampton and Welsh TV used him, as did Scottish BBC, where the presenter was Mary Malcolm. Sandy, being an Argyllshire man, knew of the Malcolm Family. He was rather taken aback by Mary's make-up in the brightly lit studio!

Television documentaries are shown worldwide. Many people wrote to the Professor from all over.

The Carnac Experiences

Thom had set himself the enormous task of surveying as many sites as he could. The megalithic culture is found all over Europe and he already knew that one man could not hope even to visit all the sites in Britain. However, when the BBC *Chronicle* and Glyn Daniel invited him to go to Brittany in 1970, he decided to act.

Carnac was irresistible. It is the megalithic metropolis of Europe, the Mecca of the megalithic world, with its thousands of massive stones standing there in great battalions, line upon line of them striding across the countryside for miles on end. The conundrum of their meaning persists: Carnac is one of archaeology's most enduring mysteries, recognised to be one of the world's greatest sources of Neolithic culture.

With three generations of his family, and friends from America and Australia, Sandy descended on Carnac to begin what was to be the first of six family visits spread over eight seasons, to make the first accurate surveys of the alignments and relative positions of many of the interesting single outlying menhirs in the precincts.

The work has been carefully documented. Here follows a list of some of the site work done. Many of the stones have been re-erected and an unknown number removed.

Complete survey plans were made of Le Menec; of Kermario; of Kerlescan and Petit Menec. The largest stones in Le Menec and Kermario are concentrated at the west ends. Quick-growing recently-seeded maritime pine covers much of the area and to check prehistoric intervisibility, miles of theodolite traverses involving line and level were run over a rectangular area 11,000ft by 14,000ft. The exact co-ordinates of many backsights and the two main foresights, namely the Manio Stone and Er Grah, (called Le Grand Menhir Brisé), were thus determined.

Remains of several cromlechs such as Crucuno were surveyed and an accurate plan was made of the fan at St Pierre similar to the fans in Scotland used for calculation on the ground — megalithic graph paper, for want of a better description.

Some discoveries from the plans include the following — Spacing of the rows is integral in megalithic yards. Distances between stones in the long rows yield the megalithic yard found in Britain. Bends or corners in the rows are built round integral-sided triangles, to keep continuity of running dimensions in distances between stones. Geometry of cromlechs is of the same type as already discovered in Britain. The Manio Stone and Er Grah are centrally placed lunar foresights observable from backsights many kilometres away. Kermario consists of one geometrical system with another system superimposed, indicating that the designers were in the middle of re-arranging the site. Some seven of the Kermario rows are curved, with a radius of 2,500 meg. yards, and so the engineers knew how to set out circular curves. No alignment proper has an astronomically useful direction, but lunar and solar lines are found between several large single menhirs, K, S and M. (See JHA ii (1971) Fig.1.)

Er Grah (Le Grand Menhir Brisé), has been an intriguing puzzle for long enough. Aubrey Burl writes, "This obsessive undertaking bewilders the modern mind.". It lies in four fragments. Sandy was sure it was erect once and proved to his own satisfaction that it was used as a universal lunar foresight for observing the rising and setting moon at the major and minor standstills from eight marked backsights, 3 to 15 km away. (See Arch Jour Vol 137. Le Grand Menhir Brisé, 27-39 by AS Thom).

The first Carnac expedition took place in 1970. Fourteen people were in the team. It was decided to camp, with Beryl and David Austin's caravan used as centre, cookhouse and office. A large tent housed a worktable at which Sandy sat. Sandy made the porridge in the big tent every morning but apart from that Beryl did all the catering and cooking. She became well known at the local market, where the stall holders were sure she had a very big family!

Three theodolites were 'begged borrowed or stolen'. They were in use for most of the three weeks. Many of the team had no experience of 'Boy Scout Surveying'. They had to be taught how to measure the stones in plan, carefully booking and sketching in pocket-sized notebooks which were going to be used at home later by Sandy.

The party on this first Carnac trip comprised Dr Ray Colton (Inorganic Chemistry, Melbourne University), Bob Merritt of

Cleveland,Ohio, Andy Merritt, Norman Merritt, Beryl Austin, David Austin, Jilly Austin, Marian Austin, Sandy Austin, Lindy Austin, George Luff, Hamish Gorrie and the author.

In March 1971, a smaller group went in one car. Tom Foord and Beryl, Skipper and the author were the party. This time the Hotel Celtique was used as a base. French breakfast at the hotel, and dinner in the evening was the rule. Al fresco meals in all weathers proved the easiest and best way of daytime catering. Morning shopping en route to the site(s) was quick, economical and easy.

In 1971 and the ensuing years 1972, 1973 and 1976 the expeditions were mounted in the spring, when fewer leaves were on the trees. Helen and Joanna Foord were willing workers in 1972. One year Alasdair and Avril Thom and Robert Freer helped. Professor Hans Motz and Monsieur Jean-Luc Quinio gave willing assistance. In 1977 Lindy Austin visited with the Cardiec family in the Hotel Celtique and made some final check measurements for her grandfather. Several times the Scottish party were the first guests of the season. Mr Cardiec was an excellent host. On Sandy's 81st birthday after dinner an iced birthday cake was produced, decorated with one lit candle and an 80 Watt (candle power) bulb.

A postcard sent home to Jeanie by Sandy in March 1971 reads —

"Got here Sunday noon and got to work right away. Finished Menec long chain today. Also went round two other sites. Sun causing some of us red faces. Beryl providing cream. Very good working party. The Menec peasants fell on our necks and wept — almost — but their créperie is not open yet. Town seems so very empty . . ."

For years the Skipper had taken his surveying equipment on the annual summer cruise. He wrote to Margaret and Gerald Ponting — "Years later (after his 1933 Callanish sighting) on the sailing yacht *Torridon*, but before the bridge across to Great Bernera was built, we made a quick survey of the surrounding sites including the three stones at the north end of the bridge. On this visit we noticed that a small menhir stood where I think the south end of the bridge now lands. Unfortunately we did not have time to note its position carefully. It seems likely that it is now gone."

The first time Sandy took surveying equipment on a yacht on the summer cruise was on *Torridon* in 1946. His small theodolite in its box, and the light tripod, could easily be stored on board. This ancient instrument was not heavy, but AT lightened it by removing one pound of brass from its framework. *Torridon* had a petrol-fuelled engine, a Morriss Vedette, and the Skipper came north from Oxford with a handful of petrol coupons specially applied for. In two weeks in August 1946 he surveyed eleven sites in the Outer Hebrides and northern Argyll. Archibald Niel Black was with him on that cruise.

Many sites were easy to visit from yacht anchorages on the west coast. From Arinagour in Coll for instance, the local taxi was hired. Loch Buie in Mull is too open and so Loch Spelve was the yacht haven, and the Skipper walked over the isthmus to Loch Buie to survey the two rings and outliers there.

An amusing incident occurred during his third visit, while The Skipper was surveying the outliers at Loch Buie. He was about a thousand feet away setting up the theodolite and the author was standing on top of the seven feet high lone menhir in the scrub to the north west. I was concentrating on holding the survey pole steady when I realised that a fellow human had arrived. I spoke first, "It looks like rain." Jill and her father Ken Shaw were vastly amused when I reported the incident that evening at dinner on board. They later wrote the following poem —

**The farmer and the youth at Loch Buie**
　With eyes downcast the pensive farmer
　Sauntered forth across the field,
　Thinking that it needed draining,
　Wondering what the crop would yield.
　Suddenly he sensed a presence,
　Raised his eyes and stood amazed.
　Surely this must be a madman
　Who unflinching met his gaze.
　There upon the very summit
　Of the tallest standing stone
　Stood a youth, and waved his bonnet,
　Though apparently alone.
　Looked down gravely at the farmer,

Bade him solemnly: "Good day.
Surely it must rain e'er evening
If these clouds don't roll away."
"Yes", the farmer stuttered feebly,
Glancing swift this way and that,
But he saw not one companion
To the youth who waved his hat.
"Do you wonder what I'm doing?"
Asked the youth with flashing smile;
"I am signalling my father
Who is distant half a mile.
"He is hidden in that coppice.
Struggling to ascertain
The azimuth and declination
Of a flipping standing stane!"

This episode brings to mind a question once asked by Skipper's grand-daughter Susan, "What does Grampa do when he stands on the stones?" This time her father was "standing on a stone"! Later she was to accompany Skipper on an expedition and have her name given to the backsight at Kintraw, on the pathway at high level.

From North Harbour Barra, the long walk round to the west coast took quite a time. Kenyon Shaw was with us, when I myself walked back over the col in the island's main ridge to report on a large fallen menhir there — from the coastal site it must once have looked like a rifle site in the notch. One August the yacht was sailed right to the very top of Loch Eynort in South Uist, about eight miles from the entrance. The anchorage was relatively near to the stones on the west machairs.

On occasion the Skipper and one or two others would row ashore and keep the dinghy there while I hove to off shore and waited, a feasible proposition as long as the shore party could row back out again if the wind freshened against them. Uig Bay, North Skye was surveyed this way, (John Adamson was one of the crew), and Tarbert, Canna, north shore, (when John Harding was in the crew), Ardnacross (Sound of Mull) and Stillaig (Loch Fyne). Once, after dropping him ashore on the west side of Tiree I sailed round to anchor safely off a sandy beach on the east side of that island. He was picked up by the dinghy and we sailed on.

The search for standing stones using sea transport frequently took us into inlets not often explored. Dry land exploration was of course the same. We explored areas of country seldom visited by outsiders. Loch Eport, North Uist is eight miles long from the Sea of the Hebrides to its top. We navigated right to the top and anchored in soft mud. Leaving the yacht the next day to begin a long walk to Craig Hasten on the west shore of North Uist we looked back to see *Torridon* grounded on the mud and heeling over, a site not usually seen by west coast yachtsmen who prefer never to touch bottom at all! Skipper's calculation of the time of low water was, however correct. That night the shore party upon return were invisible in the dark to Jill Shaw rowing ashore. A piece of paper was lit to guide her to the tired and weary surveyors on the beach.

The Sound of Harris is eight miles wide and eight miles long, littered with rocks and islands of all sizes. The Skipper wanted to visit sites on some of these islands and so he shared the cost of hiring a motorboat with helmsman for the day with an archaeologist whose interest was exploring kitchen middens. Needless to say the helmsman's local knowledge did not cover the whole 64 square miles of the Sound, and the Skipper's largescale Admiralty chart was extremely useful. Later he described gleefully how the boatman lessened his vessel's draft by pumping the bilges while crossing shallow sand bars. Many years later, in 1970, the Professor was to have a shorter trip by boat across to Gavrinis (goat island), south of Carnac, Brittany, to see the submerged stone circle there.

Shetland was visited by air, and a hired car was used to explore the mainland, Burra, Yell and Unst. The party on that trip included R L Merritt. En route home we stopped off at Orkney where Mrs E M Thom (Aunt Jock) joined the party and more work was done on the outlying parts of that island. Later I was to fly to Orkney with T R Foord to explore the megaliths on Eday Island. The short flight across from Kirkwall to Eday was an unforgettable experience — wet cow pats splashing up on to the underside of the tiny monoplane's wings at London Airport, on London Bay, where the airport was a small wooden hut.

An unexpected stone ring was found on Berneray Island, by the side of the track from the jetty to Barra Head Lighthouse some 628 feet above sea level on the top of the cliff. We had been sailing southwards round the headland and the lighthouse attracted our attention. It was a clear and bright summer afternoon and the crew wanted to go ashore and visit the place. The Skipper agreed to anchor in the east end of the Sound of Berneray off the jetty, poor holding ground and rocky bottom notwithstanding. He would stand by the ship while we explored. He explained however that we would have to sail by sunset as the next depression was coming in from the west and he wanted to cross the Sea of The Hebrides there and then. We had been seen by the lighthouse crew at least an hour before and when we anchored, down came a Land Rover to welcome us. That lighthouse was clean — no industrial dust, no smoke — only fresh air and water. I shall always remember seeing through the clear atmosphere the three lighthouses of Dubh Artach, Oigh-sgier, and Neist Point (the Stallion) as though I was looking down on them from a much greater altitude than 628 feet! The lighthouse crew explained to us that during gales salt spray fills the lighthouse yard eighteen inches deep with sea water — the scuppers are not big enough. Obviously visitors were few and far between.

On the way down, testing echoes from Mingulay across the sound, we spotted the ring of stones. When we got back on board AT went ashore immediately to see and record it for himself. We were told that in long spells of bad weather landing is impossible at the jetty. The mild steel shear legs on the jetty were usually dismantled for the winter. We went to sea after dark, heading for Gunna Sound which we found in the dawn. The gale came. We lay the rest of it out in Bunessan.

Determined resolution and knowledge of local conditions often brought archaeoastronomical reward. One time we were lying in Tobermory Bay and the Skipper wanted badly to get round to Loch Cuan to have another look at a site at Dervaig. A depression was in the offing and he reckoned he could get his ship round to Cuan, finish his survey and get back to Tobermory before the gale came.

Loch Cuan is no anchorage in bad weather. Sandy took his ship to sea and his was the only yacht going out westward that afternoon. The other cruising boats were coming in and they made a pretty sight. We anchored in Loch Cuan, Sandy went ashore, was duly picked up and we scurried back eastwards. With a freshening wind it was a wet sail and we made Tobermory by 3am, mission accomplished.

Cars were a necessity for transporting personnel, instruments and camping gear. Sandy had bought Andrew Tindal's 4.25 litre

Bentley in 1938 and he began using it immediately on survey trips. He constructed a huge home-grown sycamore wooden box which he fixed on the substantial luggage rack to hold camping gear. The earliest papers on standing stones refer to his survey of the stone circle at Torhouskie, Wigtownshire, carried out on 17th August 1938. This appears to be the first of about twenty surveys made in south-west Scotland during August 1938 and May 1939. William MacGregor helped with some of the 1939 work. In July 1939 at least 35 sites were visited in Kintyre, Knapdale and Lorn all within 24 days. All of this pre-war survey work was done on camping expeditions.

I know of no survey work done by him in Scotland using bicycles for transport. During the war, while he lived at Fleet, Hants, he did manage to do a little preliminary work at Stonehenge and Avebury in September 1943, and he investigated a site at Winchfield, Hants in April, 1944. As there was no petrol and as his car was in Scotland, he must have used his bicycle for transport to get to these sites from Fleet, Hants.

Early in the war he had a fair-sized collection of data and realising how much more there was to collect, he began acquiring one-inch to the mile Ordnance Survey maps. He would take one map at a time and carefully examine it square by square, searching for the Old English printing used to show standing stones. His maps have pencil crosses in their margins marking each site he considered worth visiting. Many of his Ordnance Survey maps were issued before the British Metric Grid system was superimposed on the Greenwich zero longitude system. The new map numbering system must have given him headaches to begin with. During one period only thin paper maps were on sale. They tore easily in wet and windy weather. Linen-backed editions were preferable.

If a standing stone alignment appeared to have been of any astronomical importance to its builders, its present orientation had to be carefully recorded by the Prof. On sunny days he used a theodolite, the orientation of its base plate having been determined by observing the sun. A good watch was needed, to be used like a ship's chronometer. Its rate of gain or loss was checked frequently by listening to the BBC's time signals — "the Pips". He laterally used one of the early types of electronic watch, its rate being controlled by a 'tuning fork' device. (The author himself has used the BBC radio Pips as far apart as Norway, Sweden and Brittany.) If no radio was available Sandy would put in a GPO telephone call for the 'Girl with the Golden Voice'. A plumb bob was usually hung below the theodolite and the position below the bob carefully marked on the ground. This mark was carefully referenced in (by measurements from three or more nearby permanent objects) and the plate bearing of a referring object at least 400 feet away carefully recorded. For open traverse work when this survey point would have to be sited from the next theodolite position, a suitable wooden peg would be driven in. Frequently the peg hole would be marked by, say, a piece of silver paper easily found later. Pegs were too easily seen and removed by prying people. Sometimes during a survey involving many short lines we would run out of pegs, metal rods, arrows, etc, all within the confines of the site, and "anything did" for a marker.

On one such occasion a visitor approached the site — it was at Clava Cairns, Inverness. After a look round he asked, his curiosity having overcome him, what was the smoker's pipe doing on top of the metal pin? AT had obviously been reduced to feeling in his pockets for something with which to distinguish this point on one of our centre lines in use at the time. He wanted something visible through the theodolite telescope against the background of brown bracken.

Frequently much of the measuring described above would be done before a sun-shot could be taken. With two people, a 70-second glimpse of the sun was enough for a leading-edge timed observation, followed by a trailing-edge timed shot. Mean of the times and mean of the angles were used in later calculation. In ideal conditions a set of three such pairs of shots was always made. On occasion, with fleeting cloud, there was time for only one single shot of the centre of the sun's disc. This procedure yielded excellent results, as verified often later, but Sandy recommended at important sites that a second set of solar observations be made by a second observer, or on a different day, to ensure correct use of the almanac tables of the sun's declination etc, as well as correct application of the rate of the watch and of the date.

On days with heavily overcast skies he would use his prismatic compass placed on the theodolite stand which of course had brass metal fittings only. A surveyor with steel framed spectacles soon found out their (unwelcome) magnetic property. At other times Sandy would obtain the true bearing of the referring object by arithmetical calculation, using the latitude and longitude of his theodolite and of the referring object, the easily identified corner of a farm building, or a lighthouse or a hill top cairn shown on the map. His astronomical expertise made him however prefer a sun-shot, or a planet-shot if it were dark, even although the theodolite circular scales had then to be illuminated.

I once unbolted the headlamp from my car and carried it and the heavy battery, with the help of Jim Tindal, to the Kame of Corrigal on Orkney to let the Skipper sight on to a survey point, the target on which we could not see during the day. The weather, though clear enough overhead for sun-shots, was not clear enough for viewing the target on the horizon some three or four miles off. When he had set the vertical diaphragm hair on the light he sent a signal by portable radio. I drove down. It was dark by this time, and booked the plate circle bearing as his sight was not too good. Hans Motz and Jim Tindal were with us that trip.

At Carnac, one sightline of ten miles across Quiberon Bay was too long for the theodolite telescope to resolve any target we could have erected. We wanted to know the true bearing of Le Grand Menhir Brisé from the large menhir at Goulvar on the end of Quiberon peninsula. David Austin's Land Rover battery and lamp were fitted on a tripod on the huge fallen menhir and a pre-arranged pattern of flashes every fifteen seconds was begun. It was a warm evening and the mosquitos were hungry. A crowd of curious French tourists was genuinely interested in watching the procedure. We stood stock still, in silence, staring into the dusk. The spectators were silent. I am sure they were beginning to be certain that these eccentrics were really mad, when to our relief and to cries of "Aaa-h", the "all clear" flashing of headlamps across the sea indicated success. In fact it had nearly been a failure, because our lamp had been too bright and AT had been obliged to adjust the theodolite tangent screw while seeing the vertical diaphragm line in the illumination from only the dying filament of the lamp ten miles away. For obvious reasons that evening was called the highlight of the trip.

Our work at Carnac involved the determination of the relative co-ordinates of many complex sites and single large menhirs spread over an area of five square miles. Because of the dense woods, few of the sites were intervisible and we had to run closed traverses linking the areas of interest. A closed traverse is merely a polygon whose sides and corner angles are measured carefully. After a complete round, calculations are expected to show that we are back where we started. Spurs can come off at any corner, but they can not be checked. They explore outwards like a spider's legs or later can be rejoined to the original closed ring at any point. Spurs were sometimes checked by independent tacheometric measurement. Any closed traverse is self-checking and it was good practice to shoot the sun at each theodolite stance. All of this work allows the surveyor to plot his plan on a flat sheet which can be imagined as being tangential to a point on the earth's surface (not a sphere) at the starting point. Meridian lines of different longitude are parallel only at the equator: at the latitude of Carnac they are converging. This convergence is calculable for a traverse having an easting of, say, two miles. True north as measured by a sunshot at the eastern end of such a traverse will obviously differ from the north as determined from the plotted plan on the flat sheet of paper.

This careful surveying encompassed two French 'trig' stations, whose co-ordinates (within a centimetre) were supplied to the Professor by the authorities in Paris. To the dismay of the Skipper (and his crew of surveyors), the Scots could not close their measurements within their own acceptable limits. Many months later, after Bob Merritt had written to Paris, word came via USA that a set of co-ordinates supplied to the maestro was incorrect. The correct pair of co-ordinates indicated that the Scots had not been in error after all. Sighs of relief all round!

Many people suggested that aerial surveys might have helped the Professor in his work, but he made no use of the technique for accurate work. He did refer frequently to a clear print of a photograph of the area at Carnac taken by a proper aerial survey camera. By the time his traverse work was completed he could take check measurements from this photograph and knew the difference in scale between opposite ends of the print. It was very useful in verifying traverse lengths. Often individual menhirs were not easily identified on the print, principally because of thick undergrowth.

This all shows how careful Sandy had to be with his calculations. When he was satisfied that he had done everything possible, he knew that he could state the value of an azimuth between any two points on the area in question to plus or minus 1.25 arc minutes.

In the wooded areas short traverses were run along various lines to examine the ground levels where it appeared that the line of sight

246

between the backsight and the foresight might not clear the ground. Use was made of two prominent water towers which on occasion were visible from clearings in the woods.

Linear Measurement in the Field

At Carnac, the long centre lines, the back-bones of the alignment surveys, were measured by steel tape. On sloping ground the tape was held horizontally, supported every 25 feet by small rods with adjustable clamps, steps up or down being made using 1/4 inch aluminium rods fitted with specially made spherical bubbles clamped on the rods to check and maintain verticality. Such methods enabled Sandy to be very sure of his distances between stones, so vital in his analysis which led him to insist that prehistoric erectors had been using standard units of length in places as far apart as Orkney, Stonehenge, Avebury and Carnac. We had a plethora of steel and aluminium rods of all sizes. A particular steel rod was in great demand as a strong enough weapon with which to swipe and split up the huge gorse bushes which made our lives miserable at times.

Kermario alignments were divided transversely by a modern pond. Here Sandy's problem was, how to measure across the pond accurately. He used the well-established method of telemetry, repeatedly measuring the angle between points ten feet apart on our tacheometer staff laid horizontally and used as a target on the other side of the water. The old Tavistock theodolite read angles to seconds of arc and the distance across was easily calculated.

On the traverse work detailed above, long lines of up to 1,000 feet had on occasion to be measured. Using a 100 feet long chain meant that 10 chain lengths had to be counted. Great care had to be taken that a chain length had not been dropped by default.

Sandy often talked of his surveying experience on the Canadian Pacific Railway. His leg was pulled aplenty. He produced a small piece of soapstone which he had kept since he used it in Canada for chalk marking.

Sandy taught his chaining team of two what he had been taught to do "on the CPR in Canada" in 1913. The rear man stood with his pointed metal rod over the zero mark of the line, where the theodolite had been set up. This man held no steel arrows (ringed, with red cloth tabs and about 12 inches long). His task was to hold the chain exactly over the zero mark and to line the leading chainman, who had the front of the chain and a metal rod, straight for the far end of the line, a red and white marker pole, say 850 feet away. The leading man had a stock of arrows in his belt and used them one by one each 100 feet. The pair advanced simultaneously, 100 feet apart, the rear man lining in the leading man, and as he advanced he lifted each arrow as he vacated the stop-over point. By the time that the rear man had 8 arrows in his possession, at his end of the chain, he could categorically state that he was 800 feet from zero.

Dropping a chain length as described above is an occupational risk which has to be recognised. One way of checking lengths is to use the tacheometric hairs on the diaphragm of the theodolite and a tacheometric staff, which method gave an accuracy of about 1 in 500 depending upon bright sunlight on the staff. Surveyors' chains had to be calibrated frequently against a standard steel tape, carried specially on each expedition. If the chain was found to be wrong, a correction had to be made while plotting the long lengths. Cloth tapes had also to be checked.

At Carnac, the long traverse lines and back-bones of the alignment surveys, of up to and over 1,000 feet long were measured by steel tape.

Long rows of stones and small groups were measured by measuring offsets by cloth tape from the chain laid out along a survey line. Individual stones were surveyed by distance measured from the theodolite along two tangential lines whose plate bearings were recorded. A "box" drawn in the field book encompassing the plan of the stone drawn at ground level defined the stone's position. If needed, more measurements could then be made easily and booked. The measurer had to think always of how the final plan was going to be drawn in.

Stone rings were easy to measure by theodolite using the above method. One man at the instrument set up near the centre, read and booked his two radial angles, and drew a "box", made a note of the stone number and listened to the pair at the stone while they measured and recorded in their book the two distances from the instrument and the shape of the stone. The radially placed tape was anchored below the theodolite all the time. A second tape, usually of linen, was used at the stone. Between 30 and 50 stones could be measured and booked per hour in the above way. Strong winds could hamper the work, making verbal communication difficult.

On a sunny day the instrument could be carefully levelled over the hub, and sights taken of a referring object recorded. After three sun shots for calculation of the plate orientation, angles and sizes for a 25 stone ring could be completed in about 75 minutes from start to finish. If angles and distances to outlying stones had to be taken, along with horizon profiles, more time would be needed.

Avebury

In the book *Megalithic Sites in Britain* published in 1967, Sandy used his plan of the geometry of the huge ring at Avebury as a frontispiece. He had surveyed this some years before and was rightly proud of the geometrical shape which he superimposed on the actual plan of the large menhirs. Avebury village is almost entirely built within the ring — at least one of the huge menhirs is too near the road for its own safety. An overhanging load on a lorry could quite easily knock it out of position. It has to be remembered that positions of stones relative to its neighbours and to the environment was all-important to Sandy.

One of the sides of his carefully measured polygon crossed the very busy main road near a sharp corner. For years Sandy had worried about the measurement of this side — life and limb had been at stake at the sharp corner, and so in 1974 he led a party to re-do the whole survey. This time the party consisted of Alexander Strang Thom (Alasdair), Avril Thom and their two young children (the fourth generation), Tom Foord and myself with Margaret. Alasdair and Avril surveyed the Avenue. One helper who came along for a few days was Professor Kennedy McWhirter, a member of the well known family of writers and journalists. Like many people over the years, Kennedy wanted first hand experience with AT to observe what was done and learn how to do it.

A completely fresh plan of Avebury was made forthwith and no error was found in the previous work. Mrs Lance Vatcher, the curator of the Alexander Keiller Museum kindly allowed us to use a table in the curators' day room for plotting the new plan. Mr Peter Tait, the curator, made us very welcome. The survey was plotted as work progressed, a new experience for us. Sites showing the megalithic yard were not so numerous in England as in Scotland and this was why Sandy had been so keen to be certain of his ground at Avebury. About this time Norris McWhirter was so impressed by two of Thom's books that he put an entry in the Guinness book of records (now in 33 languages) citing the megalithic yard as the oldest known unit in metrology.

While the party was at Avebury, Bruce Wilcock and a colleague, both of the editorial staff of Oxford University Press came to discuss arrangements for AT's next book, *Megalithic Remains in Britain and Brittany*. This book was forthwith rapidly written but publishing was held up by the press for nearly three years because they were overwhelmed by their own fifth centenary publication work. Our book finally was published in 1978 many months out of date.


Stonehenge

So much had been written about Stonehenge that, although Sandy had visited the site often, he had never surveyed the monument. In his early analysis he included dimensions of Stonehenge obtained from published plans and duly acknowledged the source. He almost always made a point of using his own measurements for analysis, because he simply did not trust the accuracy of the survey work of people unknown to him. The Ministry plan for sale to the public had been produced over the years. It was not good enough for Sandy because it had a scale drawn on one corner which did not exactly agree with a second scale drawn on the other corner. A new accurate survey was badly needed.

The major part of Sandy's hypothesis on the geometry and astronomy of the prehistoric builders of megalithic monuments had already been done before he surveyed Stonehenge. Bob Merritt very much wanted him to tackle Stonehenge and so he arranged a meeting with Dick Atkinson who invited Skipper, Bob and myself to dinner in the Oxford and Cambridge Club in London.

To the three of us, Dick Atkinson was "Stonehenge". He knew more than any man alive about the monument and he was realising that it was time that an accurate plan of the surface features was made. Who better to make it than AT who had after all made surveys of so many other megalithic monuments and brought forth a completely fresh way of looking at their shapes and sizes? At first Sandy held back, and Bob the lawyer kept the discussion going. I was of course keen to do the survey, and I knew within myself that AT really needed to do it, although I had not actually heard him say so. We were in the throes of the work in Brittany (it was 1972) and perhaps AT was tiring a little. He was seventy nine at the time. I made up my mind there and then to say that I would do the survey knowing full well that Sandy would involve himself deeply. Later Dick was to publish very flattering remarks about the Thom Family team's work in Brittany.

We agreed to go ahead and Dick Atkinson co-operated fully. With Lance Vatcher he carefully pricked out the Aubrey holes for us to survey. Our party lived at The Fairlawn Hotel in Amesbury. Leaving the hotel at 5.30am, before breakfast, we worked on the site in peace until 9.00 when the public were allowed through the tunnel. Two abreast they came, coloured anoraks, rucksacks etc, for all the world like Hannibal's troops crossing the Alps, but the elephants were lacking. By 08.50 the Skipper had porridge and bacon and eggs all ready for his team, cooked on the tail gate of the Range Rover. The team consisted of Alasdair, Avril, baby Steven, Tom and Geoffrey Foord, Bob, Ethan and Beth Merritt, Margaret and myself. Most evenings we returned after dinner at The Fairlawn Hotel to work until dark. On many days we found it possible to do our work on the site as long as we were fairly far removed from the ring proper. For long sights to horizons we set the theodolite up on the official bronze peg 'Beta' which for safety was buried six inches below ground level nearly at the centre of the monument.

Working in a busy site one seldom gets ten consecutive minutes of peace: I had deposited the theodolite near to Beta and had begun to scrape away the gravel. I knew where it was within a few inches and as I worked, a group of say thirty tourists collected round me in dead silence. Then a voice said, "What are you doing?" I could not resist the temptation and blurted, "Digging a hole in the ground". Another voice, amidst the laughter said, "You asked for that!"

Tumuli Surrounding Stonehenge

While Sandy and his party were measuring up Stonehenge, one Mr Van Millingen met him by arrangement with a view to asking if his son Ben, an Oundle schoolboy, could help in any way with a school computer project. Sandy suggested that it might be suitable if Ben could investigate azimuths of tumuli alignments in the vicinity of

Stonehenge. Ben did this with the help of the computer in his school, by reading off the co-ordinates from a 1:25,000 scale map of the district within 3 km of Stonehenge. His paper was published in *Griffith Observer*, California, in December 1976. The conclusion was that, whatever the reason for which many of the tumuli alignments were laid out at particular azimuths, it did not seem to be for astronomical reasons. 213 tumuli were used, and because the tumuli are about 15 metres in diameter, a precision of co-ordinates of about 5 metres was deemed sufficient. Solar and lunar movements were considered.

Cecil August Newham (Peter to his friends) and AT had become good friends by this time and they shared many thoughts on Stonehenge. Peter had a fine sense of humour. We met him by arrangement in Amesbury one April en route home from Brittany and after the pair of them had been yarning about "The Boys" as they did frequently, Peter said, "Sandy, if they could hear us talking like this, they'd be laughing their bluddy 'eads ov".

Peter had spent years since 1958 thinking about Stonehenge, theorising and measuring it up. By 1962 he had established that lunar alignments existed within the monument, and reported his findings to Richard Atkinson, Glyn Daniel (editor of *Antiquity*) and others. Atkinson was impressed but Daniel, after three months delay, replied to the effect that "he did not think that it would be of interest to his readers." A letter from Peter to the *Yorkshire Post* in March 1963 was published. There was no response to it whatever. Publication of the article Enigma by Peter was delayed for seven months (until 1964,) because of a fire at the printers. Peter received the first proof copy on the day that Hawkins' article on 'Stonehenge Decoded' appeared in *Nature*, 26th October, 1963.

About a week later a letter appeared in *New Scientist* from a reader asking "why the necessity of Americans to discover things about our own Ancient Monuments; were British scientists incapable?" Peter thought this was too much and wrote to *New Scientist* pointing to the fact that Atkinson and other well known archaeologists were already aware of lunar alignments at Stonehenge nearly a year before the publication of the above article by Hawkins. (See *Archaeoastronomy* 4, 1982, pS74).

On June 24th, 1964 Hawkins published again in *Nature*, his article 'Stonehenge: A neolithic Computer', quoting in the bibliography, Newham's 'Enigma of Stonehenge, a private publication 1964'.

Peter later published 'A Supplement to The Enigma of Stonehenge' (1970), and 'The Astronomical Significance of Stonehenge' (Publisher John Blackburn, Leeds, 1972) in which he acknowledged Professors Atkinson and Thom, and Major and Mrs HWFL Vatcher. Subject headings included The Sun, The Moon and Early Indications of Lunar Investigation.

The only way that one can know how a man of a previous generation thought is to read what he wrote. One message we can get nowadays from prehistoric men (The "Boys" as Thom called them) is to measure up the shapes and patterns of their megalithic monuments.

While at Stonehenge, Thom took the opportunity of visiting Newman, the astronomer, at his home in the vicinity.

It must be understood that Thom surveyed only stones visible on the surface. On occasion he would probe the ground with his bayonet. Quite rightly a large fraction of the area of Stonehenge monument has not yet been excavated. Irreparable damage is always done to a site by excavation. New techniques are being developed as the years pass, and it is absolutely right that as much as possible should be left untouched. Post holes and stone holes are important. An opportunity arose some years ago which unfortunately was missed by interested workers. After a long hard spell of deep continental-type frost the migration of moisture which occurs and allows formation of lenticular-shaped crystals in post holes raised the ground level above each hole. When archaeologists arrived back on the site in the spring, the ice had melted; the wardens explained what they had seen. Nobody had thought of using white-wash to mark each low frost-created hummock.


For many years AT financed his work practically all by himself. He did not use hotels in the beginning, preferring the freedom of car-camping. Small tents can be pitched rapidly, he had no difficulty with plain cooking, and only occasionally had he to sleep in his car in very bad weather. A tent covered with an inch of April snow is well insulated — it can be too warm!

During periods of petrol rationing he obtained coupons for his car and for the auxiliary engines of two separate yachts.

Thom enlisted the help of many friends for the vast amount of field work needed. He often paid expenses to those who he thought needed cash. Others came at their own expense. He expected loyalty and reliable attendance to the tasks in hand.

Robert Lloyd Merritt of Cleveland Ohio became interested in Sandy's work and about 1970 began to help with expenses for Scottish travel, monies being supplied by the CT Lloyd Foundation. Thereafter cash came regularly from Bob for work in Brittany, Orkney, Shetland, Stonehenge, Avebury, Norway, Sweden and Denmark. Other monies came from the Hulme Fund, Brasenose College, the Carnegie Fund, from the British Broadcasting Corporation, from the Royal Society and from the Department of the Environment, Northern Ireland. These grants certainly eased the drain on his purse, but he never made any attempt to determine how much archaeoastronomy actually cost him. Car mileages, air fares, ferry tickets, hotel expenses for helpers, drawing-office materials, theodolites (of which he possessed four), sextants, prismatic compasses, good watches, reliable radio sets, international carnets, insurances, steel tapes, measuring chains, cloth tapes, surveyors' poles, projector slides, camera, postages (to all parts of the world), telephone expenses, calculating machines and pocket calculators . . . the list of items is endless. The few hundred pounds received in book royalties, for broadcasting, and for fees for small articles, would pay for only a small fraction of his expenditure. Yacht expenses were never considered, although to have visited many of the sites he surveyed from yachts would have been very costly by public transport. He had always sailed each summer and the standing stone work merely added another facet to his enjoyment of the Hebridean environment.

His surveys were co-operative efforts on the part of many people. I quote his own acknowledgments for the help given for the expeditions mounted in 1970/1 — David T Austin, Beryl Austin, JB Austin, MJ Austin, AKD Austin, LK Austin, Dr TR Foord, JM Gorrie, G Luff, Robert L Merritt, Norman and Andrew Merritt. He was good at persuading folk to work for him. In this he was like his uncle Sam Fulton Strang who easily got crews to man his yachts year after year.

In his first paper reporting the Carnac surveys, he acknowledged the loan of surveying instruments, etc from Messrs Vickers, Messrs WF Stanley, Mr Alister Brown and the Geography Department, University of Glasgow.

In the preface to *Megalithic Lunar Observatories* he acknowledged financial assistance from the Butkin Foundation, Cleveland, Ohio.

Cup-and-ring Marks

Ronald Morris describes in detail the history of Sandy's discovery of the existence of Megalithic Inches in 1967.

Ronald's samples of rubbings of the cup-and-ring markings and spiral carvings had shown up the existence of the unit which turned out to be exactly one fortieth of Sandy's already discovered megalithic yard, and one hundredth of the megalithic rod. The megalithic inch as Sandy dubbed it, had clearly been used in the scribing of the small circles, semi-circles, ellipses and semi-ellipses carved on many flat rock surfaces. Other researchers have since found more evidence of use of the megalithic inch. For example at Temple Wood, Dr Orkney took rubbings of the triple spiral petroglyph on one upright stone. The design proved to be built up from alternating quadrants of circles of integer megalithic inch radius and ellipses based on 3-4-5 and 5-12-13 triangles in megalithic inches. The design is self-checking by virtue of its complexity and the way the groups or series run through it all.

Sandy had an idea that cup and ring markings were the megalithic builders's way of passing on a message, a method of writing. He felt that, as cup marks often occurred near lunar backsights, they might probably display lunar information. He dictated the following notes for a letter to Mrs Catherine Merritt, dated 16th March, 1979 —

Dear Mrs Merritt,

I have been looking again at the very good photographs you sent of the stones at Ballymeanach and Temple Wood. Cup and ring markings intrigue me. We do not know what they are for. I think they are probably a form of writing or a form of communication telling what the stone is for, astronomically, when they are on a stone. But of course they need not all be astronomical by any means. I do know that the big central menhir in the meadow opposite Temple Wood has a lot of cups and two rings and this stone is on two lines; one to the northwest and a line to the southwest. Over a year ago we found a particularly good lunar line at Skipness in Kintyre. The stone, which was small, had been pushed over (I had seen it vertical, some years before). The stone hole was clearly discernible. On exposed living rock nearby to the south, there were cup marks, probably telling that this stone was a lunar line also. There are cups also on a large menhir at Manemur in Brittany and this stone is a calendar stone as far as I can see.

And so it goes on, but nobody has cracked the code which I am sure exists somehow. The idea of putting writing in lines up and down or across had probably not occurred to the makers.

This has been a long winter for us, but now the snowdrops are fully out and the daffodils are growing. In fact Spring is in the air, but the forecasters tell us that there is more snow to come.

> With best wishes,
> Yours sincerely,
> Sandy

## Archaeology and Anthropology
### Flints

Interest in archaeology and anthropology led Sandy to add some general books to his library in the 1920s. As a cyclist in Hampshire from 1939-1945 he was very conscious of the hard sharp flint chips on the road surfaces which wore his tyres so badly. He began to collect flint tools, listing where he had obtained them. One intrigued him greatly. He had picked it up on Lunga, the largest of the Treshnish Islands off Mull in the Inner Hebrides. I was with him at the time. We were climbing to the top of the islet when he spotted a flint knife on the loose soil at the mouth of a rabbit hole. Sixty five millimetres long, it fits the fingers well, and one wonders how it got to Argyllshire, all the way from flint country.

### Excavation

The only excavation which Sandy allowed himself was occasionally to roll back turf from the edge of a fallen menhir in order to find its edges. If such procedure was not possible he would probe with a sharp metal rod or with the 1870 French bayonet usually carried for the purpose. He had scant praise for the damage done by so-called archaeologists, professional and amateur, who have dug up so many sites and scattered the contents over the countryside, in houses or museums, making no records. It is reported locally that after a dugout canoe had been excavated from a lake dwelling site in north Ayrshire, the vandal, this time a known individual, took a saw and cut the dugout in two to let it into the lorry.

I myself had the pleasant experience of using Colonel Hawley's field sketches of excavations made in 1922/23 near the Heel Stone at Stonehenge. I was dismayed, however, to read a report that pottery sherds had been discarded. Nowadays such fired clay is used to date the layer.

There is a large whinstone rubbing stone in the field behind Thalassa. Tenant farmer John Mitchell decided, in the absence of the owner in England during the war, that to save himself some time and effort while ploughing and harvesting the crop of oats he would fell the stone, burying it below plough-share level. This did not please Sandy who was by this time an expert on upright rubbing stones, steles, menhirs or whatever. After the war, nothing would do but that John had to re-erect the huge splinter of basalt. When John arrived one evening to do the job, they could not find the buried stone. Sandy went into Thalassa and emerged brandishing the French bayonet used for probing. He could not resist challenging, "Swords or pistols John?" The rubbing stone was soon found and re-erected.


Oxford One Conference

The following paper was presented by the author for the Professor at a conference on Archaeoastronomy (later to be dubbed "Oxford One") in the University of Oxford in September 1981 — *Statistical and Philosophical arguments for the Astronomical significance of standing stones with a section on the solar calendar* by A Thom and AS Thom.

Extracts from the first two pages are indicative of the Professor's thinking in the summer of 1981 —


"The histograms of declination give strong support to the lunar hypothesis, because of the clustering of the alignments round the expected values.

"Our knowledge of megaliths can come only from the remains themselves. These consist of standing stones, their positions relative to one another, relative to tumuli, to mounds, and to nearby tracks on the ground. In addition

some of these stones have cup and ring markings. It is
generally accepted that some of the standing stones are
arranged to indicate the rising/setting points of the solstitial
Sun, but why stop with the solstice, and why not consider
the Moon as well?"


(He then goes on to write on the necessity of accurate surveying
described elsewhere and goes on —


" . . . We calculate the declination of the foresight and so we
know, to within a minute of arc, the declination of any
heavenly body that rose or set on the foresight. We then
examine the declinations thus obtained.
    "If the standing stones have nothing to do with
astronomy then the declinations will be spread at random
throughout the range. If on the other hand the declinations
fall into clumps around significant points then we know that
we are dealing with stones erected for astronomical use. Up
to 1967 we had observed about 260 declinations. These are
shown plotted in Fig. 1. It is evident that the points group
around germane declinations. Our critics say that we
perhaps unintentionally use subjective methods in selecting
our foresights but we can not have done this every time. We
consider that our choice was not subjective, and this is
where the matter rests at present. We have several times
stated that megalithic man was able to detect the small nine
minute perturbation $\Delta i$ of the lunar orbit. This needs much
more careful consideration and in our analysis we must use
much more sophisticated methods."
    " . . . In our long investigation into the astronomy of
Megalithic Man the greatest difficulty all along has been to
decide just when a line should be neglected. On the one side
people are asking for evidence, on the other, statisticians are
waiting to point out any irregularities. No matter what
terms of reference are decided at the beginning, however,
there are always borderline cases. We want to produce the
answer to the question, Did Megalithic Man really use
advanced astronomical methods for calendrical purposes,
for eclipse prediction, or had he perhaps purely scientific
reasons? We wish to find the answer in a form that will be
acceptable to archaeologists but we find much greater

difficulty in satisfying statisticians who wish to apply rigid statistical methods thus excluding any philosophical approach."

"When in 1955 the senior author gave his first paper to the Royal Statistical Society (Thom 1955 *A statistical examination of the megalithic sites in Britain* JRSS A118,275-295) the atmosphere was quite different. For example when he asked an eminent statistician how to obtain a proof of a certain idea of his, the answer was, It does not require proof. It is obvious. That particular idea has since been attacked several times."

## The Calendar

Thom believed that early men in Britain used a solar calendar based on the observation of the sun made without instruments as we know them today. The Egyptians seem at one time to have controlled their calendar by observing what are called heliacal risings of certain bright stars, but this method is unsuited to northern countries with their long twilight. Moreover, the movement of the sun along the horizon is much greater in Britain than it is in Egypt and so use of the sun on the horizon makes a more suitable calendar.

From a histogram of the declinations shown by most of his measured lines Thom showed in 1965 in *Vistas in Astronomy* that there were sixteen calendar dates definitely marked. The year was divided into epochs of 22 or 23 days. He was also sure that there existed a further subdivision into 32 half-epochs of approximately 11 or 12 days.

## True North

In his file on azimuths of stones in circles, an interesting sketch exists of how Thom thought prehistoric man could obtain true north from the stars. The observer's eye position was fixed. A horizontal bar was arranged like the bar over a goal post, at such a level that it lay on the line representing the diameter of the circle described by a circum-polar star. The diametrically opposite ends were marked on the bar — a plumb bob was suspended from the centre of the two marks. From the eye to the plumb bob gave the true north line and a foresight could be easily marked in daylight.

Thom was always thinking about archaeoastronomy. The

following manuscript came to light and speaks for itself, indicating that he was exploring various ideas all the time. As far as the author knows it was never published, although it was carefully printed out by hand in the fashion he used in the interim between leaving Oxford and beginning to employ the help of a typist.

Could a star have been used?

"We can speculate about a method which might have been of considerable assistance in setting the backsights. Suppose that one site had been definitely established and that the observers noticed that a star appeared on the foresight exactly. Then this star could have been used for setting the backsights at other observatories in the same latitude. The effect of latitude on the Moon's apparent position is small. It comes about because the parallax effect on apparent declination depends on the latitude. But a difference of 1° in the latitude has an effect of only about 0.5 arc minute and so would not be appreciable if the method was used inside any one district. The star must be bright, otherwise its extinction angle would be greater than the altitude of the foresight. There was no star suitable for the north declinations. Castor is slightly too far north and Pollux too far south. There are two which might have helped with the extreme south declination, namely α Canis Major (Adhara), magnitude 1.6, and β Lupus (beta Lepus) magnitude 3.0. But the number of foresights with a sufficiently high altitude to be above the extinction angle is very small. One pair where the declination could have been transferred by Adhara is from Quinish in Mull to Brackley in Kintyre. Another pair using β Lupus is from Brackley to Campbeltown. No other pairs have been noticed and so it appears that the possibility that the method contributed anything to the accuracy of the site is small."

Looking back and attempting to describe how AT's mind worked, the author sometimes wonders if at that time in life when he did not require as much sleep as younger and older people do, he lay awake at night thinking out his theories. He never complained of sleeplessness. I do not know when an idea on any one subject germinated. Ideas seem to have arrived after sometimes years of work. For instance it took him about a decade to come to his decision about the Hill o' Many Stanes at Mid Clyth. He had a one track mind as far as his hypotheses were concerned — he was always thinking about them. Did his mind work in this way while he slept? I can not say. His work on applied mathematics blossomed in the same way.

Cassegrainian Reflector Telescope

The inadequacies of the three-inch refractor telescope used by Sandy from 1912 until 1921 led him, like Galileo, to make his own reflector telescope. He must have hankered after this for years. It was only after his retirement in 1961 that the opportunity arose at last to build his telecope at Thalassa. Having read up how to proceed he began in 1962 to experiment. He decided to have a twelve inch reflector, and made a concrete dummy to gain experience in making his grinding apparatus.

In a letter to Stuart Wilson from Thalassa in April 1962 Sandy indicated, "I have been grinding concrete discs (with power) to get my hand in for a glass mirror. I don't think they would silver very well!!! and one can only say that the surface is spherical by eye and template."

By the time he had mastered the technique and ground both mirrors he was the leading amateur telescope grinder in Scotland. (vid. *Testing a hyperboloidal mirror for a Cassegrainian telescope* 1965, JBAA 75, 322-327)

Mirror grinding was not very popular with my mother Jeanie, however, because the jeweller's rouge used for the final polishing transferred from his hands to the seat of his pants, thence to the cushions of the house furniture in Thalassa.

He built an observatory, complete with clock drive for the telescope, horizontal and vertical circles and adjustable seat. The shelter was supported on rollers running on a single rail, the large ring which had been used by his father for the second waterwheel. A pair of custom-built double doors allowed him to observe in any direction. He took a photograph of part of the moon's limb with the telescope, but as his eyesight was failing no more work was done with it. He finally sold the telescope to Mr Stanley Beaton of Prestwick.

About this time he built a 4.25 inch refractor telescope, the object glass of which was a lens from a German submarine periscope. Professor Curt Roslund of the department of Astronomy in Gothenburg University and his research student Claes G Carlsson photographed this. They were visiting Dunlop in 1987 to gain background information for Carlsson's thesis on the history of Archaeoastronomy.

Roslund had published an excellent paper on Archaeoastronomy, describing his discoveries at a site in South Sweden. (C.Roslund. *Ale — forntidsmatematiker och astronom?* Forskning och Framsteg 5 1979)

Mr Harry Palmer from Paisley, a member of the Fire Brigade and an amateur astronomer, frequently visited Sandy about this time. Mr Harry Clough of Wee MacNairston, Joppa, befriended Sandy. Harry was grinding a 24 inch mirror. In the spring of 1973, Sandy and the author helped him to perform the Foucault test whereby the shape of the mirror is checked by reflecting a beam of light past a knife edge.

Sandy was 'telescope lens conscious' and always on the look-out for suitable lenses. He obtained from somewhere a range-finder for use from the bridge of a ship. It was of no use to him other than for the telescope on the instrument.

He also possessed, before 1958, a Huet artillery range-finder or director, but he made no use of the lenses. The circles were graduated in grades. The instrument was, in a sense, a theodolite with a very restricted vertical circle. Sandy had made some fitments for object glass and eyepiece; their purpose is, however, unknown.


Sandy Thom's subject was so interesting that he was in great demand as a lecturer. For years he attempted at each lecture to present some new material. This was relatively easy because he was working steadily on fresh surveys all the time. He was developing his subject as he went along and he was for ever making new slides. His audiences were as far apart as Campbeltown in Argyllshire, London and Ulster. Always he was reminding his audiences how the megaliths were steadily being destroyed.

The Extra-Mural Department of the University of Glasgow arranged a conference on Stone Circles and Henge Monuments in November, 1969. Burl, Roy, Thom and E MacKie lectured in turn. About seventy people enrolled. Thom spoke on the astronomical function and geometrical design of stone circles. Six days later he lectured to the Dumfriesshire and Galloway Natural History and Antiquarian society in Dumfries.

As well as being in demand to give talks, the Professor never knew what to expect in the mail. In 1984 one interesting letter which he passed on to the author to deal with was a request from the Area Manager of British Rail at Bristol. It concerned the 150th anniversary of the passing of the Parliamentary Act authorising the construction of the London to Bristol section of the Great Western Railway.

IK Brunel, the famous GW Railway engineer who built the line, was born on 9th April, 1806. He had built the track through a two mile long dead straight tunnel rising steeply from the village of Box. Twice per year the sun shines down through the tunnel. The burning question was simply this; did Brunel intend the sun to shine through on his birthday?

Brunel worshippers were, in the end, disappointed. Accurate calculations showed that the sun, on 9th April, 1835, did not shine through the tunnel. This phenomenon occurred on the 6th and 7th of April, (and 5th and 6th of September) 1835. The inference is that Brunel, had he really wanted to, could have built his tunnel so that the sun did shine through on his birthday. By accident or design he chose an azimuth about a degree nearer south.


In Search of Ancient Astronomies.

Dr Krupp and his artist wife Robin were en route to Orkney to see for themselves what Sandy was writing about. They met by chance in the waiting room of Inverness airport. Beryl and Trude MacKie were in the Thom party. A friendship sprang up immediately and the outcome was that in 1975 Ed Krupp invited the Professor to fly to California to give a pair of two-hour lectures, part of a post graduate course "In Search of Ancient Astronomies" to be run by the University of California in Los Angeles and in San Diego.

By this time Sandy was well through his eighty second year. He was secretly pleased, but decided not to accept the invitation. I had experienced the trials of air travel and I felt that it was too much for him. It would have been too exhausting. I went in his stead, going on a lecture tour which included Los Angeles, San Diego, Berkley, Victoria, Vancouver and Rose Polytechnic, Indiana.

Ed Krupp arranged the Californian end of the business, finally producing out of the course of lectures a seven chapter book written by the four or five participants in the series.

The lecturing was hard, rewarding work. I shall never forget the audience of four hundred in San Diego. An examination question was set on my subject. I did not correct the scripts! The complete book of the course was published in 1977 by EC Krupp, called *In Search of Ancient Astronomies*. He was awarded by the American Institute of Physics/US Steel, a prize of $1,000 for the best science writing in 1978. The book has been published in English by Doubleday, McGraw-Hill and Penguin, in German by Beck and in Portuguese by Europa-America. A follow-up publication came in 1984, edited again by EC Krupp, called *Archaeoastronomy and the Roots of Science*. It reported the AAAS Selected Symposium 71.

In 1954 Sandy had published *Some Refraction Measurements at Low Altitudes*, in the Journal of the Institute of Navigation. Twenty-three years later he was remembered. He was asked to read The Duke of Edinburgh Lecture, presented to the Royal Institute of Navigation normally not more than once every two years, on subjects related generally and culturally, rather than technically, to navigation. Sandy was invited to give the lecture, which he duly prepared on Megalithic Astronomy.

Lecturing had begun to weary AT and the author took over almost all of the invitations. I travelled to lecture in many places like the Isle of Mull, Aberdeen, Southampton, Los Angeles, San Diego, San Francisco, Victoria, Vancouver, Terre Haute, Cleveland Ohio, Colchester, Nottingham, Hereford, Preston, Cardiff, Liverpool, Glasgow School of Art, Stirling University. On vacation in Grenoble I was invited to lecture to an interested audience of academics. I used AT's slides along with my own action photographs taken at many sites.


In the process of writing this book, it has gradually dawned on me that my father had a gift of man-management. Somehow or another he could make people work for him in the way he wanted. His experience of really hard work in Canada undoubtedly helped to develop this ability.

During the 1914-1918 war when he was with the Norman Thompson Flight Company, Sussex, working as chief draughtsman and designer on flying boats, he was complimented in writing by Air Ministry Officials on the expedition whereby his drawing office staff carried through the task of standardising the 120 drawings required to put one of the boats in production.

Others noticed this. One to express it being Herbert Gravenell who wrote a glowing testimonial for Thom in 1919 when leaving The Norman Thompson Flight Company himself. Gravenell wrote 17 years later,

> "Hearing that Mr Thom is applying for an Engineering Chair, I endorse this reference by stating that his tact and resourcefulness in efficiently controlling a mixed staff was the primary consideration leading to his appointment."

Like his Uncle Sam Strang, Alexander Thom had the type of personality which allowed him to make people work for him and with him. The results show in his Departmental work in Glasgow University, in his leadership of teams of constructors and researchers at Farnborough (the High Speed Wind Tunnel never broke down), in his successes in Oxford University Engineering Department, in his handling of crews on his yacht cruises, and finally in his leadership of hard-working volunteer surveyors all over the British Isles and in Brittany.

It is not easy to skipper a mixed crew of six or sometimes ten or twelve on sailing yacht cruises when incipient seasickness and the cramped living quarters on board are always an unknown element. Professor AN Black noticed this and wrote to the author as follows;

> "I have never forgotten the time when a crew came up on a tiring overnight journey from the South to join *Torridon* at Tobermory. As we went up the sound of Mull in the steamer somebody said 'The Old Man has been at anchor all day, he'll be trying to sail this evening'. It was unanimously agreed that if he tried that there would be a mutiny. I need not say that about two hours after we arrived we were under way without a murmur. It was a superb piece of man-management."

Leading his expedition of twelve or fourteen hard-working volunteer helpers to make accurate plans of thousands of standing stones at Carnac in Brittany was no mean task.

Very few individuals disagreed with his methods. Lazy ones kept away. Several asked to join fieldwork parties to be taught how to survey, to see for themselves how this man worked.

Writers of prehistory came to see how his mind worked — how he saw into the minds of prehistoric ring-builders and 'Astronomer Priests'.

Alexander Thom had the ability to enjoy a fine morning along with someone — the postman for instance, or his scout in Brasenose College. One scout came, before his own retirement, specially to see Sandy to thank him for the way in which he had treated him as a man. Men like these had great admiration for him. He was sensitive to their need to be recognised as individuals.

As a thinker, however, he worked alone. A deep thinker, he was always "a lad o' pairts" among men of intellectual qualities.

Sandy enlisted the help of his family and many friends for the vast amount of field work needed. He often paid expenses to those whom he thought needed cash. Others came at their own expense. He expected loyalty and reliable attendance to the tasks in hand.

While at the theodolite the Professor needed to concentrate. One time in the field at Carnac, Hans Motz the Austrian was talking eloquently in French to Monique, a French archaeologist who had joined the party for a day. While making his point, Hans's voice waxed louder and louder until Sandy was forced to exclaim, "Do you mind. I'm working."

The good lady had been brought along for a day by her friend Jean-Luc Quinio, who helped the team day after day in Carnac.

Some years before, Jean-Luc, an amateur archaeologist, had been visiting the alignments, had seen and heard our sizable parties at work and had made himself known to AT who invited him forthwith to join the expedition. His help was invaluable. His native language was Breton.

Alexander Thom's annual correspondence was huge. For office work tasks — filing, dictating, typing etc — he employed casual helpers, Mrs Halstead, Mrs H Forrest at Dunlop, Lynne et al at Banavie.

About 1975 he acquired a pocket tape-recorder with head phones for the typist and with the foot controlled start-stop device for her use. The small cassettes were collected by her or anyone going in the direction of her home, or posted. This system worked well until his voice became so frail that the typist could not make a good reproduction of what Sandy wanted to say. When he became blind he evidently could not check the typing.

Towards the end of his active calculating life he felt that it would be a good idea to have help for the theoretical scientific calculations needed. Mark Wallace was very interested in the subject at the time and visited Thalassa several times, but the arrangement did not work out. Mark later went on a fairly long expedition surveying with Ron Curtis in the Hebrides. Sandy could not work for very long at a time and tired easily. Hilda M Gustin helped him greatly about this time with secretarial work and by writing out and tabulating the work as he was calculating it. On occasion he began to make mistakes which were picked up and corrected by his co-author before publication. Some leaves were beginning to wilt and fall.

# PART IV

## AUTUMN

# 1975-1985

"Short of time."
Alexander Thom

Every day in life Jeanie had a cold plunge outside in 'the tub' until twelve days before she died in 1975 in her seventy ninth year. Honour and Andrew Tindal very kindly helped with nursing her in her terminal illness. Sandy thereafter had to live alone.

He gradually adjusted. He had a 'home help' for a time, then help three times per week for a few hours from two persons. Soup was made for him frequently. He did not eat large amounts of meat. Very soon after Jeanie died, Margaret began to do Sandy's washing and he came every evening to the Bungalow, 140 yards distant, for his meal. In good weather we often dined in Margaret's caravan on the blaes at the front door.

His daughter Beryl visited him frequently. Mrs EM Thom, (Jock), Wastle's widow, visited him once for several days. Andrew and Honour Tindal came frequently from Uplawmoor, usually in the evening. He loved their company. Harry and Joan Clough visited regularly from Joppa. When Sandy went off to visit Beryl at Banavie for a few days, he arranged for James Thomson to sleep in Thalassa at night, acting as caretaker. The thought of having his papers rifled and stirred up appalled him.

The Department of Extra Mural and Adult Education of Glasgow University ran a conference on archaeology in September 1975. The Professor attended and contributed. He was very well looked after by the organiser, Dr WC Hutchison. The attitude of many of those attending was a restrained politeness. They seemed to be completely satisfied with unsubstantiated drawings of elevations of buildings made with only the evidence of post holes. Many of them were not yet in the mood to accept the Professor's analysis using objective evidence from accurately made plans of many stone rings. I suspect that they were not understanding the difference between subjective impression and objective data.

Objective (concrete) evidence consists of data observed by the senses of sight, hearing, taste, smell, or touch; subjective data is one (or more) individual's unsubstantiated belief (hypothesis), and must be tested and verified before qualifying as evidence.

Perhaps the conference could be summed up by quoting Archie Roy's observation that from then on archaeologists would consider more carefully the orientation of sites being investigated. My memories of the conference are that the Skipper was developing a heavy cold which took three weeks to clear away.

Skipper liked nature but did not appreciate the attentions of wood pigeons to young succulent garden vegetables. He also liked to be up in time to unlock his door to pass the time of day and receive mail from the postman who usually arrived about eight am. One morning while stepping out of his pyjama, Skipper spotted a pigeon in the field on the south side of Thalassa. He loaded the shot gun, but did not attempt to open the window. Instead he stealthily unlocked the north door, crept round the house and shot the pigeon on the wing as it flew away southwards. Unbeknownst to Skipper, Postie had arrived to witness the shot.

"Goad that wis a guid shoat!" So it was. An instant killer because it got the bird up its feathers — a head-on shot is never so lethal with pigeons!

About 1977 he took a bout of flu, the variety that destroyed sense of balance. Beryl nursed him at Bridge of Weir. From that time onwards he never shaved and grew a beard like his father whose cheeks had never felt a razor.

The snowdrops which had been brought to The Hill in 1901 from Carradale show their first white spears between Christmas and New Year. Skipper was as conscious as the rest of us of 'the Victory of Spring' being more certain than 'the Defeat of Winter'. One midwinter I picked the first snowdrop and took it to him on one of my evening visits. "Well, that's one more", I said. He grinned.

About this time in his life he remarked, "Middle-aged people do not realise that as a person grows older the mechanics of living become more difficult and time-consuming." He did his own shopping in Dunlop, usually on Saturday mornings, when I took him out in his car. He had given up driving when he was about eighty six. One morning in the street, a village worthy asked him, "How are you today?" His reply was quick and to the point. "Bloody but unbowed!" Laterally he had difficulty in recognising people and had to ask, "Who is it?"

272

*Alexander Thom at The Hill, Monday 1 September 1975*

*Alexander Thom taking a reading surveying with the author in Shetland*

On his final surveying expedition in August 1977 the Skipper was Margaret's guest in her caravan. We had a perfect evening for the theodolite survey of the north-eastern horizon from Brainport, Loch Fyne, a site being examined by Col PF Gladwin. Next day we moved to Skipness, parked the caravan near to the ferry terminus, and surveyed the site he called Skipness. This turned out to be a very good lunar site. (See JHA 1979 AA 1 S97-98)

We visited Marion Campbell at her ancestral home at Kilberry Castle. Author of *The Dark Twin* (publisher Turnstone), she knew most of the standing stone sites in her area.

A passing look at Temple Wood reminded the Skipper of his work showing its importance as a lunar site. He had first surveyed here in 1939. Ring A2/8 is described by him in *Megalithic Rings*. Of the inner ring, he wrote,

"This beautiful little ring became a Mecca for visitors from all over the world until in the late 1970s it was torn to bits by the Ministry of Works. Subsequently Mr JG Scott has further excavated the site on behalf of the Scottish Develoment Department. It is hoped that the SDD will complete this careful work by restoring the inner ring destroyed by its predecessor . . ."

Probably the inner ring shown on Skipper's plan is the only record of what the place once looked like on the surface. He once told Beryl that he felt guilty about having drawn attention to Temple Wood which the archaeologists then proceeded to destroy. All was not lost, however. The original geometry of the little ring was accurately recorded for us all by Jack Scott with Ian Orkney, (see Thom, Thom and Burl, *Megalithic Rings*, BAR 81, 1980. page 145).

Later we had another long careful look at the stones near to the ruins of Barbreck House, re-surveying them and exploring the valley to the north. AT was booking while I took the theodolite sights.

These were the last times that AT timed my sun sights.


Thom received criticism aplenty. Sometimes he reacted instantly, putting his thoughts down on paper — thoughts which he did not publish. If he was upset he might write a strong letter which he never posted. He seemed to benefit by expressing himself in this way.

He dictated the following about August 1981 —

"Archaeology and Students
    We can divide people who tend to study
archaeoastronomy into three classes —

    1. Those who believe that our forefathers were able to do these things;

    2. Those who are uncertain but are prepared to read and learn, and

    3. Those who do not believe and refuse to be convinced.

    The third class is the most difficult to deal with, because its members do not want to spend the time reading; they are so convinced that they are right. Perhaps they do read a little but as they find this cuts across their preconceived ideas it makes them annoyed and they will not read any more."

Once, at a conference, the author had to listen to a critic of Thom's hypotheses ranting on at great length about refraction, showing slide after slide of sunsets with most interesting effects caused by very stable layers of air with obvious different temperatures. The critic either had not read or did not want to understand AT's two papers published in the Journal of the Institute of Navigation (1954 and 1958). Later, at a similar conference, the same customer tackled Thom (again in his absence). This time he was quietly reprimanded by Richard Atkinson saying, "Words such as these are not in my book." The critic has not been heard since that day. Nor has any of his edited work come the way of the author. He had not taken the time necessary to read what AT had done — he was unwilling to accept Thom's field work.

    The Professor's aim had been to continue surveying sites accurately in order to gain more and yet more information before they all disappeared. Contrasting those sites he identified as 'functional, scientific', (Thom,1971), with the ones that are less precise. He tagged the latter 'symbolic, mystical.' The 'symbolic' and the 'mystical' were not really the target of his research.

    He approached the problem by using a modern analogy. Every one of today's buildings is not a church or meeting place and so why should he include every megalithic site as being 'functional, scientific'?

    He felt that he had the right to use only those alignments which fitted the functional, scientific hypothesis. He knew that standing stones had been erected over millennia, that dates given by archaeologists for each site would make his task easier all round. The

*On the same trip to Shetland (aged 82) with RL Merritt at Staneydale Druid Temple, Shetland*

dates were simply not there. Co-operation of the archaeologists was also needed to find out if any of the sites had been re-erected. Assuming that the cult lasted for several centuries the obliquity changes would make it desirable to move the backsight.

When the professor had collected enough data, he began to search around for somewhere to publish his findings. By that stage in his life he had published many papers on applied mathematics. No editor in the UK had been interested in his archaeoastronomy. He tried the USA. A refusal came six months later. One of the leading archaeologists to whom he submitted a paper, OGS Crawford, founder and editor of the prestigious magazine *Antiquity*, returned the paper, with the blunt remark, "I do not believe your thesis."

Unrepentant, the Professor sent his material to the Royal Statistical Society which body lapped it up with delight in 1955. Statisticians, accustomed to working on data like the incidence of horse-bite in the German army, had here a completely new set of measurements. The paper was read worldwide and thereafter editors began to accept his material.

Not satisfied with this way of spreading his knowledge, he finally wrote his first book, *Megalthic Sites in Britain*, published in 1967. Much of the manuscript of this book was handwritten, in fact printed by hand, for the publisher.

Jean Hunt points out in her book *Tracking the flood survivors* that Thom was very badly treated by many archaeologists, his information sometimes refused publication, and ridiculed when it did reach print.

"However, by the time of his death in 1985," she later wrote in *Astronomy and Mathematics*, "he was acknowledged the "Father of Archaeoastronomy", both in Europe and the USA. That gives me hope that, if an idea has merit, it will survive. Thom surveyed so many sites and wrote so much, that I am overwhelmed with admiration for his patience and perseverance; he must have made up his mind early that, if it was necessary to drown the critics in a tidal wave of evidence, then so be it!"

Hunt writes —

"With this sort of evident myopia, it is understandable that archaeologists have come to be seen as the eunuchs of the academic world. The reality is that, in the past fifty years, there have been at least four archaeological 'breakthroughs'

by 'outsiders' relative to the dawn of modern human history
in the 12,000-3,500BC period for which we have previously
had no written records: Willard Libby's development of the
radiocarbon dating technique (Libby's training was in
physics); Alexander Marshak's demonstrations of man's
record-keeping propensities as far back as possibly 20,000BC
(Marshak, up to that time, had been a journalist, although he
is now a research fellow at Harvard's Peabody Museum);
Alexander Thom's demonstration, through geographic site
surveys, that a standard system of measurement and
recognisable astronomical alignments were in use in the
megalithic-constructing cultures of Great Britain, Egypt and
America (Thom's training was in civil engineering); and
Martin Brennan's observations of the lumiere effect inside
passage/chambers constructed by the megalith builders
(Brennan began his career as an art historian)."

Hunt goes on . . .

"As a psychologist engaged in measuring and predicting
human behaviour, and as an 'archaeology buff' for many
years, on the basis of the facts outlined above, I think it
would be reasonable to say that one of the factors to be
looked for in predicting the probability of success for a
person engaged in archaeological research would be that
s(he) not be trained in it."

Like Alexander Thom before her, in 1986 Jean Hunt had sent an article
to Glyn Daniel, editor of *Antiquity* hoping that he would publish it.
Failing that would he please comment on it. Five weeks later, back
came the article — "unsuitable for *Antiquity*". The relevant parts of
the editor's comments were,

"It seems to me just an uncritical acceptance of the theories
of Thom, von Daniken, Landsburg, Fell and others. Fell's
'Ancient Inscriptions and Alphabets' as you call them are
not valid scientific data but glacial scratches, plough marks
and natural features.
    Von Daniken's theory of visitors from outer space has
long been exploded, while Thom, though he showed himself
to be a good surveyor, his theories are now discredited . . . I

am afraid you have clearly landed yourself on the wilder shores of Archaeology — a very dangerous country."

To this letter, part of Jean Hunt's reply reads,

"You mention 'the wilder shores of Archaeology — a very dangerous country: not when you're trained, as I am, in the scientific method. Any person can repeat and verify my research: any person who does so is very likely to come to much the same conclusions that I did."

Later, AT had likewise little or no patience with his critics who were mainly statisticians, called in by archaeologists to help them understand the procedure. They accused him of 'deciding first what he was looking for, and going into the field and finding it.' He denied this. His approach was positive, described by himself in a letter to Margaret Ponting — "The stones are there, they have a message, let's find it." Had he applied a negative approach he would never have surveyed any stones at all.

In his contribution to 'Hoyle on Stonehenge: Some Comments', in *Antiquity* (41, 95-96), the Professor wrote —

"Somerville in 1912 drew attention to a possible lunar line at Callanish and in my 1955 (JRSS) paper's declination histogram a number of possible lunar lines are to be found. But in the atmosphere of 1955 it would only have complicated the issue to have drawn attention to these lines; I had no proof. But proof came when in 1965 I brought together all the lines collected to that date (*Vistas in Astronomy*). The double hump produced by the lunar lines can be seen, one hump for the upper limb and one for the lower. To my mind this was a completely objective proof because the two humps simply appeared without having been expected. He had not 'decided first what he was looking for, and gone into the field and found it.' His discovery that at megalithic man's equinoxes the sun's declination was not zero but about $+0.5^0$ was made in the same way.

To quote Thom's own words, he 'kept on recording what he found', making plans and measuring azimuths.

### The Golden Rule; Phi-geometry

For years Sandy had known about the Golden Ratio (Phi), the aesthetically pleasing proportions found in ancient works of art and architecture from the times of the ancient world. But he had never considered the possibility that prehistoric ring builders had been using what is now called Phi geometry. Mona Phillips, an artist from Cleveland Ohio, obtained a copy of *Megalithic Rings* and to Thom's delight discovered that Megalithic Men, as AT called the builders, had been using what is now called Phi geometry. During all of the years he had been surveying rings, Phi-geometry in connection with the geometry of standing stone rings had never entered his head. So much for the above criticism of statisticians.

Mona Phillips used his published plans to great effect. She wrote and delivered, at the (1981) XVIth International Congress for the History of Science, a paper *Thom's Stonehenge Trilithon Pattern: A Megalithic Design?* There had been some correspondence in which she had asked some questions, the first one being, "Am I correct in stating that you (here I mean the collective Thoms) have never identified Phi in megalithic geometry?" His answer to this was 'yes'. He wrote her on 7th January, 1981 —

"Dear Madam,

It is indeed a pleasure to know someone in US who is prepared to believe that my work is correct. How different this is from the attitude of the editors of the *Scientific American* who treated me so nastily over Glyn Daniel's recent letter.

I began to survey megalithic remains more than forty years ago. As time went on I realised that not only for the geometry but also for the astronomy the surveying had to be done with the greatest accuracy. You have perhaps seen Professor Giot's translation of our work in Carnac. This is a considerable improvement on earlier days when people who should have known better simply scrawled across my submitted paper, 'I don't believe your theories'. But

281

eventually I got some recognition from the British
Astronomical Association and then from The Royal
Statistical Society, but it was hard uphill work. Then I got the
support of a United States citizen, Robert L Merritt, and then
of Ed Krupp of Los Angeles.

When I came to survey Stonehenge I knew that the
survey work had to be of the highest possible quality. I also
knew the value of the megalithic yard within very small
limits.

It gives me great pleasure to know that someone really
believes in my work and is prepared to carry it further. But
judging by my experience you will have an uphill fight. Are
you not ascribing to these people the knowledge of a ratio?

Good Luck and good hunting!
Yours sincerely,
Professor A Thom"

Mona Phillips delivered her 1981 paper at Bucharest. She visited the
Professor en route home. We advised her to obtain a copy of *Megalithic
Rings*. She used the survey plans to great effect and wrote up her
material. Her papers, thesis and book ms duly arrived. The author
read out aloud her 100-page letter to the Skipper who dictated the
following letter on 12th December, 1984 —

"Dear Mona Phillips,
I am now well into my 91st year. My eyes are so bad that
I can not read without electronic assistance. My son Dr
Archibald S Thom has, however, read me your work on the
Phi-ratio yesterday and today.

I do not understand why your approach gives the same
results as mine. It sounds like magic.

I accept your work, however, and your methods of
applying Phi-geometry to the plans I have made since the
1930s. Archie will now attempt to answer your main
questions.

I have known about the Golden Ratio for many years but
never thought of applying it to megalithic geometry.

With best wishes, yours sincerely, Alexander Thom"

282

He was accused of changing his mind about specific sites on second publication, of revising his already reported observed azimuths and calculated declinations. His reply to these challenges was instant, direct and simple, "Yes, I change my mind — it is a growing subject — as it develops I frequently return to a site to check my observations in better weather conditions, often with a better theodolite." Some work often had to rely on compass azimuths or on azimuths taken from OS maps. He much preferred time observations taken using the sun as referring object, moving though it was.

Referring to his sometimes frequent revisits to a site, for which he was criticised, my mother likened him to a molecatcher, who usually left a pair of moles to breed so that he would have to come back next year again!

Skeptics scoffed at Thom's insistence on his lunar theories. He maintained that the Moon was until recently mankind's lamp in the dark — its light allowed safe walking over rough terrain during the night hours. In an agricultural community it was seen that the pattern of rising times of an Autumn Moon is such that the nightly delay of about an hour is decreased by the cyclically increasing declination as the Moon comes north. The result is that great help is always available from moonlight in the early autumn evenings. The working day can be extended — hence what we term now the Harvest Moon. (Much grain is harvested now in the dark by a small number of men using machinery with bright headlamps in the fields). The next lunation is for similar reasons the Hunter's Moon.

Why should Neolithic Men not have studied lunar phases, watched the monthly changes in horizontal rising and setting, etc, and recorded the relevant sightlines by the only permanent method they had, the erection of menhirs?

Thom pointed out that 'Carriage Moon' candles were on sale as late as the 1920s, and that in Dunlop, after the installation of the gas works, the lamp lighter did not light the gas street lamps (installed in the streets in 1884) during bright phases of the moon. In the wartime blackout, wise secretaries of engineering associations always arranged city meetings to suit the moon.

The Glasgow University Department of Archaeology were running a small symposium on Archaeoastronomy. One of the bright research students had said let's call it 'Thom Foolery and Mega-Lunacy?' In fact the senior staff man in charge advised against using this name. The incident illustrates, however, the attitude of established teaching at the time. It has been said that knowledge is not knowledge until it has been taught in universities for twenty years.

By December 1981 his cataract was so far developed that the operation had to be done on both eyes. The four inactive days so weakened him that Beryl took him to Banavie to convalesce. He had been given a temporary pair of spectacles with which he could not see at all well. On a frosty morning in January 1982, while out for a short walk he fell on the rough frozen mud fifty yards from the house door and broke his femur. He was then in a predicament. In Inverness hospital no optician could be found who could prescribe a reasonable pair of spectacles. He was weeks convalescing from the thigh operation, and he could neither read nor see well what was going on around him. Beryl was nursing David, her husband, in his terminal illness, and she could not keep her Dad at Banavie. He returned to Thalassa, was fitted with a reasonable pair of spectacles and did his best to adjust to the new circumstances. His mind was still active. He worked on, contributed three more papers on archaeoastronomy and finished the drafting in manuscript form of his part of what was to become a 557 page book, *Stone Rows and Standing Stones* finally published in 1990 in two volumes.

After his return to Thalassa in January 1982 it became obvious that the treck to the Bungalow for his dinner was too much for him, especially in the dark winter evenings with frozen ground. We improvised a hot-box, loading it carefully with his dinner on hot plates, the while ringing Thalassa on the telephone to say his 'Meal on Feet' was on the way. He enjoyed his 'kitchen' on a tray beside his own fireside.

Hilda Gustin came occasionally for several weeks at a time and helped him with his manuscript writing and calculations.

John Leask, a BBC Radio travelling programme commentator came to Dunlop and interviewed the Professor in Thalassa. He was broadcast for about ten minutes, answering Leask's questions, the programme being *From Langholm to Lerwick*. On the same programme Leask put on our neighbour Mrs Nancy Miller and James Thomson, who was working part time at The Hill. The three of them did their best to portray 'Old Dunlop'.

*Alexander Thom in his own home Thalassa, still expanding a point in the summer of 1982*

Each one was asked for a favourite piece of music. Sandy chose Mendelsohn's *Spring Song*. He had played it on his violin some sixty years before.

Sandy was not asked to talk on archaeoastronomy on BBC Radio but the author was roped in by BBC editor Peter Beer, (son of Arthur Beer, who had been editor of *Vistas in Astronomy*), to be recorded for a BBC overseas programme. Sandy was getting too frail by that time.

The time came in December 1983 when he could not live alone any longer. I asked the family doctor on a Friday for permission for the 120 mile journey to Beryl's at Banavie. Sandy spent Saturday quietly deciding what to take with him, and after packing the car to the roof with his arm chair, his big radio, his books, pocket calculators, the lot, we left on Sunday. As I drove down the avenue he said, "I remember coming up the first time in 1901. I'll not be back."

In the fall of 1984, in his 91st year, at Banavie, AT's mind was still alert. He wanted still to contribute but it was becoming more and more difficult as he had to dictate into the pocket recorder and his words had to be typed and read to him. By this time he was registered as a blind person. He had been thinking about the book *Megalithic Astronomy, A New Archaeological and Statistical study of 300 Western Scottish Sites* by CLN Ruggles, (BAR Series 123, 1984) and also about the paper published by Ruggles in BAR 1981 'Astronomy and Society in Britain during the period 4,000 BC - 1,500BC' edited by Ruggles and Whittle, 'A critical examination of the megalithic lunar observatories'.

He had known that Ruggles was resurveying many sites and was quietly pleased that no serious errors or mistakes had been reported. He dictated the following on 6th November, 1984.

"Clive Ruggles has shown that he has surveyed a large number of sites on the west coast of Scotland. In the book he carries out a careful analysis of these surveys. He finds that these indicate certain declinations and avoid other declinations. This does not make sense and we must look further.

"But he pays no attention to the unequivocal metrological conclusions arrived at by myself, namely that these people were capable of working to a precision of an arc minute.

"If they used the same precision in their astronomical work then Ruggles' conclusions must be wide of the mark.

"It is to be noted that Ruggles's work is to $\pm 1^0$. It seems to me that he has merely introduced a new set of problems for statisticians to solve when they try to explain his peculiar results."

# PART V

## FALLEN LEAVES

"The Art of successful living
is to perform unimportant tasks gracefully."
Alexander Thom

Alexander Thom died peacefully on 7th November 1985.

Beryl wrote to Barry Nicholas, Principal of Brasenose College, "My father was in hospital for a week before he died. I should like to have had him at home but he died before he could be returned to me. My father often spoke of his days at Brasenose College. They had been happy ones."

Oration and eulogy at the cremation service near Ayr were given by the Reverend David Reid, son of Lily Tindal, Alexander's cousin.

David Reid related the experience of his late father when the Professor took him home from a Brasenose dinner on the tandem. David omitted to give the detail about the red tail light having been strapped round the passenger's waist.

Among those attending were Jack Maclay; Ronald Reid (from Australia); James Thomson of Dunlop; Mrs M McMillan of Inver Guest House, Dunbeath, Caithness; Peter Lund, his wife Helen and John Allen (head of Maintenance) from Oxford University Engineering Laboratory.

Among the wreaths was one from The Principal and Fellows of Brasenose College Oxford. We wrote our appreciation to Principal Barry Nicholas. Lindy Austin took the flowers home and so they were fully appreciated.

I tend to be more numerical than literate. I am however of the opinion that the writing of good English is most important. How do we know what a man thought about, a hundred years ago, other than by reading what he wrote? We can not talk to him; nor can we talk to megalithic men. They have left no written records. This is why Alexander Thom always maintained that all we can do is to study the shapes of the stone rings they built, along with their positions relative to the surroundings, expecially the horizons where they could observe the rising and setting points of heavenly bodies. In this way we can attempt to see how they thought. Sandy was of the opinion that some cup and ring markings were in a way the efforts of 'The Boys' to make records — a form of writing. He said, "the only writing is in the stones themselves."

After 1983 I had brought many wheelbarrow loads of books from Thalassa and the cabins. By December 1987 I managed to take time to cull through the books, lay those aside which I did not require, and invite Glasgow University Library to take their choice. Finally over three hundred volumes ended up in the University library.

He had already given his huge 1908 *Encyclopaedia* to Kilmarnock Academy and his early British Astronomical Association journals to the BAA.

His reading tastes were varied. He read many books.

He enjoyed Masefield's sea yarns, Conrad, Arctic exploration, the voyage of De Long's *Jeanette* and Greely's scathing remarks about Nansen's incredible plan, Nansen's *Farthest North*, HG Wells, Jack London, Kipling's *Hymn to Steam* and the *Rhyme of the three Sealers*, Rabbie Burns, Fraser Darling, Neil Gunn, yachting voyages, mountaineering books, *The Southseaman*, Claud Worth, Thor Heyerdal, *The Earth* by Jeffreys, Neville Shute, the *Ruba'iyat* of the old Persian Omar Khayyam. He kept himself up to date with books on modern astronomy and cosmology. He read some books on Egyptology, but did not steep himself in that subject. He was extremely interested in modern books on Greek mathematics. He enjoyed modern translations of Homer.

Thor Heyerdal's description of his spelaeology on Easter Island did not appeal to Skipper at all; he detested the feelings of claustrophobia engendered by Thor.

He possessed the necessary books on statistics and used them. His shelves were laden with Ordnance Survey maps, books on surveying, geodesy, aeronautics, aerodynamics, numerical analysis, mathematics, applied mathematics and mathematical tables.

He enjoyed detective stories and in the last thirty years or so of his life he read these in German, jokingly saying, "It makes the story last longer!" He often chose German translations of books by English authors.

That was his life!

Alexander Thom lived through nine decades and well into his tenth. He maintained that the art of successful living is to perform unimportant tasks gracefully. His aim was to grow old gracefully. He had the habit of shaking hands with one upon meeting after a few days.

Jeanie and he had similar feelings about home-made things, "A poor thing but mine own!" They built Thalassa together. Their philosophy might be expressed in the saying, "It's the journey that is interesting, not the arrival."

As he grew older it was obvious that he was saving his energies by becoming more and more tidy with his tools, papers, filing systems, cabinets and books. He found it easier to live and work in this tidy fashion, with his short term memory deteriorating. He maintained, however, that any filing system was no better than the memory of the the person running it.

Alexander believed that engineering is one of the main springs of a progressive society. His work was his hobby; his applied mathematics was his hobby. Study of the geometry and astronomy of prehistoric men in Britain and Brittany began by being a hobby; it became his work. He became more and more obsessed with it as it took over. He was to have a distinguished second professional career in a different field.

After Thom realised that the megalith builders had an intelligence equal to his own, he began to reason out their thinking by placing himself in their situation, "wearing their mocassins". They lived most of their lives in the open air, observed the skies by day and night, and the rising and setting positions of the heavenly bodies on east and west horizons. He reasoned that they kept a record, memorised it and passed it on by word of mouth. The relative positioning of the astronomical megaliths was the permanent recording of the calendar, both solar and lunar. At each observatory the astronomer priest would know what to expect each season; his students would be well instructed.

He had often to change his mind about a particular archaeo-astronomical site — smaller minds criticised him for this. His answer was, "What else could I do? It was a new subject, growing daily as I worked at it!"

Astronomy as practised by Neolithic Man was also a growing

subject, spread over millennia. No wonder Thom occasionally changed his mind.

He had his critics, but he thought deeply, formulated his hypotheses and published his results.

It was as though a sentry had fired off some shots between sleeping armies in the dark. The shots may not always have been accurate but at least they served to wake sleepers from their beds.

The dogs bark, but the caravan rolls on.

He was always going ahead to seek new horizons. Thom was one of the great discoverers.

He was invariably 'short of time'. In his 'autumn' he always had the feeling, "I must get on with this or that (new discovery) and write it up before I die." He did not stop to write a popular volume, a concise, up-to-date full statement of his various hypotheses.

In the *Ruba'iyat*, the Old Persian Omar Khayyam wrote —

> *"The stars are setting and the Caravan*
> *Starts for the Dawn of Nothing —*
> *Oh, make haste."*

Rarely have advances in stone circle research been made by an archaeologist. Most of the discoveries about the rings from the seventeenth century onwards have been made by non-archaeologists, surveyors, engineers, clerics, astronomers, solicitors, an illustrious pageant of true amateurs amongst whom Alexander Thom occupies an honourable place. Thom the engineer, statistician and field surveyor joins this illustrious band of men. He stands with John Aubrey and William Stukeley as a person who investigated outside the boundaries of archaeological convention, less concerned with pots and flints than with the hitherto neglected aspects of shape, design and orientation.

Alexander Thom's work has influenced scholars far beyond the confines of his own homeland. He raised the engaging question, "do the remains of ancient civilisations reflect a knowledge of astronomy by virtue of the way they are laid out in the landscape?" This aspect of his work has had a great catalytic influence and has aroused the greatest controversy.

His book *Megalithic Sites in Britain* had the effect of a delayed-action bomb. It seldom happens that a single book, by an author who made no claim to be an archaeologist, compels archaeologists to re-examine their assumptions about a whole section of the past. His first book did this. He radically altered the current view of the intellectual calibre of man in Britain in the late third and second millennium BC. A whole chapter had to be revised in the accepted history of science, in which primacy in the development of geometry, mensuration, observational astronomy and the calendar had been ascribed hitherto to the literate civilizations of the Ancient East.

Whatever arrangements politicians may make for the use of land by our populace, it has always to be remembered that the soil must be nurtured and cared for in order to provide food.

In the early parts of this biography I gave many details of the farms worked by the Thoms, from Finnock Bog in the early nineteenth century to The Hill today. Continuity of the soil, of the land and its husbandry comes to the fore. To remind me of the continuity, I still have and use some of my grandfather's tools.

When there is a decision to be made a good husbandman always does what he considers to be the best thing for the continuity of the fertility of the land. Soil of any kind is so necessary for all living things. Living rock is seldom more than a metre below the surface.

Throughout there is the continuity of the seasons. Spring, Summer, Autumn and Winter follow one another inexorably. The dawn chorus of birdsong, the nesting, hatching, feeding of fledglings, the empty nests and the silence in leafy June all take place. Passerine birds visit in autumn and winter, vixens scream and howlats cry in the night. In summer, house martins, swallows and swifts criss-cross the fly-laden air in the lee of the woods. Herring gulls, wood pigeon and feral dove visit but lapwing, snipe, corncrake, and lark are no more. Gaggles of silent geese overfly in season. Some rabbits have survived. Occasionally mad March hares, those loneliest of fauna, circle in the fields. Unexpected wet spells and droughts are nothing new in the weather pattern. Bitter drying east winds in spring wreak havoc with the husbandman's crop planning, but spring zephyrs come, summer breezes follow on, and luscious grass grows to be grazed by contented dairy herds. Some hay is cropped for winter silage.

Deep frosts are few and far between. Blizzards seem never to occur now; open air skating and curling are things of the past. Equinoctial gales and winter hurricanes continue to destroy and kill.

Plants other than grass thrive: dockens, nettles, bun-weed, thistle, cow parsley, cow parsnip, rushes, etc, colonise areas. Deep rooted trees and weeds do more good than harm bringing minerals from the hard pan below to the surface, increasing the fertility. Tonnes and tonnes of timber are burned annually. The ashes go back to the soil, helping to maintain ecological balance. Annual trimmings from miles of hedges are burned and the ashes scattered. Edible mushrooms occasionally flourish in unpredictable profusion in the fields. Worms pull fallen autumn leaves down into the soil, adding to fertility. Moles come and go.

Although appearing to be dormant in winter, most plants are consolidating their position, ready to begin the next round of seasons. If the bark of sycamores is damaged in early spring, it bleeds like maple. Tree buds swell visibly, en masse, when seen against the sky, branch silhouettes darken, weeks before burgeoning. Not easily perceived against the sky, the first tree flowers seen, before the leaf buds burst, are the delicate pink elm flowers. Hawthorn, sycamore, horse chestnut, elderberry, gean, wild damson, all flower in profusion as the season progresses. Bees and flies make the most pleasant of sounds in the flowering sycamores on a sunny June morning.

Each and every one of the Professor's many farming forbears, salt of the earth they were, experienced the trials and tribulations of farming. They knew of the back breaking labour, but they could also enjoy the spring snowdrops, daffodils, wild hyacinth, hawthorn blossom, elderberry blossom, the soft fruit, apples and plums, the fresh butter and Dunlop cheese. They survived. They enjoyed the autumn crocus, the mellow fruitfulness and above all, the harvest moon.

Undoubtedly there is a time to work, a time to play; a time to plough, a time to sow; a time to grow, a time to harvest and a time to sleep.

Alexander Thom took part in it all.

I must go down to the sea again,
to the vagrant gypsy life,
To the gull's way and the whale's way,
where the wind's like a whetted knife.
And all I ask is a merry yarn
from a laughing fellow rover
And quiet sleep and a sweet dream
when the long trick's over.

John Masefield

# NOTES

1 Family tree

Archibald Thom, his father, was born at Finnock Bog Farm, Inverkip, on 7th December,1857. Archibald had come to Carradale as a young man when his parents flitted to The Mains about 1870. Archibald was the surviving brother — his older brother John was born in 1848; he died sp 4/11/1891. Archibald had sisters Mary, Maggie, Alexandrina and Janet; and another brother or sister (all dsp).

Archibald's father was Alexander Thom, born 1808, died 19/11/89, farmer at Finnock Bog and Mains of Carradale. That Alexander's father had been Archibald Thom, farmer at Finnock Bog, Inverkip.

Archibald's wife was Mary Thom, born 1820, died 19/6/99.

Alexander Thom's mother, Lily Strang (Mrs Archibald Thom), was born c1862. She married Archibald on 11th March 1892. Lily was the oldest girl in her parents' family of eleven boys and girls. The first born was Walter, followed by William, Lily. James, Martha, Marian, Andrew, Margaret, Robert Winning, John Nairn and Sam. One only of these brothers and sisters died sp, namely William.

Lily's father was William Strang; her mother was Lilias Stevenson.

The father of William Strang, Alexander's grandfather, was James Strang, married to Marian Craig (née Nairn). This William Strang married Lilias Symington.

The parents of Lilias Symington were Walter Symington (1804 – 1837) and Lilias Stevenson (1806 – 1877). Lilias Stevenson's parents were Robert Stevenson of Shutterflat and Margaret Cochrane of Beith; her mother was Jeanie Burns.

Walter Symington's father was William Symington, born 1761;

his mother was Marion Brown.

A cup without handle, once in the possession of the Professor's brother WAS Thom, was a wedding present to the above Margaret Cochrane when she married Robert Stevenson. This cup is evidently not one of the set of twelve presented to the above Lilias née Stevenson by her father (Laird) Robert Stevenson in place of the tocher coo (cow) always given to a farmer's daughter upon her marriage. Beryl has the teapot, sugar basin and two cups and saucers of the set. She also has a ring which belonged to Mrs Robert Stevenson (née Margaret Cochrane). On this is seen the inscription "L.S. from her mother" presented, we think, on her 21st Birthday. The Maclays have one cup of the set.

The above is the record of Sandy's family tree from about 1820 on his father's side and 1761 on his mother's side. He had thirty-seven full cousins and one brother.

Alexander Thom married Jeanie Boyd Kirkwood on 10th August 1917. They had a son Archibald Stevenson born 10th July 1918, a son Alan Watson born 11th July 1923, and a daughter Beryl born 13th November 1926.

2 Replacing the continuous field of integration by a rectangular mesh, net or grid of side a and replacing the derivatives in the differential equation by finite difference equivalents, Thom was able to write a series of finite difference equations instead of the differential equations. He related the value fo at point 0, of the dependant variable f at the four surrounding points 1,2,3, and 4 by the algebraic equation 4fo= f1 + f2 + f3 + f4.

|   |   |   |   |
|---|---|---|---|
|   |   | 2 |   |
|   | 3 | 0 | 1 |
|   |   | 4 |   |
|   |   |   |   |

The boundary for the purpose of this explanation is considered to pass through the contiguous mesh points 1, 2, 3 and 4 on the square. Generally the smaller the mesh length the better is the approximation.

The Method of Squaring begins by assigning guessed values of f to every mesh point in the field. In its elementary form squaring then takes the above equation and applies it to each point in turn, systematically interpolating by means of that equation an improved value for fo at each point, calculated from the most recent values of f standing at the surrounding points.

The elementary form of squaring is slow and is used in only a few specialised problems. The four-square application was greatly speeded up by using a formula for sixteen-squares all at once. Within any 'square' of mesh length a x root 2, the 'diamond' of mesh length a could also be involved. It is in this speeding up that Thom excelled: his publications detail the short cuts.

WALKING IN ALL OF THE SQUARES

# BIBLIOGRAPHY

Atkinson, RJC *Stonehenge* Pelican (1960)
'Megalithic astronomy: a prehistorian's comments' *Journal for the History of Astronomy* 6 42–52 (1975)
*Stonehenge Decoded* Souvenir Press (1966); Fontana (1970)

Beer, Arthur (ed) *Vistas in Astronomy* Volume II Pergamon

Cooke, JA; Few, RW; Morgan, JG & Ruggles, CLN 'Indicated declinations at the Callanish megalithic sites' *Journal for the History of Astronomy* 8 113–33 (1977)

Freeman PR 'Thom's survey of the Avebury ring' *Journal for the History of Astronomy* 8 134–6 (1977)

Heggie, DC 'Megalithic lunar observatories: an astronomer's view' *Antiquity* 46 43–8 (1972)
*Megalithic Science* 174–9 (1981)

Hoyle, F 'Stonehenge: an eclipse predictor' *Nature* 211, 454–6 (1966)
'Speculations on Stonehenge' *Antiquity* 40 272–6 (1966)

Kendall, DG 'Hunting Quanta' in Kendall et al *The Place of Astronomy in the Ancient World* 231–66

Kendall, DG; Piggott, S; King-Hele, DG & Edwards, IES (organisers) and Hodson, FR (editor) *The Place of Astronomy in the Ancient World* a joint symposium of The Royal Society and The British Academy OUP (1974); also published in a paper-bound edition by the Royal Society in its series Philosophical Transactions A 276, no 1257

Mackie, EW 'Archaeological tests in supposed prehistoric astronomical sites in Scotland' in Kendall et al *The Place of Astronomy in the Ancient World* 169–91
*Science and Society in Prehistoric Britain* Paul Elek (1977)

Merritt, RL & Thom, AS 'Le Grand Menhir Brisé *The Archaeological Journal* 137 27–39 (1980)

Morrison LV 'On the analysis of Megalithic lunar sightlines in

Scotland' *Journal for the History of Astronomy* 11 S65-S77 (1980)

Newton RR 'Introduction to some basic astronomical concepts' in Kendall et al *The Place of Astronomy in the Ancient World* 5–20

Patrick, J & Butler CJ 'On the interpretation of the Carnac menhirs and alignments by A and AS Thom' *Ulster Journal of Archaeology* 35 29–44 (1976) (with reply by AT & AST)

Porteous, HL 'Megalithic yard or megalithic myth?' *Journal for the History of Astronomy* 4 22–4 (1974)

Roy, AE; McGrail, N; & Carmichael, R 'A new survey of the Tormore circles' *Transactions of the Glasgow Archaeological Society* 15 59–67 (1963)

Ruggles, C 'Megalithic observatories: a critique' *New Scientist* 577–9 16 September 1976

Thom, A 'A statistical examination of the megalithic sites of Britain' *Journal of the Royal Statistical Society A* 118 275–95 (1955)
'The egg-shaped standing stone rings of Britain' *Archivs Internationales d'Histoire des Sciences* 14 291–303 (1961)
'The geometry of megalithic man' *Mathematical Gazette* 45 83–93 (1961)
'The megalithic unit of length' *Journal of the Royal Statistical Society A* 125 243–51 (1962)
'The larger units of length of megalithic man' *Journal of the Royal Statistical Society A* 127 527–33 (1964)
'Megaliths and mathematics' *Antiquity* 40 121–8 (1966)
*Megalithic Sites in Britain* (1967)
'The metrology and geometry of cup and ring marks' *Systematics* 6 173–89 (1968)
*Megalithic Lunar Observatories* Clarendon Press (1971)

Thom, A & Thom, AS 'The astronomical significance of the large Carnac menhirs' *Journal for the History of Astronomy* 2 147–60 (1971)
'The Carnac alignments' *Journal for the History of Astronomy* 3 11–26 (1972)
'The uses and alignments at Le Menec, Carnac' *Journal for the History of Astronomy* 3 151–64 (1972)
'The Kerlescan cromlechs' *Journal for the History of Astronomy* 4 169–73 (1973)
'A megalithic lunar observatory in Orkney' *Journal for the History of Astronomy* 4 111–23 (1973)

'The Kermario alignments' *Journal for the History of Astronomy* 5 30–47 (1974)

'Further work on the Brogar Lunar Observatory' *Journal for the History of Astronomy* 6 100–114 (1975)

'Avebury (2): the West Kennet Avenue' *Journal for the History of Astronomy* 7 193–7 (1976)

'Megalithic Astronomy' *Journal of Navigation* 30 1–14 (1977)

'A Fourth Lunar Foresight for the Brogar Ring' *Journal for the History of Astronomy* 8 54–55 (1977)

'A reconsideration of the Lunar Sites in Britain' *Journal for the History of Astronomy* 9 170–179 (1978)

*Megalithic remains in Britain and Brittany* Oxford (1978)

'The standing stones in Argyllshire' *Glasgow Archaeological Journal* vi 5–10 (1979)

'A new study of all lunar lines' *Journal for the History of Astronomy; Archaeoastronomy* 2 S78—S94 (1980)

'Astronomical foresights used by Megalithic man' *Journal for the History of Astronomy* 11 S90– S94 (1980)

'Statistical and philosophical arguements for the astronomical significance of standing stones . . . in DC Heggie (ed) Archaeoastronomy in the Old World Cambridge (1982)

'Observations of the Moon in megalithic times' Archaeoastronomy no 5 S57–66 p S57 (1983)

'The two major Megalithic observatories in Scotland' *Journal of the History of Astronomy* 15 S129–S148 (1984)

Thom, Thom and Burl, *Megalithic Rings* BAR Megalithic Rings: Plans and Data for 229 monuments in Britain (1980)
*Stone Rows and Standing Stones Britain Ireland & Brittany* BAR International Series 560 (i) (1990)

Thom, A; Thom, AS & Foord TR 'Avebury(1): A new assessment of the geometry and metrology of the ring' *Journal for the History of Astronomy* 7 183–92 (1976)

Thom, A; Thom, AS & Gorrie, JM 'The two megalithic lunar observatories at Carnac' *Journal for the History of Astronomy* 7 11–26 (1976)

Thom & Thom in ed Heggie (1982) *Archaeoastronomy in the Old World*, CUP) 'Statistical and philosophical arguments for the astronomical significance of standing stones, with a section on the solar calendar' 53–82

Thom, A; Thom, AS & Thom AS 'Stonehenge' *Journal for the History of Astronomy* 5 71–90 (1974)
'Stonehenge as a possible lunar observatory' *Journal for the History of Astronomy* 6 19–30 (1975)
Wood, John Edwin *Sun Moon & Standing Stones* OUP (1978)

# APPENDICES
## ARTICLES

Journalist William Dunbar made an appointment to interview Sandy and Jeanie. The following is the text of his article in the *Scottish Sunday Express*, 7th October, 1962, by which date the Professor had published only eight papers on megalithic sites and related subjects.

ONE SCOT WHOSE NAME WE SHOULD KNOW
by William Dunbar

The lean grey man with the Maigret pipe clenched in his teeth was at his desk when I opened the door of the book-lined hut in the garden. I had come to meet a very eminent but very shy professor.

Professor Alexander Thom, who looks more military than academic, agreed that he was busy. "It's true that I have retired, but we seem to work harder when it's all over."

Unless you are deeply interested in the nuclear age or the megalithic age, you possibly have not heard of Professor Thom. For this Scot whose achievements in the study of the future and the past have won him international renown, has side-stepped publicity all his life.

Yet if ever a man deserved a nation's thanks it is the professor. If only for one thing.

When greater speed was essential to British fighters in the furious air battles of World War II if the Germans were to be defeated, a backroom team led by Alexander Thom helped to find the extra 20 miles an hour.

The rest is history.

A year ago when he retired as Professor of Engineering Science at Oxford University, Professor Thom was awarded an LLD from Glasgow University and then disappeared back into the peaceful rolling farmlands of Ayrshire that he has loved since boyhood.

But solitude, seclusion, rest — what could these mean to a man who had devoted his life to technical progress?

THREE HUTS

I found the answer within the grounds of The Hill - his home set among 80 acres near Dunlop, countryside that Burns knew well: for this man has never lost the joy of working with his hands.

The cottage that the professor and his wife Jeanie built with their own hands in 1922, has been entirely modernised , repaired and freshly painted - by them.

In the sheltered grounds there are three huts. One is his study. Another houses an astonishingly accurate rain gauge driven by electricity, which the professor designed and built himself.

The third is his workshop where he makes intricate instruments to serve him in his three main interests - engineering science, astronomy and the mathematics of the ancients.

The professor has examined meticulously some 500 of the mysterious circles left by prehistoric man up and down Britain.

As a result of his studies he has established that prehistoric man - usually depicted as little above the animal level in intelligence - had in fact an astonishing mathematical knowledge.

He had adopted a scale of linear measurement which resembles our yard, and as this was in universal use it shows that there was communication between isolated areas even then.

The professor hopes to visit every prehistoric circle before his days of camping and tramping are over.

So after a career of 47 years he is not yet finished. As he started as a boy building his own playthings - clocks, canoes, even a glider - on his father's farm, so he goes on seeking new horizons. What is his secret?

" It is the basic belief that engineering is one of the mainsprings of a progressive society," he said.

PROPHETIC

Professor Thom is so convinced that the engineer need only be articulate to become twice as valuable, that before he retired from Oxford he included a compulsory essay paper in his students' final exams.

His own record is imposing. Before he graduated from Glasgow in 1915 he had worked on the final stages of the Canadian Pacific Railway. By the end of World War I he was helping to pioneer aircraft development.

He received his doctorates at Glasgow University in 1926 and 1929, and then lectured at the university right up to the Second World War.

During that time, with a prophetic glance into the future, he introduced an aeronautical department equipped with a small wind tunnel. It was a revolutionary step that was to lead him to his most important work.

He was recruited to Farnborough in the war and put in charge of research into subsonic planes. Working all day and often all night, he and his team carried out top-secret tests.

The vital extra 20 miles-an-hour were found in a massive wind tunnel, parts of which had been designed by Alexander Thom. It is still used today in tests of supersonic air liners.

THE DREAM

Taking the professorial chair at Oxford after the war was the fulfilment of one ambition for this brilliant Scot. To enlarge two-fold the number of engineering students, and the space for them to work, was his next.

When he retired last year with the honoured position of Emeritus Professor and Emeritus Fellow of Brasenose College, the dream was almost complete.

Soon students at Oxford will move into a costly new sky-scraper building equipped for studies of the nuclear age.

The lead he has given his fellow men and the humility he has shown all his life put this quiet professor in the category of great Scotsmen of this century.

HIS BELIEF

Professor Alexander Thom says: " Man is judged on his ability to express himself and to present a coherent report of his works. So the status and present-day importance of engineers can be raised by giving them more training in the use of the English language."

Article in *Glasgow Herald*, 12th December, 1967, by Samuel Hunter. By this date the Professor had published 15 articles and one book on the Geometry and Astronomy of Standing Stones.

WHEN A YARD WAS 33 INCHES MEN WERE GIANTS

Alexander Thom, who is 73, has a cold tub every morning even if he has to break the ice on the top first to slip in.

It keeps him exuberantly fit. He looks faster over any distance than most men half his age by a good yard - a megalithic yard.

In fact, Professor Thom is not just the fastest but the first man in the modern world over the megalithic yard. He discovered the thing.

A megalithic yard measures 2.72 ft - and that may be the only clear, comprehensible sentence you will get out of me this morning.

It was the standard unit of length which megalithic man used to build things. Just what he was building does not seem to be clear yet, any more than it is why he bothered. No matter.

It is how which fascinates Alexander Thom. With theodolite and steel tape he explores the Britain of 4,000 years ago. Megalithic circles, alignments and isolated standing stones have him in thrall.

He has hiked all over the country to survey about 5,000 of them - as I understand it, this is what makes him different from most megalith-maniacs - as engineering sites.

[Only one was difficult to get to - a good 17ft stone near Campbeltown and next to the cottage of Beatle Paul McCartney, who likes his privacy.]

"Being an engineer myself," Alexander Thom says, "I realised I was dealing with other engineers.

"It is remarkable that 1,000 years before the earliest mathematicians of classical Greece, people in these islands not only had a practical knowledge of geometry but could also set out ellipses based on Pythagorean triangles."

Professor Thom has written a book on his findings (Megalithic Sites in Britain) and on Thursday leaves his study - a hillside shack outside Dunlop, Ayrshire - to lecture to the Royal Statistical Society in Glasgow.

Presumably they will know already about nominal diameters, meridians, and, heigh-ho, azimuths.

But the simple, inescapably marvellous thing about the megalithic yard is that it was the same from one end of Britain to the other.

All these years ago somebody stood up and said This is a Yard, and a yard it was.

"Undoubtedly it was universally used, perhaps universally sacred," Alexander Thom says.

He does not think much of the theory that the yard was just dreamed up somewhere and the neighbours borrowed it the way neighbours will.

If the yard had been borrowed all the way, say, from Cornwall to Cape Wrath, its length would have gone in and out like a yo-yo. This did not happen.

In England Professor Thom has worked out the length of the megalithic yard to 2.721ft and to 2.719 in Scotland. He shows that stone sites were set with an accuracy approaching one in 1,000.

If you want to know how, please ask the professor or go and hear him on Thursday.

For what I want to know is how megalithic man passed the time when he wasn't building these stone things to tell the time with, or whatever.

I mean: if he used standardised building methods to stick

30-ton stones in the ground which are still sticking he must have had some other good tricks up his megalithic sleeve.

"Yes there presumably must have been some common culture, or common something," Alexander Thom says cautiously. He thinks it may have covered all Europe.

"Some people have this picture of megalithic sailors sitting in a bar in Marseilles one night and deciding to go to Genoa because the beer is good there and the girls are all dark-eyed," he says. "And, you know, it may have been like that, who can tell?"

Culture

But Professor Thom does not enjoy such speculation. He likes to stick to what he can prove with his theodolite and tape measure.

Still, it is good to think that Europe may have been full of truly great men once who had a sound, stone-built, common marker of culture based on a common 33 inches.

Even Alexander Thom cannot resist it entirely. "There are about 20 of these things just from Kintyre up to Mull," he says.

"You may be sure they didn't put them up for fun."

PROFESSOR Alexander Thom was professor of engineering science at Oxford University from 1945-1961. He spent the war years on aeronautical research at the Royal Aircraft Establishment at Farnborough.

He is a Glasgow graduate and an Hon LLD.

His lecture on Thursday to the Glasgow section of the Royal Statistical Society will be held in the McCance Building of Strathclyde University at 7.30 pm.

Samuel Hunter

Article by Tom Shields in *Glasgow Herald* Saturday, February 22 1975

FROM ACADEMIC OXFORD TO THE MYSTERIES OF
MEGALITHS.
(Tom Shield visits Professor A Thom, the Scottish
engineer who has won considerable fame - and provoked
controversy - with his theories about the astronomical
significance of ancient standing stones.)

Professor Alexander Thom has a quote by Bertrand
Russell on the wall of his study. It says: "To be perfectly
intelligible , one must be inaccurate. To be perfectly accurate,
one must be unintelligible."

Professor Thom will keep this in mind, I hope, when
reading anything in this article about megaliths,
mathematics, solstices, statistics, archaeology and
astronomy. These are all elements of the work which has
brought the professor not a little fame in the sections of
society which take an interest in these things.

In 1961 Alexander Thom became emeritus professor of
engineering science at Oxford University and began to
devote all his time to his work on the geometric and
astronomical significance of ancient standing stones. His
scientific papers ( collected into books in 1967 and 1971), it
could be fairly said, put the cat among the pigeons in the
archaeological world.

He was 67 at the time and officially had retired - except
that people like Professor Thom do not retire; they simply
switch careers late in life. Alexander Thom, son of an Argyll
farmer (transplanted at the age of seven to Ayrshire) was
single-minded in pursuing engineering,, his first career. He
shunned a normal school education in favour of Skerry's
College and the Royal Technical College.

From the Royal Technical College ("They call it
Strathclyde or something now") He went to Glasgow
University. He graduated with distinction in 1915, designed
flying boats for a spell, returned to Glasgow as a lecturer,
and earned his PhD and DSc degrees.

His rise to professor was halted in 1939 when he was

called to Farnborough to do research into high-speed planes. His younger son, who also worked at Farnborough, was killed in a airplane accident in 1945. The same year Alexander Thom became professor of engineering at Oxford.

Parallel with this distinguished career ran his interest in astronomy. He joined the British Astronomical Society in 1912. Records of the West of Scotland branch recently entrusted to his care show he failed to pay his dues in 1914.

The young Thom read a paper by Admiral Somerville, published in 1912, on archaeology and astronomy. The story passes on to 1933 when, on one of his yearly sailing expeditions in the Outer Hebrides the Thom yacht was anchored in Loch Roag and Thom saw the standing stones of Callanish silhouetted against the moon. The seeds of the work on megaliths and lunar observations were sown.

In the 40 years since, Professor Thom has visited about 500 sites initially on his own or with his son, daughter, or grandson. More recently he has had a team of about a dozen helpers.

UNPERTURBED

He applied his skills as engineer, surveyor and scientist to recording the sites. The positions of the stones had previously only been noted in sketches made by archaeologists. Using his detailed recordings he began to piece together facts about the astronomical significance of the positioning of the megaliths.

He was ignored at first by the archaeologists. He was unperturbed, though this cool reception to his work may account for a certain degree of antipathy to archaeologists with a classics background. He says they never seem to be happy unless they're digging and scraping away looking for bits of pottery and carbon.

Thom's tools are different - his theodolite, measuring tape, and such back-up information as a computer print-out of the position of the moon in the period 2000BC to 1300B. He also has a bayonet which he uses to poke for stones underground, the extent of his excavations.

His most recent work in Brittany on sites such as Carnac has been described as one of the greatest single pieces of archaeological research this century - and that from an archaeologist. He has awakened many archaeologists to the need for a scientific and mathematical stiffening of their work.

FARM IN DUNLOP

In so far as astronomers and and megalith experts can be, he is in great popular demand. He has to turn down invitations to lecture. His son Archie, a lecturer in engineering at Glasgow University, and the middle one of three generations of A.Thoms more or less in the same mould, has just returned from an American lecture tour on the subject.

Meanwhile Alexander Thom remains at home revelling in his work. A paper on Stonehenge, his second, which comes out next month should cause something of a stir he says, with a hint of amusement in his voice.

But what of the man himself? I visited him at home on the farm in Dunlop where the family have lived since they moved from Argyll in 1901. Driving up the snow-drop lined drive you see two fine stone-built houses. Professor and Mrs Thom, however, live in the humblest of the three houses they own. It's a small cottage hidden in a clump of trees. They built it themselves (after the Kaiser's war) as a stop-gap home and now are very happy to retire into it.

They lead an almost spartan life. But one area where the professor will not stint is in heat for the solid wooden hut in the garden which serves as his study. He has a wood stove, a paraffin heater, and an electric fire.

Before starting work in the morning, he leaves the hut to heat up while he saws logs.

FIELD WORK

If you didn't know from "Who's Who" that Alexander Thom was born in 1894, it would be very difficult to guess his age. His gaunt figure might have been hewn from one of his standing stones, so impervious does it seem to the years.

His world is one of scientific and mathematical complexity but he is not without humour. His field work has taken him all over Britain, including the most beautiful parts of Orkney, mainland Scotland, and England, yet he says the scenery does not particularly interest him. He spends hours at the megalithic sites yet refuses to be caught up in the natural tendency to picture the daily lives of the men who built them.

He does allow himself to stop and admire the engineering talents of these people and the determination of the squads of workers who moved the tons of rocks on the instructions of the megalithic engineers (as a student his summer job in 1913 was on the construction team pushing through the Canadian Pacific Railway, the conditions of which exercise were not too far removed from the megalith constructions).

I asked him which had given him the most pleasure of his two careers. He said he had to make a living and ended up professor at Oxford. But the work on megalithic sites was all his own and there could be nothing better than that.

What if he hadn't taken up the megalith work? "I would have been dead, I suppose. People who do nothing in retirement die, don't they?"

# APPRECIATIONS

Shortly after Alexander Thom died Clive Ruggles offered to edit a Festschrift in the form of a volume of papers to be written in his memory. The book finally took the form of contributions from about twenty writers, each one a specialist in his own discipline, usually a branch of archaeology. The intention was to present a broad spectrum of opinions on the relevant subjects, not merely one end.

The book is named *Records in Stone*, an appropriate title, because Alexander Thom maintained that the shapes of the rings and the positions of the stones relative to each other and with regard to the horizontal rising and setting points of heavenly bodies were recorded for all time. No writings were left. He often said the stones themselves contained the only evidence available.

I quote here in full the personal appreciation written for *Records in Stone* by the late Professor Hans Motz, along with extractions from other contributions to the same volume written by men who appreciated Alexander Thom's work.

Additional appreciative writings of Herr Fikentscher and Ian Orkney are also given.

The Oxford 2 conference on Archaeoastronomy was held at Merida in Mexco in 1986, from 13th to 17th January. At the very beginning, as part of the introductory welcoming comments, the meeting was dedicated to the memory of Alexander Thom and Travis Hudson. One minute's silence was held.

A Personal Appreciation of Professor Alexander Thom by
Hans Motz (1909-1986)

Professor Thom came to Oxford in 1945 to take up the
Chair of Engineering Science vacated some time earlier by
Sir Richard Southwell. I met him at that time, when I was a
departmental demonstrator who had come to Oxford in an
unusual way. Having been interned as an Austrian National
in 1941 and released in the same year, I was directed to
Oxford by Dr CP Snow, the novelist who was then in charge
of deployment of scientific manpower at the Ministry of
Labour. The Reader in Electrical Engineering had left on war
work and I was to take over the teaching of Electricity in the
Engineering school. It was very small at the time; we had
about 15 undergraduates per year. By the time Professor
Thom retired in 1961 it was a big department and he had
designed the ten-floor building named after him which was
needed to house it.

Southwell had developed numerical methods for the
solution of problems of Mechanics and Elasticity. They are
known as Southwell's Relaxation method. The term is
somewhat misleading, because it involved weeks and
months of tedious work turning the handle of a mechanical
calculator, an occupation which was not exactly relaxing. I
know it because I became a member of the team but was
lucky enough to acquire an assistant, (Dr Laura Klanfer, an
able and patient lady paid by the Admiralty) who helped me
with my research on Radar. I had adapted Southwell's ideas
to the solution of problems of electromagnetism, in
particular microwave problems in Radar research.

Professor Thom, not entirely by chance, was the
independent originator of another method of dealing with
the same class of problems. In solving partial differential
equations according to both methods, values of the function
were calculated at the points of a discrete net. Partial
differential equations approximately valid at these points
were used. Starting from arbitrary values, the errors at every
point were calculated and successively removed. In the case
of the relaxation method this was done by intelligent and
purposeful actions by the operator; in the case of Thom's
method it was achieved by a process which could eventually
be automated. This is why, with the advent of digital
computers, the Thom method was used and is still
employed to this day. Professor Thom may therefore be
regarded as a pioneer of modern computing methods. His

contributions are by no means confined to this field. He did important work in fluid dynamics, and he designed one of the first large wind tunnels for testing high-speed aircraft.

When he came to the department, after an interregnum, I had regrettably already made my decision to leave, largely because I anticipated a certain resentment at Oxford (in the College) for having been planted there by Government intervention in war-time and because I did not want to block a position needed by young people returning from the war. I went to California, but not before making friends with Professor Thom and his family. I met Mrs Thom and Beryl, his daughter, and I was often a guest in their home. Mrs Thom, the kindliest of persons, had an unpretentious charm and directness with a heartfelt warmth; one simply had to love her.

I had some extremely fruitful years at Stanford. But somehow I felt catapulted into the twenty-first century and I was already too old to 'Americanise'. I must have spoken about this when I visited the Thoms at Oxford on the occasion of a half-year mission to Cambridge when I was on leave from Stanford. A year or so later Professor Thom wrote to me to say that the Donald Pollock Readership was vacant, because EB Moullin, the holder, had accepted a chair at Cambridge, and he suggested that I might apply. It was Professor Moullin's teaching which I had taken over during my war-time stay at Oxford. I applied, and to my great joy was elected and returned to Oxford.

My work hardly overlapped with Professor Thom's, but there were points of contact between his fluid dynamics and my electricity. He took a great interest in the 1953 tidal surge which had devastated the East Coast of the country and he had constructed a model of the North Sea which correctly represented important features. He had a theory about the resonance of the wind driving the sea with tidal waves which resembled one which occurred in my work on electronic amplifiers.

At Oxford he built up a loyal and devoted staff; harmonious collaboration was essential in a school of non-specialist general engineering, and he made some excellent appointments. Compared with the present standards he was rather cautious with money: his rule was one of enlightened autocracy. His method of discretely consulting people was, in my opinion, preferable to government by committee voting.

He became the great old man of Brasenose College. He computed corrections to a sun-dial to be applied during different months of the year. They can be found on a plaque on the opposite side of the quadrangle, recessed in a porch, and serve as a permanent memorial. College servants as well as laboratory staff who go back to his time still enquire after him.

I now come to my association with Professor Thom's archaeological field work. I went with him, his son Archibald Stevenson Thom (Archie) and the other camp followers to Stonehenge, Avebury, the Orkneys and Carnac. The ventures left me with some of the best memories of my life and I only regret that I did not come with him more often. I suppose the trouble was that he was so unassuming when he vaguely suggested that I might come that I had hardly noticed the hint.

The parties consisted of the Professor, Archie, Archie's wife Margaret and their son Alasdair Strang, and Beryl Austin, the Professor's daughter. I remember Robert L Merritt, an American benefactor, his son Ethan and his daughter Elizabeth at Stonehenge, and a young Frenchman Jean-Luc Quinio at Carnac; there may have been others.

Professor Thom was a Grand Master of the theodolite. Whoever has seen engineers use it to survey street corners would probably not suspect that, in his hands, it could become a delicate precision instrument capable of measuring seconds of arc. In the department he laid great stress on the art of surveying, always in danger of being supplanted by some new-born engineering subjects. He believed that working carefully with a theodolite is the best introduction to experimental science. I am afraid that on these outings he never gave me a chance of acquiring the gentle art. It is true that I could never have emulated him successfully: I had to be content with taking turn with others in taking down the readings in a carefully-laid-out book.

Surveying was the alpha and omega of his observational art. Theorising came later. On a site, whatever its nature, and even on territory separating points of importance, exact measurement of positions and distances was the order of the day. Exacting measurements were needed to determine the right ascension or declination of stars, the sun or the moon; perhaps the most delicate measurements I remember pertained to events of the lunar cycle as evidenced by the setting or rising moon at spots marked by special features of the landscape at the horizon.

Professor Thom was a tall man with a pleasant somewhat gaunt face, a small moustache and a kindly expression. He kept his manly bearing into old age and there was something about him that commanded respect wherever he went. He had a natural aristocratic gentility; he was a Laird, perhaps, by nature. When we put up somewhere, the landlord would know that he needed to produce the best food or wine. Yet Professor Thom did not give himself any airs, not in the least; he never sent a bottle back; one just knew. His natural authority extended, of course, to his family and it was a pleasure to be with them, to watch them love, tease, spoil and respect him.

I found the surveying at Avebury particularly impressive. It is hard to describe the beauty and charm of the site and I can strongly recommend a pilgrimage. It had been surveyed a long time before by Alexander Keiller, the marmalade king, and his helpers. His researches are recorded in a book written by Dr IF Smith, who had been Keiller's secretary, and published by Oxford University Press (Smith 1965). On the occasion when I was there we were entertained to tea by Dr Smith, by then an old lady, who had settled down in a cottage near the museum. Her book is a most impressive document. Unfortunately the Press kept no copies, so that it is now available in libraries only. I wish to state my disappointment with the practice of publishers to dispose of their stock of important records, thus not showing a responsibility transcending their mere commercial interests.

There were many uncertainties left by the earlier survey which Professor Thom wished to clear up by his own. The Ministry of Works had constructed a little museum in the village and the permanent custodians were very helpful to the professor and his team when we went there. They put a room, which is part of their office, at our disposal for making drawings and carrying out calculations on the spot. Some years later I visited Avebury and was recognised by a custodian who remembered Professor Thom and spoke highly of him.

I was a modest acolyte helping with taking down the professor's readings of the theodolite dials. The site is not altogether easy to survey. Several traverses had to be made, and we went back and forth and round and round until we came back to the initial point of the survey. When the work has been done correctly, the final point must lie near the

WALKING IN ALL OF THE SQUARES

initial point. On that occasion Thom was out by no more than six inches which is extremely good.

The visit to the Brogar Ring in the Orkneys in 1974 started at the professor's home at 'The Hill', a seventeenth or eighteenth century steading near Dunlop in Ayrshire. At that time Archie and his family lived in a large house on the farm and Professor Thom, with his wife, in a wooden building which they had built with their own hands. In the courtyard there was a bathtub filled from a continuously-running private water supply, in which Thom had a dip every morning: this probably explained his long-lasting state of health. In the bungalow, there was the professor's study, equipped with drawing table, pantograph, his files and manuscripts. He had a home-made telescope, with a mirror which he had ground himself in countless hours of patient work. With this he watched the stars and when he found that a tree cut out a portion of the sky he resolutely cut it down.

The journey to the Orkneys was undertaken in Archie's Range Rover. If a person has never ridden this marvel of engineering he or she does not know what comfort of travel can be. I could have written this contribution by hand, no less legible than usual, during such a journey. The beauty of the mountain ranges, the heather and the castles was enhanced by the explanations and anecdotes of the professor. We traversed the whole of Scotland right up to Sutherland and Caithness , to Thurso and finally Scrabster where we crossed on the car ferry to the mainland of Orkney. The Standing Stones Hotel, near the Brogar Ring, offered every comfort one might desire.

I believe that the fierce wind which we experienced is a constant feature of the climate in the Orkneys. Here the wisdom of the aerodynamicist Thom came in useful. He made us lie down flat in the hollows of the ground, in the quiet boundary layer where one could get respite from the elements.

I can not go into the details of the work (see Thom & Thom 'A megalithic lunar observatory in Orkney: the Ring of Brogar and its cairns' JHA 4, 111-113; 1973) but I do want to give an account of a most impressive episode. The Brogar Ring is surrounded by foresights, both in the shape of cairns and in features of the not-too-distant hills such as the Kame of Corrigal, a steep part of which has the same slope as that of the moon at maximum declination at a major standstill.

This had been investigated by the team on previous occasions, but this time many things needed to be checked. In particular the azimuthal angle under which the feature of the Kame of Corrigal appears, when viewed from the circle, had to be measured with great accuracy to identify it with the azimuth expected at a major standstill during a night observation by neolithic man.

The skies were too cloudy for optical observation in daytime and the following strategy was employed. The Range Rover was driven up as high as possible near the Kame. The headlights were then screwed off and carried, together with the car battery, up to a cairn which stands at the site. The Thoms had not examined the site before, but inspection revealed a platform to which large stones had been brought, presumably from a location nearby which could be clearly identified as a quarry for large stones. If this platform could be identified as being of megalithic origin, this would strongly support Thom's hypothesis, that the Brogar Ring had amongst other functions that of a lunar observatory. We were equipped with walkie-talkies and it had been agreed that a car light should be lit in the darkness of the night, when the professor had set the hair-line of the theodolite precisely at the azimuthal setting predicted by the astronomical theory. I was with him when the signal was given and the light spot appeared, exactly on the hair-line. There is, in validating science, always a difference between accurate prediction and comparison with existing data. Witnessing confirmation of a prediction is indeed very impressive.

I shall always regret that I did not take part in any of Professor Thom's expeditions to Carnac prior to 1973. When I joined him there in that year he was already known in Carnac by some city notables. He had booked into a very good hotel where the owner was also the chef. His choice of wines was superb (perhaps this is not too difficult in France) and the quality of the sea food, caught locally, was excellent.

At lunch time the fare was much simpler. We were fed from the back of the Range Rover with beverages prepared by Beryl and also by the Professor himself. To the casual onlooker we must have looked more like a bunch of Stonehenge hippies than a party of respectable archaeologists.

According to Thom's theory, the sites at Le Menec and Kermario served as gigantic computers to carry out interpolations between lunar measurements. The centrepiece of the theory is Er Grah, sometimes known as Le Grand Menhir Brisé, which now lies broken in four pieces near Locmariquer. Its length must have been at least 67 ft and from its cubic content its weight may be estimated to be over 340 tons. The great mystery is how the megalithic engineers managed to transport it and erect it. It might have been observed from various places: Le Moustoir, Kerran, Trevas, Petit Mont, or from Quiberon. The names of places like Kerlescan, Kervilor, and Kermario still ring in my ears.

There were problems connected with the line of site from these places to Er Grah. Professor Thom was ready to assume that runners from observation posts might have carried information to the man busy at the 'computer' because they did not yet have walkie-talkies, despite their advanced skills in engineering. But it was of great interest whether territory, now heavily wooded but which was almost certainly bare in their days, allowed direct sighting. I remember most clambering through the woods, traversing when the terrain was almost impassable, and measuring changes of elevation as we made our arduous way. The professor would issue his usual 'Let's get on with the job' when we showed signs of tiring.

After a good dinner we would reassemble again to work out the results. Formulae of spherical astronomy had to be evaluated in order to relate the repeated sun observations to our measurement net. A certain water tower from which one could observe Er Grah figured prominently as a reference point. For his computations the professor used a gadget (a Curta calculator) looking like a cross between a Tibetan Prayer Wheel and a Turkish Coffee Grinder with a rotating handle. I had brought along a Texas Instruments programmable calculator, but he did not altogether trust it and checked everything.

Professor Thom was regaling us all the time with anecdotes, stories and jokes, sometimes quite bawdy, but none the worse for that. All this was with his inimitable Scots accent, in a matter-of-fact dry manner. He was jolly good company.

Hans Motz

An abridged version of a chapter written by Ronald Morris but not included by Clive Ruggles in the memorial volume for want of space and because of a certain amount of overlap.


Professor Alexander Thom
An Appreciation by Ronald WB Morris 1986

I am a lawyer - accustomed to weighing up the evidence presented by a client and deciding whether a case can be proved. It took nearly twenty years for my old friend Professor Thom to convince me that nearly all his ideas were right. When I first met him at Thalassa, he was already over seventy years of age. Retired from the Chair of Engineering Science at Oxford, he was devoting a great deal of his time to studying and classifying Britain's standing stones and so-called stone circles. I was to find from others that he had no less than four doctorates, two for his work in mathematical engineering and two honorary ones, I rather think for his work in archaeoastronomy. Modestly he never mentioned this to me himself, and indeed I doubt if this is mentioned in any of the archaeoastronomical papers he was to publish in his retirement. He struck me as a man of high intelligence and integrity, with a tremendous drive towards whatever goal he had set himself.

We spoke much about his hypothesis that early man must have used a standard unit of measurement in arranging the stones in these rings. He had already worked out the geometry of many rings, egg-shapes and ellipses. In all cases he showed me how this had been achieved by using a standard unit of measurement (the megalithic yard) and I must confess that at that stage I was far from convinced that he was right.

A keen amateur astronomer nearly all of his life, he showed me his big twelve inch reflector telescope, most of which he had made himself. He told me proudly that he had spent many months grinding and polishing the two mirrors. All his archaeological papers and records were in The Cabin, a big henhouse erected in his garden. He could always find anything he wanted to show me, almost immediately.

Professor Thom had got in touch with me after reading my first paper on prehistoric rock carvings. In some cases 'my' rock art appeared on 'his' standing stones. Classification in these pre-computer days was often a tedious job and the Professor had worked out a system using punched cards. With his help I worked out and began to use a punched card system of my own. The Professor told me how he had first been attracted towards the study of prehistoric standing stones, relating the episode in the yacht *Hadassah* at Callanish in 1933.

Quite early in our acquaintance the Professor discovered that I was taking rubbings of some of the many cup-and-ring and spiral carvings which I had found on sites in Southern Scotland. He invited me to send some of these to him - he wanted to analyse them, thinking that perhaps he might find there evidence of some smaller standard unit of measurement than the megalithic yard which he had found used so extensively in the stone rings. So I sent him a big random sample selection of rubbings. This included rubbings of all the few rare spirals I had recorded.

A week or two later the Professor telephoned and asked me to come over to Dunlop to see him. He had now analysed the rubbings and wanted to go over the results with me. The Professor was almost jubilant. He had found what he thought was clear evidence that a Megalithic Inch existed. It had been used in making those cup-and-ring carvings. This new measurement, he had shown, was exactly one fortieth of his megalithic yard. The new megalithic inch fitted nearly every cup-and-ring rubbing I had sent him. He demonstrated this to me, using in all cases either his new megalithic inch or its half-inch. There were, however, a few of my rubbings of cups-and-rings where he had been unable to obtain a fit. He was inclined to dismiss those as being either 'badly drawn' or 'irregular shapes'. Some of them undoubtedly were. Now I'm something of a "Doubting Thomas", and like to see good solid proof of things before accepting them. Because of these misfits, I still felt very sceptical about his findings.

However, he next went on to show me his analysis of all the spirals whose rubbings I had given him. Using a series of either semi-circles or half-ellipses, drawing these from alternate centres, increased in radius in each case by a series of exact megalithic inches or half-inches, he proved to me beyond doubt that in every single case a standard unit of measurement had been used - his newly-found megalithic inch or its half-inch. There were no exceptions - no 'mistakes' or 'irregularities'. This was how these old spirals had been made. The Professor's findings about spirals went a long way towards making me think that, after all, he might be right - a standard megalithic inch, not just based on some anatomical measurement like a thumb joint, might exist. But I still could not understand, and cannot understand to this day, how such a standard measurement could have been communicated from tribe to tribe from the Northmost part of Scotland to the Southmost part of England.

I had been taking Professor Thom with me on some expeditions to rock art sites, so that he could see these old carvings for himself and make his own measurements. One day we went to a site I had recently discovered on the Gourock Golf Course. There were actually two sites there. The lower site comprised two groups of cup-marks. One of these groups consisted of five cups arranged as a chevron, with what looked like a right-angle in the middle. Professor Thom became quite excited when we examined this. He said the cup-marks in the chevron looked very like a 3-4-5 right-angled triangle in megalithic inches. "I tell you what we'll do" he said. "You've made no rubbing of this site yet. I'll go home and etch out on a piece of perspex a 3-4-5 triangle in megalithic inches. I'll bring it back and we'll see if it fits".

A few days later we went again to the site, this time armed with his sheet of perspex. The Professor had etched out on it his 3-4-5 megalithic inch triangle - three of the five cup-marks on each of the first two sides. He put it over the carving. It fitted exactly. I was stunned! The Professor was delighted. This, he felt, proved his case. Megalithic Man must indeed have used this standard measurement in carving this petroglyph at any rate. I began to feel that the old man must be right. His ideas about the existence of a megalithic inch definitely seemed to "hold water". However, I still felt doubtful, and still do, as to whether a standard unit of measurement was used in the majority of cup-and-ring markings, and in spacing the majority of cup-marks, in the British Isles. I simply have not tried to check this. Others will have to do more research to reach a decision.

I often argued with him about his assertion that the megalithic yard was a standard one, not the measurer's pace length. I pointed out that all his theories about the geometry would have worked equally well on any site, as long as the one man measured out the whole site with his one standard pace length. The Professor, while agreeing that this was so, pointed out that so many of his measurements of these prehistoric rings came out exactly in his megalithic yards, and continued to maintain that this standard was used throughout and kept on publishing his results to prove this. I gradually became more and more sure that the Professor must be right, but I still cling to my idea that a standard pace for any one site would have given the same results.

In 1975 a conference was held in Glasgow so that professional and other archaeologists might hear what the Professor had to say about his revolutionary theories and might question him on them. At that time very few archaeologists and virtually no professionals believed that the Professor was right. In spite of all he had to say, the conference broke up with most of those present politely incredulous. Professor Archie Roy pointed out however that from then on, people would be considering and talking about archaeoastronomy at each site. This soon came to pass.

Five years later another conference was held at Newcastle-upon-Tyne. By now the Professor was too frail to attend and his son Archie put forward a spirited defence for the various hypotheses. It was well attended by archaeologists from all over Britain, some from overseas. At the outset, many present were still strongly sceptical. I had the feeling indeed that most of the professional establishment still regarded Professor Thom's ideas as being on what was called the "lunatic Fringe", and not to be taken seriously.

As the conference went on, some of this feeling began to change. I was startled when Mr Jack Scott rose to give a paper on his work at Temple Wood stone ring complex. Mr Scott, a fair-minded professional archaeologist of note, like many others, hitherto had not believed Thom's findings, despite the Professor's undoubted mathematical qualifications and integrity. Mr Scott had made an accurate plan of what was there; it turned out to be a ring laid out with the standard type of egg-shaped Thom geometry. He was surprised to find that most measurements came out in exact terms of megalithic yards. At what had been the centres of three of the arcs used to complete the egg-shape, he found, at original ground level, small upright stone markers, like large potatoes. These confirmed to him that he had found the right geometry for the main ring. The radii of these three arcs were also in exact megalithic yards. Mr Scott had now shown to his own satisfaction - and perhaps astonishment - that the newly-found measure must have been used in laying out this Bronze Age site. He made no bones about it - illustrating his paper clearly with diagrams.

Unfortunately Mr Scott's paper is not included in the Newcastle Conference volume. A summary of it is, however, included in Thom, Thom & Burl (1980). This independent 'evidence' is very important. It convinced me that Professor Thom was right, that a standard megalithic yard was in use throughout Britain in the times around 2,200 to 1,600 BC.

I was soon to be reminded of other 'independent' evidence. Professor Archie Roy had published a paper 'A new survey of the Tormore circles' (Trans Glasgow. Arch Soc 59-67, 1963). Years before, he had discovered that these circles had been laid out using the megalithic yard as standard measure.

At last, Professor Thom's work is beginning to be recognised and accepted. Like all new ideas, it has taken a long time - nearly 25 years - for this to happen. The world owes a debt of gratitude to this learned engineer for his long perseverance, in the face of so much incredulity and even opposition, in proving his case.

To sum up, as a lawyer, if I were sitting in judgement, my decision would be —

1. Megalithic yard's existence and quite general use: PROVEN.

2. Its universal use in all stone "circles": NOT PROVEN.

3. Megalithic half-inch's existence and almost universal use in Scottish carvings of spirals: PROVEN.

4. Its use in many cases of multiple rings round a cup- and in some cases of cup-mark spacings: PROVEN.

5. Its universal use in carving petroglyphs: NO.

In *Archaeoastronomy* (Vol VIII 1-4), 1985, Merritt wrote:

Although initially Professor Thom's megalithic studies were largely ignored by archaeologists, and were rejected for publication in professional archaeological journals, the geometry, metrology and astronomy proposed in his *Megalithic Sites in Britain* (Oxford, 1967) occasioned the following favourable review by Professor RJC Atkinson in *Antiquity* 42.77 (1968) —

It seldom happens that a single book, by an author who makes no claim to be an archaeologist, compels archaeologists themselves to re-examine their assumptions about a whole section of the past. This one does. If we accept the evidence here presented by Professor Thom (in such detail that the reader can check all the stages of the argument), and if we concur in even a part of his conclusions (which are drawn with the most scrupulous regard for the legitimate limits of inference), we must alter radically our current view of the intellectual calibre of man in Britain in the late third and second millenium BC. Indeed, we must consider the revision of a whole chapter, in the accepted history of science, in which primacy in the development of geometry, mensuration, observational astronomy and the calendar has been ascribed hitherto to the literate civilizations of the Ancient East.'

Anthony Aveni, in his essay in *Records in Stone*, 'The Thom Paradigm in the Americas: The case of the cross-circle designs', introduces his subject immediately with a reference to Alexander Thom's work —

Alexander Thom's work has influenced scholars far beyond the confines of his own homeland. As Baity's (1973) survey of the literature has demonstrated, once the results of his investigations began to appear at regular intervals in the Journal of the History of Astronomy and in his textbooks, investigators all over the world took seriously the possibility that astronomy might have been a motivating factor in the placement and orientation of ancient ceremonial architecture. Nowhere has the impact of the Thom methodology been more deeply felt than in the Americas, where alignment studies have been conducted with varying degrees of success in cultures ranging from the prehistoric period to the Spanish Conquest and from New England and south-west Canada to Peru. Indeed, archaeoastronomy, as astro-archaeology came to be known in the Americas, developed into a fad indulged in by many members of the scholarly set as a leisure weekend pastime in some cases.

. . . Thom raised the engaging question; do the remains of ancient civilisations reflect a knowledge of astronomy by virtue of the way they are laid out in the landscape? . . .

Thom offered us a methodology for seeking the answer to this question. His method has consisted of making precise measurements at the site and expressing the resulting alignments in the framework of an astronomical reference system.

Mr Barry Don, a post-graduate Cambridge student in 1990, in a private communication on the subject of megalithic yards, sent the author the following extract from his thesis on Pythagoras —

Thom's work represents the only fundamental and thorough-going presentation of the possibility that the Pythagorean theorem was known long before the Babylonians learned of it. Before 1960 his work would not have seemed quite so revolutionary. Archaeology was dominated at that time by the theory that the great discoveries originated in the civilisations of Egypt and Mesopotamia and then slowly made their way across Europe to England. It was thought that sites such as Stonehenge were younger than the pyramids of Egypt. Such ideas were put in jeopardy when carbon-dating techniques supplemented by tree ring corrections became widely accepted. The application of those techniques to sites in England indicated they were much older than the civilisations of the Middle East. Thus, Thom's work suggests the rise of an advanced, indigenous geometry in Britain prior to that in Mesopotamia, and that the origins, or an origin of the Pythagorean theorem occurred much earlier in Britain than elsewhere.

A much abridged version of Dr A Burl's chapter in *Records in Stone* —

Without Sharp North . . . Alexander Thom and the great
stone circles of Cumbria.

Discussing how Thom had surveyed and made plans of
19 Cumbrian rings, Aubrey Burl concentrates his attention
on Castlerigg and Long Meg and Her Daughters and on
Thom's analysis of the geometry of his accurate plans and
their possible astronomical alignments.

It was an objective analysis of a stone circle (Castlerigg),
the work of an engineer that revealed potentials for stone
circle studies never before so clearly presented either by
amateur investigators or professional archaeologists."

It is strange how rarely advances in stone circle research
have been made by an archaeologist. .... Most of the
discoveries about the rings have been made by non-
archaeologists, surveyors, engineers, clerics, astronomers,
solicitors, from the seventeenth century onwards, an
illustrious pageant of true amateurs amongst whom
Alexander Thom occupies an honourable place. He stands
with John Aubrey and William Stukeley as a person who
investigated outside the boundaries of archaeological
convention, less concerned with pots and flints than with the
neglected aspects of shape, design and orientation. These
had been disregarded, quite deliberately, by a majority of
archaeologists as illusions fostered by romantics who had no
understanding of the realities of prehistoric existence."

. . . His work has compelled other students to consider
the implications of his data. No longer is it possible to
dismiss a 'circle' as devoid of any clues as to its function
simply because excavation has produced nothing tangible.
Even without artifacts or dating evidence a ring possesses
size, shape and design and it was Thom who made
archaeologists think about such matters.

Burl finishes his discussion —

This may have been what a stone circle was to its people, a
place where axes and gifts were exchanged, a place where
annual gatherings were held, a place to which the bodies of
the dead were brought before burial, but, above all, a place
that was the symbol of the cosmos, the living world made

everlasting in stone, its circle the circle of the skyline, its North point the token of the unchangingness of life, a microcosm of the world in stone, the most sacred of places to its men and women.

Should this interpretation be correct, then it will not have come out of the work of excavators but from the plans and analyses of Alexander Thom and others before him without whose information and stimulus such research would not have begun. Years ago John Aubrey wrote that he had brought the stone circles ' from an utter darkness to a thin Mist' (1665-1693, I:25). The mist remains, a little thinner today, but through it, with the work of Alexander Thom, the sun is rising.

Thaddeus Cowan has studied megalithic ring patterns and in his chapter in *Records in Stone* on Megalithic Compound Ring geometry, refers to Thom as follows —

The volume 'Megalithic Rings' seems to have a certain style of pattern, and we are indebted to Alexander Thom who took the first steps towards understanding the geometric structure of these monuments (Thom 1967). First steps are always the boldest and most difficult, and Thom deserves considerable praise for taking them. But they are necessarily faltering. As with all profound theoretical accomplishments, however, the errors tend to be less than first perceived, and there is a significant element of truth that remains after the obstacles of criticism have been removed. We will offer a suggestion as to what that element of truth might be. We will then use it to point out a rather surprising and heretofore unknown feature of many of the compound rings. . .

Ronald Curtis, who loves old stone arched bridges and who has written the history of Wade Roads in Scotland, used the following wording in his introduction to his chapter in *Records in Stone* about 'The geometry of some megalithic rings.'

> For many years I have been interested in stone, in stone structures of all kinds and particularly in megaliths. This latent spark was kindled on the day I watched Professor Thom on a television programme drawing out his various rings on a Sandy beach. Then I read his first books and was immediately convinced of the truth of his findings. Later I had the benefit of kindly and informative discussions by letter and by meeting him in his home.
>
> As a direct result I started serious surveying at the Callanish sites during a family holiday in Harris, and I have continued to do similar field work, mostly in the Outer Hebrides, with the help of many friends.

In his chapter in *Records in Stone* on 'The metrology of Cup-and-Ring carvings', Alan Davis refers to Thom as follows —

> Among the many contributions of Alexander Thom to the study of megalithic remains, his hypotheses concerning cup-and ring carvings have been surprisingly neglected by other researchers. It is clear however, that Thom himself considered the subject to be of some importance. In his foreword to Morris, Prehistoric Rock Art of Argyll (1977) for example, he writes:
> 'Do they contain a message? Are they the beginning of a form of writing? The fact that these questions can be asked shows the enormous importance which must be attached to their study and interpretation.'
>
> Similar comments may be found in many of Thom's publications. . .

# SELECTED CORRESPONDENCE

Mr Stan Beckensall wrote to the Professor about cup and ring prehistoric carvings in Northumberland and Argyll. The Professor replied (4th November, 1978) —

> There cannot be the slightest doubt about the connection between the stones and cup and ring markings. The geometry is identical in the two . . . If we are ever going to decipher the cup and ring markings every one left should be reported so that they can all be brought together and an attack made on the problem. The ones near backsights for lunar observation or solar observation are of first rate importance at the moment because we suspect that these tell us what the backsight was for. I realise that to get all the information together is an enormous task, perhaps a lifelong work.
>
> Yours sincerely, A Thom

(Author's note. Doug Scott of Tain has been following up the above suggestions. Thom would have been delighted with his findings at Scottish sites.)

In a private communication to the author dated 23rd October, 1990, Jean Hunt of Louisiana wrote:-

> Most of the 'modern' or 'current' books by archaeologists are useless except as catalogues or inventories. Your father's books are almost the only exceptions. He knew how to draw

conclusions and state them scientifically. He never went 'beyond his data' without identifying his further 'speculation' as just that; however, I would substitute the word 'hypothesis', and the substitution suggests the desirability of further testing. Most current archaeologists regard 'speculation' as being the same as 'myth' and don't realize that refusing to 'speculate' means that they are not developing further 'hypotheses'. I still think his hypothesis about the cup-and-ring marks and other art work of the same era found at megalithic sites may well be 'instructions' as to how to use the construction.

Letter from Mrs H Forrest to the author, dated 23rd September, 1988.

Dear Archie,
    I am just writing to thank you for my copy of Records in Stone. I very much appreciate your kindness and it will always remind me of the interesting and amusing times with your father. He never failed to impress me with his memory and stories of "the olden Days" in Dunlop. He was a truly remarkable person and I feel privileged to have known him.

    Many thanks again, Yours, Hattey

In *Records in Stone*, 1988, photographer Chris Jennings wrote a Chapter on Megalithic Landscapes. Sixteen of his excellent photographs embellish that chapter and I now quote him —

Many artists have been impressed by the standing stones and stone rings of the British Isles not only because of their beauty in the landscape but because of the mystery of their role in prehistoric culture.
    In making a photographic survey of megalithic sites my intention was to record and document the stones in their surrounding landscape. As an artist I looked at the stones with particular reference to their siting in the landscape; often the stones appeared to act as a focal point unifying sky, horizon and land.
    An art which is integral to society and incorporates geometric and astronomical science is a major concern for some contemporary artists. My own enthusiasm for the

stones was reinforced by the theories of Professor Thom as proposed in his book Megalithic Sites in Britain (Thom 1967).

Encouraged by Professor Thom, and with the assistance of a Leverhulme Fellowship, I photographed over three hundred sites; these photographs are my 'portraits' of the stones and I hope that they might go some way towards inspiring the preservation of megalithic sites in Britain.

Chris Jennings' photographic work was exhibited along with Professor Thom's plans at several ICA Exhibitions, in London, Edinburgh, Glasgow.

Ed Krupp had written to AT asking about visiting megalithic sites. The following letter to the author explains how they met.

Dear Archie, 8th June, 1990

Meeting your father, Beryl and Trude in Scotland in 1973 was one of the more unexpected and memorable experiences in my life. I had written to your father in the fall of 1972 for advice about visiting megalithic sites. I did not have his address. I only had a copy of Megalithic Lunar Observatories. And so I wrote to A.Thom, Dunlop, Ayrshire, Scotland.

The letter reached him, and he wrote back promptly. He offered good advice and emphasized the importance of Orkney, which was not on my itinerary. He suggested that I change my plan, and I did. Of course, neither of us had any idea we would be travelling to Orkney at the same time.

On Friday, 7th September, we checked in at the Inverness Airport for the flight to Orkney. I was a little sorry to leave, for the Japanese Loch Ness team had just arrived at the airport. I thought monster hunting would be a lot of fun. We were delayed somewhat in the airport, and I overheard a gentleman - who turned out, of course, to be your father - talking about megaliths to two women (Beryl and Trude MacKie). Megaliths were interesting, too, but I really could not interrupt a stranger.

We finally boarded the flight, and as it turned out, Robin and I were seated against the bulkhead, facing the rear of the plane - the only seats like that. Beryl and your father were seated across from us. I still did not know who they were, but every once in a while they talked about megaliths. I was growing more alert. We flew about as far as Wick, and then the crew announced we would have to return to Inverness. Fog was keeping the plane from landing at Kirkwall. The stewardess said it was unseasonable and unusual weather.

So we returned to the Inverness airport and waited some more. During that wait I heard your father refer to "four generations" working at Stonehenge. I knew he could only be talking about the Thoms and so finally got enough courage to introduce myself. I do not remember what I said, but it had something to do with my having heard them talking about Stonehenge, that I was Ed Krupp from Griffith Observatory in Los Angeles, and that we were visiting sites in Britain to see firsthand what Professor Thom was studying. Beryl then said, "Well, this is Professor Thom!" Your father clearly remembered corresponding with me, and they invited us to join them.

Beryl was diplomatically protective, but when she saw all the photo-copies of site plans from your father's books in my field workbook, I think she decided we were serious and okay.

Eventually we reboarded the plane, took the same seats, and flew to Orkney successfully. When we arrived we took some time to get our rental car, while your father, Beryl, and Trude continued to the Standing Stones Hotel. They were certain we should book there, too, and they had set the reservation up with the management by the time we arrived.

We had a lovely dinner together that night - the stones of Stenness out the window, a mural of dancing stones in the dining room, a respectable wine list, and wonderful, funny conversation.

The next day we spent part of the time with your father, Beryl, and Trude at Brogar. Trude came along with us to Skara Brae and Maes Howe.

The whole sequence of events comprised grand and wonderful coincidence, all set into motion by your father's insistence we see Orkney. I have not been back to Orkney

since then and am looking forward to the excursion this
September.

Approaching the solstice, Ed
EC Krupp,
Director,
Griffith Observatory


Ed Krupp's chapter in *Records in Stone* is called 'Light in the Temples'.
The temples are of course the ancient temples in Egypt. It was
Alexander Thom's work that was, indirectly, responsible for the field
research on Egyptian temples reported.

Krupp wrote —


Although I, as many others, was entertained and stimulated
by the astronomical interpretations of Stonehenge and other
monuments detailed by Gerald Hawkins in the 1960s, it was
Alexander Thom's work that prompted me to invest time
and effort into the idea of ancient astronomy. When, by
chance, I discovered the title Megalithic Lunar Observatories
(Thom 1971) in Blackwell's catalogue in 1972, I decided I
should like to know what besides Stonehenge, and perhaps
Callanish, could have some connection with the sky. Shortly
after the book arrived in the mail, the comprehensive,
systematic approach taken by Alexander Thom convinced
me that I should have a first-hand look at these faraway
places with strange sounding names - Long Meg and Her
Daughters, Castle Rigg, Ballochroy, and Kintraw. The
importance of making reliable measurements in the field
was underlined by the care and discipline that marked
Thom's data. However his hypotheses about prehistoric
astronomy, geometry, and measure may be judged, his effort
was serious and substantive. The decades he invested and
the field data he obtained persuaded others and me that
ancient and prehistoric astronomy might yet comprise a
respectable area of study.

The 'symbolic' and the 'mystical' (sightlines) (as distinct
from functional, scientific) were not really the targets of
Thom's research. He was seeking, in prehistory, the
surviving artifacts of a developed practical astronomy. That,
however, is not what lights up in the Egyptian temples. The
astronomy that beamed into an Egyptian sanctuary probably

was 'symbolic, mystical.' But it was Alexander Thom's awesome body of work that sent me down the alignments to find whatever might be lodged within them.

In his chapter in *Records in Stone*, Euan MacKie points out that

" . . . Thom was the first to propose the existence in rugged terrain of very long, potentially accurate alignments. These consisted of a standing stone backsight pointing in some way to a distant natural foresight - a cleft or notch or mountain slope on the horizon. Some of the long ones would have been capable, for example, of defining the solstices to the day.

. . . Thom's first book presented a formidable problem for British Archaeologists.

He goes on to explain —

" . . . The evidence was mainly statistical, and was based on the claimed existence of large numbers of various combinations of standing stones which seemed to have been deliberately arranged to mark specific directions. These turned out to point consistently at places on the horizon where the sun, moon and some bright stars rose and set at significant times in their cycles of movements; often there was a peak or notch at these places."

Our knowledge of the nature of the calendar in use in late Neolithic times derives from the work of Thom."…. "The study of prehistoric calendrical sites by Thom has shown convincingly that a solar calendar was already in use by about 2000 BC in which the year was subdivided quite differently. It was certainly divided into four quarters, and very probably further subdivided into 16 solar 'months' of from 22 to 24 days; it may even perhaps have been split into 32 solar 'weeks' of eleven or twelve days.

In the Editorial of *Archaeoastronomy*, The Journal of the Center for Archaeoastronomy, College Park, Maryland, (Vol VIII, Nos 1-4, 1985)

LeRoy Doggett wrote —

> The World was ready for Thom, and Lord knows, Thom was
> ready . . . We are privileged to have reminiscences of
> Alexander Thom from two people who worked closely with
> him, his son AS Thom and his friend Robert Merritt . . . If
> there is a grand old man of archaeoastronomy, it surely was
> Alexander Thom.

John Carlson, of Maryland University, Editor of the above, published
the article "Some Observations on Alexander Thom" by Bob Merritt
in the Journal. After an introduction, a resumé of which follows,
Merritt gave some 14 letters from Sandy.

> Some years ago, when Professor Alexander Thom delivered
> the 1977 Thomson Lecture to The Institute of Measurement
> and Control at The Royal Institution, London, the proposer
> of the vote of thanks, JFM Scholes, recalled how 33 years
> earlier, during the Second World War, he was an engineering
> graduate faced with a number of difficult problems relating
> to the control of wind tunnels and the making of
> measurements in them, and found himself for a period of
> time under the tutelage of a friendly, wise and stimulating
> engineer at the Royal Aircraft Establishment at Farnborough.
> The proposer remembered the engineer mentioning that
> measurements on ancient stone circles would be rather more
> interesting and challenging.
>     Professor Thom's research, said Mr Scholes,
> demonstrated a range of qualities not often found:
> dedication, meticulous observation, logical thought, much
> common sense and brilliant deductions. Most discoveries of
> significance led for a time to contention. Prof Thom had
> clearly generated a lively discussion in this field, and set the
> statisticians an interesting problem. Perhaps before long they
> would devise a formal proof of the existence of the
> megalithic yard, which Mr Scholes thought philosophically
> seemed so evident.

Merritt continued —

Enlarging on the prior work of Sir Norman Lockyer and HB Somerville, Professor Thom devoted over forty years to accurately surveying hundreds of stone rings, stone rows and single standing stones, seeking to discern megalithic man's reasons for erecting them. These pioneering studies added new dimensions to our understanding and appreciation of the capabilities and achievements of "megalithic man". Working primarily alone at first, and later with his son, Archibald S.Thom ("Archie"), and with other family members and persons who came to constitute his "team", Professor Thom created a new discipline now known as Archaeoastronomy. His large-scale survey drawings of the megalithic rings and alignments, reproduced in British Archaeological Reports (BAR 81, and BAR volume in press [to become BAR 560]), will be of invaluable aid to future researchers, particularly as to sites which have been disturbed by man and nature since he made his surveys.

Merritt went on to say that he was impressed with Professor Thom's dedication, meticulous observation, logical thought, common sense and brilliant deductions. He had in 1968 "cracked the Stone Age Code" at Temple Wood. . . He interested Merritt in joining him in 1969 (and thereafter) by sending a report of his work in 1968. His report (reproduced below) summarized the progression of his studies of megalithic sites in Britain.

Merritt "reviewed correspondence with Professor Thom over the years and selected a few excerpts which give, together with his 1968 report, some flavour of the man and how his mind worked, his doubts as well as his self-confidence, his creativity and interpretive skills, his organizational ability, his intellectual honesty and concern for accuracy, his wide range of interests. These are reproduced following the 1968 report, with dates of writing. They bring him closer to us than do his more formal papers in the Journal for the History of Astronomy and elsewhere, but not as immediate to us as he is in the 1970 BBC *Chronicle* 43 minute colour film "Cracking the Stone Age Code".

Letters to Bob Merritt from A Thom
Report on Work Done in 1968 5th December, 1968 AT wrote —

Since 1938 I have, when opportunity presented, examined and surveyed some 500 Megalithic sites in Britain. As a result I have published 8 scientific papers on this subject. I believe it is true that although I am an engineer I have materially altered the outlook of many archaeologists. In 1967 OUP published my book 'Megalithic Sites in Britain'. Since then I have tended to concentrate on lunar sites. My book showed the existence of these and indicated their connexion with eclipse prediction.

My work in 1968 has been mainly concerned with three objectives.

(1) A complete study of menhirs in Kintyre, many of which are lunar.

(2) An elucidation of the complex site at Temple Wood near Kilmartin, Argyllshire.

(3) An elucidation of the problems presented by the stone rows in Caithness. (Unfortunately it takes twelve hours by car to get there.)

My reason for this concentration of effort is that I believed that all three were connected with Megalithic Man's pre-occupation with lunar observations. My year's work has fully justified my belief. Kintyre shows a remarkable concentration of lunar sites. In the centre of the peninsula I found a new site in a most inacessible position. I had to get help to carry up the equipment to make a full survey. At last I have obtained a complete explanation of the site at Temple Wood. It is a sophisticated double lunar site of remarkable accuracy (±1 arc minute), ie, it records the extreme positions of the setting moon (N & S) and the perturbation is shown both ways. (This 10' perturbation which shows only in the lunar standstill every 18.6 years allows of the eclipse prediction. See my book.)

But I consider my 1968 study of Mid Clyth in Caithness to have led to the greatest advance I have so far made. I have long been puzzled by the accuracy of these sites. I could not see how the builders could have made the extrapolation made necessary by the fact that the maximum lunar declination will mostly occur between two settings.

Eventually I solved the problem by asking how a modern scientist would extrapolate from two nights' observations to the maximum stake position if the thing had to be done graphically. I thereby found that I had a construction resembling the stone rows at Mid Clyth (and elsewhere). These are in fact an elaborate graphical computer. The explanation of all this demands a long article or a book. This is half written but ought not to be completed until I have examined in detail several other sites. A Thom


A Thom to RL Merritt


Reporting of Data, 26th June, 1969.

It is a relief to report that Brackley (Kintyre) is probably not lunar.

It was well that we looked at the Kilmartin and Poltalloch cairns. There seems to be in my earlier notes some confusion between the two peaks of which I thought one might be a foresight.

I should be happier if I could discard that theory (like Brackley). It might avoid difficulties about the relative dates, but if I find something then I must say so.

Kintraw, 26th June, 1969

Yesterday Mr TY Gibson gave me a lift to Kintraw. The weather was bright and clear and he took the big theodolite up to the platform and I connected the col in the Paps with the reference object you and I established. So that's that - it fitted almost exactly with my calculated position. If you think of that Megalithic Man trying to catch the twinkle of light at C (on a sketched notch) you will see that on the platform he could easily miss it. But if he had a lookout at a definite point above he could have 5-10-15-x seconds warning. I imagine this was the use of the "Merritt Stone" on the slope above the platform. (This was a "lookout stone" noticed by Merritt in June 1969. Thom photographed Merritt kneeling by the stone, which was quite low, but clearly upright and man-erected.)

Contemplating Carnac November 1969

Now I ask what the best next move will be. You will see that although I worked a lot in England and Wales the advances have always come from further North, eg 1954 Solstitial sites in Argyllshire; calendar months discovered in Outer Hebrides; Temple Wood for the perfect Lunar site: and Caithness for the stone rows showing the computing method for extrapolation. The Dartmoor "avenues" defeated me. I may be completely wrong but I feel that perhaps the hard scientific stuff is in the North and perhaps the ritualistic in the South. Having failed in Dartmoor I am afraid I may fail in Carnac. . .

Planning the Carnac Surveys 19th March 1970

After writing the other letter I thought that I had given you no real idea of my intentions. I was brought into it by G Daniel and BBC. Daniel told me there were no surveys but this is not quite correct. Burl in Leicester sent me copies of small scale surveys done by the Germans. See Praehistorische Zeitschrift, 32-33, 1941-2. But these have no azimuths and no hill horizons and are very small scale. I should hate to trust them even as surveys. They do however give some idea of the enormous extent of the stones - 3 to 6 thousand. There seem to be 5 or 6 main groups plus other stones scattered over perhaps 20 to 30 square miles.

The survey techniques will be different from that I usually employ. It will be chain surveying, each line theodolite controlled; and so comparatively inexperienced workers will be able to work alone with Archie connecting the lines by theodolite. I'll be plotting as the books come in, and trying to get hill horizons (through the trees!!)

It took me thirty years to break Temple Wood. Can I break this one ? I don't know and I am a little doubtful of the task which is frightening. We need all the help we can get, up to the limit when the party becomes unwieldy. I think I have got workers who will work; and to be any good it will mean a long working day. That is better than a lot of people working indifferently and worrying me by different methods of booking, etc. . . I'll need a chain and a tape for each group, three groups working; Archie on one theodolite, continually supervising. But on some sites the techniques will be different and will involve simultanous use of two theodolites. The third theodolite will be for me. Probably as one site is nearly finished one group will transfer to the next. (Hence the extra car).

Velikovsky and Planetary Orbits 22nd January 1974

I give you some thoughts on Velikovsky. The differential equations of motions which astronomers use to calculate the movement of the planets and satellites are based on Newton's laws of motion. We know that these work, otherwise how did we get to the moon? We know that we can predict the position of a planet far into the future. It is done every year. But since there is no resisting medium, or practically no resisting medium affecting the movements of planets, the equations work either way; ie we can work backwards into the past as well as into the future. The movements of the planets in the past have been calculated and tabulated. These calculations take account of perturbations that are the effect of one planet on another and are very involved, but they are correct and there is no sign of Venus or any other planet wandering about throughout the system. Such an idea is complete nonesense. We know just how the orbits of the planets have changed slightly over the millenium, but there is no sign of anything catastrophic. Another point is that if a planet such as Venus had been wandering about through the system, how did it get back into its nice, almost circular orbit? By any conceivable method this would have taken millions, perhaps hundreds of millions of years. I know about these things because I used to be very interested in the determination of cometary orbits from 3 or 4 observations. I once measured about a dozen positions of a comet myself with a three-inch telescope and deduced the orbit. (See I.17. Interest in Astronomy; comets; Professor Becker).This was a very long and time-consuming job which would not nowadays be attempted at all by hand, but would be put on a computer. The Astronomer Royal said that the orbit I had deduced represented things better than that from the huge observatory in Pulkovo in Russia, so I am not entirely ignorant of computational astronomy. I cannot understand the vogue which Velikovsky has in America. His ideas are simply rubbish. Does he think that all astronomers are fools?

## Encouragement of Independent Check on Thom's Work
## 2nd February 1978

Clive Ruggles, a Cambridge man who is now working in Oxford, has applied to the Science research Council for a grant of £14,000 to measure up the circles in all the important districts in Britain. His idea is quite sound. Our work must be independently checked but I do not see the Science Research Council giving him £14,000 for the two years' work and I do not know of anywhere else he can apply. It is a pity because I believe he is a very good man with a theodolite and I think he read astronomy at Cambridge. He is working at present in the astrophysics department at Oxford. It will be very difficult to find a more suitable man to make an independent check on our work, and it is obviously going to be expensive. I have written a very strong recommendation to the Science Research Council.

## Cup-and-Ring Marks 16th March 1978

I have been looking again at the very good photographs you sent of the stones at Ballymenach and Temple Wood. Cup-and-ring markings intrigue me. We do not know what they are for. I think they are probably a form of writing or a form of communication telling you what the stone is for astronomically when they are on a stone. But, of course, they need not all be astronomical by any means. I do know that the big central menhir in the meadow opposite Temple Wood has a lot of cups and this stone is on two lines; one to the northwest and a line to the southwest. Over a year ago we found a particularly good lunar line at Skipness in Kintyre. The stone, which was small, had fallen, but on a bit of living rock near there were cups, probably telling that this stone was a lunar line also. There are cups also on a large menhir at Manemur in Brittany and this stone is a calendar stone as far as I can see.

And so it goes on, but nobody has cracked the code which I am sure exists somehow. The idea of putting writing in lines up and down or across had probably not occurred to the makers.

Concern for Accuracy 10th July, 1969

Here are copies of some of the work you booked. Two sets were worked at each site and I never needed to go to a third. Except Ballochroy where the theodolite seems to have been improperly levelled at first.

But I never feel really satisfied until I get the same result on a different day or trip because of possible watch error.

Archie is going to Inverness next week. He will then take me to Caithness for 3-4 days. With him I can survey the stone rows faster than with anyone else but there will be a good deal of bayonet prodding, a slow and exhausting job.

Publication Difficulties: Sun's Semidiameter 16th January 1968

I do not know when Pergamon will complete Vol 12 of Vistas in Astronomy. (I think he was referring to Vol 11 Author). So I am sending surface mail my copy of the page proofs of my paper. You will see why I believe that the obliquity was about $23^{0}54'$.

Incidentally, I have found several more lunar sites since this paper was written but expect the usual difficulty in publishing these. I am perhaps even now not quite respectable, especially with archaeologists, and I owe a great deal to Dr Beer (editor of Vistas) for his support. In an allied field (cup-and-ring marks) it is doubtful if I shall be allowed to publish and Beer cannot help me there. I am 74 years old and do not feel like another struggle. The cost of the standing stone investigation was really more than I can afford and of course I had no "grant".

A difficulty is now that the volume of correspondence is becoming too big. A great deal of it is stupid. But I try to write. Cranks galore! It is a pleasure to get real interest and appreciation from people like you. Are you doing any more? If so the following results of a calculation (unchecked) may be of interest. Sun's semi-diameter in 2,000 BC — at Summer solstice 15'51" and at Winter solstice 16'11". I do not know if researchers have used these as modern values. It only occurred to me recently to check up.

Caithness undated 1969

Archie took me to Caithness where three of us (a girl who is doing a "project" on standing stones joined us, fortunately) had a hard three days prodding for the buried alignments. Just as we were leaving the last site we found three fallen menhirs which we had not time to survey (no tape as we were then only expecting to do azimuths). On getting home and working things out, this site works both ways. I had sent the other two across the (shallow) valley to look for traces of a foresight. Just where I predicted, there were the remains of a denuded cairn. So now I must get up to this spot and look back at the 9ft stones, to get the exact azimuth/altitude the other way. By calculation it seems OK.

After asking around I have found a retired cousin (Jim Tindal) who will help me with this and two other sites in Caithness which need more work. I have found what I think is the foresight for one of them on the Ordnance Survey but I must check visibility.

PS The altitude both ways is almost zero allowing the two limbs to be used on the same line.

The fallen items are on a platform at A (on a sketch showing a cross section of the site at Loch of Yarrows) which I did not know about. On all three visits I approached the hilltop from the other side. The distance across the valley is exactly right for the radius of the stone rows. The computer (fan) is naturally in the middle for convenience either way. Let's hope this one is OK.


Reaction to Criticism of the Megalithic Yard
30th September 1969

. . . About Hogg (see III,3 and also IV15, August 8th and 14th, 1969), Clarendon Press does not think it advisable to reply. It is as you say peculiar that he accepts the astronomy but discards the geometry. The latter is, to my way of thinking, much more rigidly established than the former, on which indeed it is very difficult to put a figure. Hogg ignores completely (1) the evidence of the fit of the geometry, (2) the manner in which the factor 10 appears at Avebury, (3) the evidence of the perimeters, and (4) the adjustments made in the diameter to bring the perimeters nearer to multiples of the megalithic yard.

I spent many years gathering as long a list of diameters as possible in order to get a reliable figure of use in Broadbent's formulae (I ignored nothing). And then Hogg goes into reverse and divides the range into parts. If he goes far enough, he will end up with groups of two diameters in each — and get anything he wants. This is a misuse of the material and of statistical analysis. Surely it was to avoid this sort of thing that Broadbent prepared his paper. Broadbent (in correspondence) would not allow any division of the material, e.g., I wanted to take the Scottish circles and say that they gave 2.72ft/my and then test this on the English circles because then I maintained I had a priori evidence for 2.72, and so could use the straight-forward analysis on English circles of his first paper. But Broadbent would have none of it and was not satisfied until I had enough diameters to use in his second method (2nd paper) which (logically) needs no a priori evidence.

I can assure you that years of work went into the thing. Why does Hogg not attack my paper on The Megalithic Unit of Length in J Roy Stat Soc? Queer that this paper was accepted by a society with a very strict refereeing system on papers. I have written to you about this matter but I have not written anyone else. . . "

Merritt's heart ailment and letter to AT

From 1969 onwards RL Merritt helped in many ways to forward Sandy's work, mainly because he felt, along with other thinking people, that Velikovsky's statements were wrong. Here in Sandy's work was evidence that no sudden changes had occurred in the solar system in recent millennia.

While on the Shetland expedition in 1978 I (the author) had noticed that Bob had not been as energetic as usual. The following letter to Sandy from Cleveland, Ohio dated 19th February 1981 explains why.

Dear Sandy, Since my heart attack I have been contemplating my life, and am writing to say what a magnificent dimension knowing you and working with you these past twelve years have added to it. I wish to thank you for this rare opportunity. Sincerely, Bob

A Thank You Note to RL Merritt 25th February 1981.

Dear Bob, Your letter was very much appreciated and I shall try to reply by hand.

I do however remember that it was from you that I received my first grant and so was able to work in Carnac.

You seemed always to believe in my work and this was a great support. Yours sincerely, Sandy (A Thom)

Margaret Ponting (now Curtis) lives a mile from Callanish Stones. She contributed to *Records in Stone* by writing about Megalithic Callanish and started off by quoting a long letter from Alexander Thom dated 21st March 1982.

The letter gave in detail his experience on that evening in 1933 when he navigated into the anchorage beside the Callanish Stones. Margaret wrote —

"... Although I was intrigued by the stones, I could find little about them in print. Thus I was unaware of Professor Thom's extensive work until a copy of Megalithic Sites in Britain (Thom 1967) was given to me as a birthday present soon after moving to live permanently at Callanish. Only then did I realise what a wealth of information had already been gleaned from megalithic remains, and my eyes were opened to further possibilities of research.

Initial approaches from amateurs are not always received kindly, but Professor Thom always replied to my letters promptly and courteously, fully answering queries and frequently adding personal touches which made his letters a joy to read."

Dr Graham Ritchie introduces his chapter, The Ring of Brodgar, Orkney in *Records in Stone* with this paragraph —

In a small hotel in Kintyre in 1968, the writer was introduced to a gentleman described by his host as 'a Professor who was interested in old stones'. Alexander Thom's kindness on that occasion in explaining his researches at Ballochroy and later in sending copies of many papers on the layout and the astronomical significance of standing stones and stone circles is part of the impetus of this note. We met later on several occasions in hotels near the Ring of Brodgar, Orkney, in the course of his survey of the circle, and a phrase used by Thom at Brodgar is the second trigger for this tribute. It reads in published form: 'We know however from the survey made by Thomas in 1849 that since then some of the stones have been re-erected. This unfortunate form of vandalism makes it difficult to be certain about the exact diameter.' (Thom & Thom JHA 4, 1973:121-2)

In his chapter in *Records in Stone*, The Stone Alignments of Argyll and Mull, Clive Ruggles notes that —

Alexander Thom was not the first to suggest that certain prehistoric stone structures might have been aligned upon the rising and setting positions of the sun, moon or stars. He was, however, the first to back up his conclusions with statistical evidence taken from many sites taken together - the product of extensive and high-quality fieldwork.

The value of what we term a 'statistical' approach is easy to perceive. Any individual alignment of apparent astronomical significance could have arisen through factors quite unrelated to astronomy. There needs to be some attempt to demonstrate the intentionality of putative astronomical alignments.

One way is through the analysis of a large quantity of data, whereby it can be shown that certain astronomical alignments are significantly more common than would have been expected by chance.

There are nonetheless dangers and drawbacks in applying a statistical approach to the study of alignments at archaeological sites. In this paper we attempt, through the example of a group of sites which has become of increasing interest to the author over some years, to illustrate some of the questions raised by applying statistical methods to a particular set of archaeoastronomical data. . .

Ruggles finishes by writing —

Alexander Thom, by opening up 'megalithic astronomy' as a field of enquiry in the 1950s and by his strong influence on the gradual development of world archaeoastronomy, has opened up the interdisciplinary arena for a fascinating exchange of views across the 'two cultures' which could have methodological consequences far beyond the mere study of megalithic remains. The reassessment of Thom's statistical evidence in megalithic astronomy has brought these issues to the attention of the present author, and has gradually helped him clarify some of his own ideas. Through examples such as the group of sites described (above) he hopes to cast a little light not only upon astronomical practice in prehistoric Britain but also upon some very much wider methodological questions.

Letter from Jack G Scott to the author

Woodrow Bank,
Creebridge 14th August, 1988
Dear Archie,

It was most kind of you to send offprints of chapters 1,3 and 5 of Records in Stone. I am delighted to have them as a memorial of one of the foremost scientists of the century, and of a man of great charm. The first time I met him was in Kintyre when I was excavating the chambered cairn at Ardnacross near Peninver. He had been working in Arran and had crossed to Kintyre to check his observations. Graham Ritchie had directed him to our site. His first words to me were. "I am Alexander Thom. I expect that you think I am mad!" Utterly disarming. I have never forgotten this.

I have read with great enjoyment your personal note on your father (in Archaeoastronomy Vol. VIII, 1985). You have succeeded in giving a vivid picture of him and I would say two things: firstly I do not think it could have been better done, and secondly, your father is clearly worthy of all that you say about him. I find it curious that I have the same birthday as your father. I certainly have no feeling for figures; as early as the lower Vth I had myself transferred to the C stream for maths, and did just enough to get myself through School Certificate and Matric after which I happily parted with the subject!

What must be said is that your father and yourself have

given to archaeology a new dimension, which archaeologists themselves — even the numerate ones! — would never have done. You have permanently changed the way in which we regard people of these far off times, and this can not be a bad thing.

I am fascinated to hear of your forthcoming paper on the gold lozenge from Bush barrow, and I am most intrigued by your idea that it may be a 16 month calendar. I take Antiquity and I shall look forward to reading what you have to say.

All good wishes, Yours, Jack.

Rolf M Sinclair had written requesting offprints and a spare copy of *Vistas in Astronomy* in 1966. He wrote again on September 21, 1970 from the National Science Foundation, Washington, DC.

Dear Professor Thom,
I am enclosing a small etching, which I hope you will accept as a token of my admiration for your work in archaeoastronomy. This etching has the following history:

I became interested in the English megalithic sites through your various writings. A year at Oxford (on leave from Princeton University) gave me a chance to visit several, and I corresponded several times with you about your work.

I conveyed some of your interest to a friend of mine - an artist, Mr Arturo Bassols, of Milton, Delaware, USA. Mr Bassols is perhaps best known for his sculptures in metal, but also works in several other media. Long after our conversations, he suddenly conceived of several etchings in which he expressed the emotional and artistic content of the stone circles in terms of the original use you had reconstructed. The enclosed "Solstice" is one of these: this particular copy is number 16 (of 30 printed). I have not framed it, because that is so much a matter of individual taste.

I hope that this print and its history interest you. It owes its existence to your studies.

Sincerely yours, Rolf M Sinclair

(The author met Rolf Sinclair at the international "Oxford 3" Conference held in St Andrews in 1990. He is still actively interested in the subject. The Professor had framed the etching and hung it in Thalassa).


Appraisals of AT's survey work and his ensuing hypotheses would be incomplete without including Dr Ian Orkney's doggerel written in 1983 when, after Ian's careful excavations at Temple Wood with archaeologist Jack Scott, there occurred "the establishment's brainless inability to take in the significance of the stone marker pegs which Jack and I found at the arc centres of the Temple Wood egg." Ian wrote, "Prof Thom deserves this doggerel and so do today's archaeologists." The author includes the verses with tongue in cheek — he has many good friends who are archaeologists of renown.


> "GIVE A GOON A MEG-INCH . . .
> AND HE'LL TAKE A MEG-YARD?"
>     "Doggerel in praise of the genius of Thom, and on the shameful inadequacy of the Archaeological Establishment. . .
>         to understand
>         to follow
>         to check
>         to expand
>         to achieve
>         or even to ask."
>     by Dr JC Orkney.
>     Archaeologists now for twenty-five years,
>     Have burbled contented in each other's ears:
>     "Thom's Rubbish, Thom's Rubbish. 'Tis writ in the runes."
>
>     What a dim-witted bunch of incestuous goons !
>     In the year fifty-five, Prof Thom did proclaim
>     Quite enough to have got all these goons at his game.
>     "'Tis Rubbish, 'Tis Rubbish. I don't understand."
>     The goons' only cry to be heard in the land.
>     Archaeologists find that this technology
>     Is light-years beyond them. It always will be.

It circles the square in triangular Yard,
And it's not just as plain as the songs of the bard.
But they won't take the word of the brainier bod
To whom it is easy to fathom the Rod.
"Stupidity's nice, and laziness free,
So let's go on barking up every wrong tree,"
So the Megalith Inch and the Megalith Yard,
To these men of dim wit, are too terribly hard,
So they don't stand a chance with the difficult bit,
Where the sun and the moon in that hill-notch did sit.
That circle's not true, like their face, it's all egg,
Conclusively proved since we found their stone peg.
"Don't you dare to confuse us! Our mind is made up!
Technology's trying to sell us a pup!"
"Contemptible, ain't it." says Dylan to me,
"What the hell have they done with their integrity ?"
"They can't understand it because they're too thick."
"Why won't the goons ask us ? This isn't a trick !"
Just one wise man had the wit to ask,
Invited me to join his task.
No egg on his face, just one on the ground,
And elliptical spirals there to be found.
So spake the wise Jack: "Come on now there, Ian,
You know that this egg should be Pythagorean !"
But it wasn't, it isn't, yet down there instead,
We found the stone pegs of those boys so long dead.
We found three neat spirals through which series ran,
With the Integer Inch of Megalith man.
Elliptical quadrants! By Pythagoras!
That'll give the profession a kick up the ass!
Thirteen years now, I've checked it, as it ought to be,
With barrow and pickaxe and trowel and knee.
They've no reason at all to reject this good work,
It's just far beyond them, so they'd rather shirk.
They won't take the word of who can understand,
It's smarter to sneer with their heads in the sand.
They don't even see what contempt that it brings,
Or the data they wreck when they just dig for things.
Archaeologists of Britain, your thickness we see,

In units of years, like the rings of a tree.
For the twenty-eight years of its good healthy growth,
You've stuck and hung on like a dozey old sloth.
So the tree is as thick as a roof-beam need be.
On your head may it fall, like our technology,
So it lets in the light as you see and expire -
You deserve all the shame and contempt you acquire.
Stratified are you all, twenty-eight layers down
In the mire heaped on you by this Prof of renown.
He's a wily old bird, a genius, by me,
You're out-gunned and out-classed, as all goons
                                          ought to be!

JCO February 1983


Lloyd Williams, a Rhodes Scholar Australian Post Graduate research student, wrote the following letter to the author in 1989—


Dear Archie,
    Your father was a fine man and had a great life. Certainly I'll always remember him with deep affection and respect. He pointed me in a most interesting and satisfying career direction when I felt my applied mathematical ability was inadequate for the relaxation studies which were the main thrust of engineering research at Oxford at the time. So Prof took me down to the RAE, and I was launched into the field of engineering ceramics. The group I left behind me in CSIRO is now the spearhead of advanced engineering material research in Australia, and is seen as very important in adding value to extracts from Australian minerals. Another feather in your father's cap!

Thanks again for your kindness in writing. L

# OBITUARIES

Obituary in *Antiquity*, July, 1986

Alexander Thom died at the age of 91 in November last year. We asked Dr Aubrey Burl to write a short piece for us in his memory, which he says he has been very happy to do.

Alexander Thom, who died at the age of 91 last November, was a remarkable and important innovator in British megalithic studies. He was also a polymath of considerable ability, reading German fluently, an expert woodworker, a first-class seaman, and a Scot who could recite the whole of 'Tam o' Shanter' by heart.

Long before he developed an interest in archaeological remains he had a career to satisfy most men of ability. In 1913, when only 19 years old he was assisting in the construction of the Canadian Pacific Railway. Later, as a draughtsman with De Haviland Aircraft he designed not only flying boats but also a high-speed wind tunnel for testing early Spitfires, a tunnel used every day between 1942 and 1945 and which never broke down. In 1945 he was elected Professor of Engineering Science and Fellow of Brasenose College, Oxford, a post which he held until his retirement in 1961.

It was in August, 1933, while sailing off the Outer Hebrides, that he anchored at Loch Roag in Lewis and sighted the stone circle of Callanish. This was the time when he decided to collect more information about as many megalithic sites as possible and from then on he made field surveys as far apart as the Orkneys and Brittany. Only Shetland and Ireland eluded him. He planned over 400 stone circles and rows including the daunting lines at Carnac where, between 1970 and 1974, over 2,000 stones were plotted in the gorse and woods. It is pleasing to record that it was the editor of *Antiquity* who invited him to undertake this task.

His plans of all these sites were of a very high standard and their quality and quantity alone would ensure Thom a respected place in megalithic studies. His influence, however, was greater than this. His archaeological publications from 1954 to 1984 show his developing conviction that prehistoric people had used a standardized measuring stick of 0.83m in length, his Megalithic Yard, had laid out non-circular stone rings by the use of right-angle triangles, and had built very precise lunar alignments into many of their stone rows. Had these ideas been professed in popular books they would have been derided but Thom was not a popularizer. He preferred to present his theories through tables, statistics and diagrams, all of them lucidly explained for anyone to analyse.

Inevitably, the publication of his first book, Megalithic Sites in Britain (1967) caused controversy, proposing as it did a model of early prehistoric Britain quite different from that of conventional archaeology. His two later books of 1971 and 1978 revealed his increasing certainty of prehistoric man's scientific curiosity.

His ideas remain contentious, perhaps always will, because the fragmentary nature of archaeological material means that too much is missing for the past ever to be completely reconstructed. It is hardly important. Thom's achievement lies in the stimulus he gave to megalithic research. None of us, believer or sceptic, can ignore the possibility of units of measurement, whether national or local, of the deliberate design of non-circular rings , or of astronomical alignments, scientific or symbolic or both, being elements in the construction of stone circles and rows. Before Thom, such matters were considered, if at all, as the playing fields of the lunatic fringe. After Thom, they have become respectable facets of our studies even though their precise nature remains debatable.

Alexander Thom was a modest, unaggressive man and in many ways a great man. He was a friend and a scholar never reluctant to share his data with anyone interested. Whether some of his conclusions were right or wrong his influence has been strong. As Richard Atkinson wrote in another context, 'Shots in the dark may not always be accurate: but at least they serve to wake sleepers from their beds'. Thom's work certainly did that.

A Burl

Obituary by Dr Charles Oakley

In January, 1986, The Grand Old Man of The Faculty, Dr Charles A Oakley was asked by William Mackie, Lecturer in Mechanical Engineering at Glasgow University, to write a Personal Note about AT for the Glasgow University Engineering Society. The note was never published. It is now given here. Charles is probably the only remaining 1939 Glasgow University colleague of Sandy Thom. Oakley graduated BSc in Naval Architecture in 1923.

I first met Sandy Thom in 1921 shortly after he had been appointed lecturer in Civil Engineering. I was a student in Naval Architecture and was to have a friendship with him for about 50 years. I found him a highly intelligent man, enthusiastic and imaginative in everything he put his hand to, as well as being vigorous and persistent.

My first discussions with him were on an issue about which we did not see eye to eye. This was over the period of study being extended from three to four sessions and the duration of each session being raised from two to three terms. I was a member of the Students' Representative Council and was a strong supporter of 'the sandwich system'.

I was a six-year apprentice at John Brown's, spending six months at the University each year and six months at the ship-yard. The Faculty of Engineering was coming into being (it was still part of the Faculty of Science), and we both thought that in itself a very good thing; but I was much keener on students getting 'practical' experience in the works. Incidentally, he had plenty of that himself, having spent a summer (1913) on railway construction in Canada and another summer (1914) on building construction in Glasgow. Of course he and his fellow supporters won on this particular issue and the Old Regulations were changed, specifying four sessions each of two terms.

In 1931 I got to know Sandy Thom better when I returned to Glasgow University as a lecturer (in Industrial

Psychology) and I recall several lively and often amusing debates. That was a long time ago, however, and I remember giving him keen support on some matter but cannot recall what it was! No doubt a search of the Faculty minutes would give a clue, but these few years before the outbreak of the second world war now have an air of unreality about them and can be left among the forgotten things of yesteryear.

In 1939 the University had advised some six of us that we were to be seconded to the Civil Service should prospects of war become serious. Both Sandy and I found ourselves in the Air Ministry (Ministry of Aircraft Production). We met once or twice at Oxford during the six years that followed, and it was only then that I realised that he had, in fact, not been one of these six, but had volunteered some months earlier and had been appointed Senior Scientific Officer at the Royal Aircraft Establishment, Farnborough. There he had soon gained a considerable reputation and was advanced to be a Principal Scientific Officer (covering, in his own words, a very wide ground). After the war he went to Oxford University and it was there that we did some reminiscing. He now held that highly prestigious appointment, the Chair of Engineering Science at Oxford University. Under his guidance, teaching to undergraduates and postgraduate research both thrived. Soon the Engineering Laboratory was too small for the ever-increasing numbers of students. As the years passed, requirements became more and more obvious. Architects were called in and action taken. The Laboratory extension was finally named, in his horfour, the Thom Building.

On retiring he switched back to one of the major interests of his younger years, astronomy. Since 1912, after reading about Callanish he had been fascinated by the circles, rings and rows of standing stones erected some thousands of years ago in various parts of the British Isles and in some other parts of Europe. They were clearly related to phases of the Sun and Moon, so incidentally showing that the people of these times were numerate and basically as intelligent and shrewd as we are today. One of the finest of these sites is at Callanish, near Stornoway, and he spent a fair amount of time there making observations and calculations based on them. Much public interest was aroused by his theories and he was sometimes embarrassed by newspaper publicity which followed. I have business connections in the Harris

Tweed Industry and more than once we chanced to meet in
the same hotel. I accompanied him on one of his expeditions
to Callanish and, while my mathematics was too rusty to
follow his equations, I was left with the impression that his
name will be remembered for his theories in this branch of
astronomy — and that goes right back to his first
appointment to Glasgow University and to a comment made
by the Professor of Astronomy who spoke 70 years ago
about the involved calculations he was carrying out and to
his "finding relaxation in our private observatory".

Charles Oakley

Obituary and an Appreciation in *The Ley Hunter* (issue 100) by John
Michell.

The writer explained how the Professor was led into a second
career, which removed him far from the peaceful world of academic
engineering into the wild country of archaeology.

In 1967 when Thom's first book was published, Richard
Atkinson described it as a "well-constructed parcel bomb"
below the foundations of orthodox archaeology. The
professors of the time thought that they had discredited
Lockyer's theories of prehistoric astronomy, which he
promoted at the beginning of this century while Alfred
Watkins was totally ignored. Thom's book reawakened the
spirits of both these old heresiarchs. . .

It was this unexpected, impeccably academic gift of ancient
alignments which really put ley-hunting in business again. . .
As to the megalithic yard, the case for it was based in the
first place on statistics, and so also is the case which has
been made against it. Thom's reply to his critics was to
deplore the quibbling approach of modern statisticians,
who, he said, are no longer prepared to listen to a reasoned
argument. . .
    Every original work, such as Lockyer's or Thom's, by
which the author sheds new light over a wide field, is bound
to attract detailed criticisms, as those mentioned above. The
component parts of Thom's work will be argued about for
years.
    But nothing can diminish the importance of what he has

done, which is to establish the reality of prehistoric science and to raise the standard of debate on megalithic monuments to an altogether higher level. . .

He felt that the monuments of ancient science had a valuable lesson in them for the present time. He greatly admired the stone circle builders, and his idea of them to some extent reflected his own personality. He was precise and economical in his Scottish manner, and he was also a true Scot by virtue of his courage, independence, sincerity, intellect, deep imagination and warm, kindly nature. In his latter years many people wrote to him, often about esoteric subjects which he had scarcely heard of, but they all received courteous replies; and so did his academic opponents. Thus he helped bring about the much happier atmosphere which exists today in the world of megalithomania. Fellow-sufferers from that noble obsession, from whatever point of view they regard our common megalithic properties, all have good reasons for remembering Alexander Thom with gratitude and affection. . .

John Michell

Obituary for the Royal Astronomical Society by Dr DC Heggie. There follows a précis —

Not surprisingly, in view of the quality of his data, Thom's findings were received with much interest by statisticians. His first comprehensive paper on megalithic science was published in a statistical journal. In some instances no satisfactory statistical methods existed for testing the hypotheses he was advancing, and this led to significant statistical developments by such researchers as SR Broadbent, DG Kendall, PR Freeman, CS Wallace, and JD Patrick. Comparable interest was shown by astronomers in Thom's work. . .

It was among archaeologists (or, rather, prehistorians) that the response could often be called hostile, and there were several reasons for this. First, some of Thom's papers are hard going even for someone with a mathematical mind. Second, there was perhaps the reluctance to admit the possible importance of the work of a non-archaeologist. Third, many failed to distinguish the nature of Thom's contribution from that of archaeology's lunatic fringe.

Fourth, megaliths are a minority interest even among archaeologists. And fifth, Thom's findings seemed inconsistent with the views of most archaeologists. . .

A number of archaeologists, recognising the somewhat flimsy and certainly shifting foundation on which their standard model was built, did put in the necessary effort to grasp Thom's methods and results. . .

Despite the indifference of many archaeologists, Thom's work stimulated a great deal of research, in the way of critical reanalysis, new statistical methods, excavations, and large field projects. Several large conferences were held, eg at Glasgow (1975), Newcastle (1980), and Oxford (1981), which were largely based on Thom's research or on work which it inspired. It is no exaggeration to say that Thom's work was much the most important single reason for this upsurge of serious interest in these aspects of prehistoric studies, not only in Great Britain but perhaps also in Europe and even in America. This interest was by no means restricted to the academic community. Thom's findings were featured in a number of television programmes, which popularised his results in the best sense for a very wide audience. Many popular magazine articles and books spread his ideas to a wide readership.

Thom's own lectures drew large audiences, and he was much in demand. His talks were liberally illustrated with plans of prehistoric sites and statistical diagrams, but he would sometimes start on the assumption that everyone in the audience was thoroughly familiar with his terminology, and sometimes even his latest preprints, which must have been baffling to some. He spoke slowly and rather quietly, in an accent which betrayed nothing of the 27 years spent south of the border.

In company he was quiet and modest, often preferring a pipe rather than lively conversation. If the criticism which often came his way did not leave him untouched, then neither did it significantly deflect him from what he saw as the right way to conduct his prehistoric studies. This imperturbable side of his intellect was partnered with a tough and wiry constitution. . .

Unfortunately Thom's excellent health faltered in his last years. His failing eyesight was significantly restored by surgery, but latterly he was considerably inconvenienced by the effects of a fractured hip. . .

How can such an unorthodox scientific career as that of

Professor Thom be summed up? Only a few other Fellows of this Society can have been known to such a wide audience, and still fewer can have established a reputation in what was essentially, and in the best sense, an amateur interest. And however the controversy over his contribution is finally settled, it will not be forgotten that he was a scholar of remarkable breadth and energy, and a genuine seeker after truth.

DC Heggie

Obituary in *Journal for History of Astronomy*, 1986 by RJC Atkinson.

It is not often that a man can be said to have created, single-handed, a whole new academic discipline. Such a one was Professor Alexander Thom, who died on 7 November 1985, aged 91. Had it not been for his relentless pursuit, over more than forty years, of megalithic sites in Britain and Brittany it is doubtful whether the subject of archaeoastronomy would have existed at all. There would have been no Archaeoastronomy supplement for JHA, and probably no Archaeoastronomy Bulletin from the University of Maryland, because his influence in the Americas has been at least as great as in Britain and Europe. From small and disregarded beginnings his work grew in stature and acceptance to being published by the Oxford University Press in three successive volumes, to forming one of the focal points of a joint symposium of the Royal Society and the British Academy, and ultimately to becoming part of the canon of the early history of science. Few men could have achieved such recognition in their own life-time; and fewer still as a by-product of a distinguished professional career in a different field.

Thom was born on 26th March 1894, and from 1913 to 1921 worked for various engineering and aeronautical firms, taking his BSc in the University of Glasgow meanwhile in 1915. In 1921 he was appointed to a Lectureship in Engineering there: he gained his PhD in 1926 and was awarded a DSc at the early age of 35. His expertise as a surveyor was betokened by the publication in 1935 of his Standard tables and formulae for setting out road spirals.

Shortly before the outbreak of war in 1939 he began his astonishing series of precise surveys of megalithic rings and alignments, initially in western Scotland. With many of these he became familiar on sailing voyages, a recreation which he continued until late in his long life. During the war he worked on aeronautical research at the Royal Aircraft Establishment, Farnborough: and in 1945 he was appointed to the Chair of Engineering Science at Oxford, where he remained until his retirement in 1961. Thereafter he devoted his time almost exclusively to megalithic enquiries, and was active as a surveyor and leader in the field into the ninth decade of his life, with an energy and a command of research strategy which all will envy but few, if any, can hope to emulate. In 1973 I took part in his survey of Stonehenge, and found it hard to keep up with him though he was 26 years my senior.

His first publication on Megalithic astronomy, mensuration and geometry appeared in 1954 and was succeeded by many others, the last of which appeared in JHA in 1984. It was not until 1966, however, that his work came to the notice of archaeologists in general, through an article presciently commissioned by the editor of Antiquity, Professor Glyn Daniel. This was followed a year later by Thom's book Megalithic Sites in Britain, which had the effect of a delayed-action bomb. His previous papers had appeared in mathematical, statistical and astronomical journals, mainly because they had been refused by archaeological editors, to their discredit, who did not understand them and would not have taken them seriously if they had been able to do so.

In the retrospect of history it is too early to assess objectively, or with much hindsight, Thom's lasting contribution to knowledge, and we cannot at short notice anticipate the judgement of posterity. Yet even now it is essential to understand that his work encompassed three quite distinct fields of enquiry and hypothesis, which are formally and logically separate, even though they share much of the relevant data derived from observation in the field. Virtue or blame in any of these fields has thus no bearing on either of the others, though this is a point often ignored by Thom's critics, some of whom have taken a single error to invalidate the whole.

Thom's recognition of the recurrent appearance of non-circular settings of standing stones is in my view the most important, as well as the least controversial, of his contributions. It does not matter that others have subsequently put forward alternative algorithms for their construction. What matters is that Thom was the first to show that the builders of these prehistoric rings were repeatedly experimenting with geometric figures which cannot possibly be explained away as bad shots at a true circle, the easiest of all plane figures to set out on the ground. Herein lie the beginnings of geometry, however tentative; and beginnings removed far in time and space from their conventionally accepted origins in the ancient civilizations of the East. This alone requires the early history of mathematics to be re-written, as even the severest of Thom's critics must admit.

The shape of sites is independent of their size. Thom's analysis of dimensions led him to posit the former use of the megalithic yard and the rod. The reality or illusoriness of these units in pre-history depends wholly upon statistical arguments, which can be as controversial and contradictory as those delivered by advocates in court. One may suspect that future analysis will not sustain Thom's claim for the universal use of the same values throughout Britain and Brittany; but arguments may be adduced for local values which cluster around a hypothetical mean figure. This remains to be seen; but the question would not have arisen unless Thom had first drawn attention to the possible use in prehistory of defined units of measurement. This is his lasting contribution in the field of mensuration.

Both the shape and size of sites are independent of astronomical implications. Most of Thom's later publications have been concerned with apparent alignments on significant risings and settings of the Sun and the Moon, and it is probably this aspect of his work which has had the greatest catalytic influence and has also aroused the greatest controversy.

Here too the real argument is statistical, with all that that implies. Given the number of significant events on the horizon, and the range of dates for their occurrence, as well as the uncertainty about how a rising or setting was defined, it is obviously impossible to assert that any one alignment was deliberate. We can try only to find out whether the number of putative deliberate alignments (within prior limits arbitrarily determined) are significantly more frequent than could be expected on the null hypothesis of purely random alignment. Because of the inevitable selection by Thom of sites which were apparently significant we cannot yet solve this problem, though there may be enough evidence already to suggest the former existence of symbolic alignments, even if these lack in detail the high precision claimed by Thom, as the re-surveys and analyses of Clive Ruggles and his collaborators apparently show. Here too it is Thom's own work, with his collaborators, which provides the starting point.

We should not ignore the influence that he has had on the standards of archaeological survey, and not before it was time. His difficulties in the dense jungles of gorse and pine in Brittany can be understood only by those who, like myself, have tried there and have been deterred.

Thom specifically disclaimed any competence as an archaeologist, and this sometimes led him into error, through failing to ascertain the status and past history of the sites which he surveyed and published. His critics have fastened on these quite disproportionately.

Sandy Thom was a most generous man who never hesitated to make his unpublished observations available to other enquirers, whatever their motives or view-point. In his published work, as a mathematician of elegance and economy, he made few concessions to the frailties of his numerous readers. This is why, perhaps, the archaeological community at large has not yet been able to assess his ideas with dispassionate understanding, but has tended to be polarised for or against in opposing camps. Time may lead to a considered and understanding view; but time already shows that Thom was one of the great discoverers.

RJC Atkinson

# INDEX

Torridon 135, 137, 178, 238, 239, 241, 265
*Tracking the Flood Survivors* 278
traverse (closed) 245–9, 321–2
Treshnish Isles 139, 256
Trevas 324
trigonometry 181, 183
The Tub 116, 271, 310, 322
tumuli 251–2
Turnbull, Alyce 42
Tursachan, Callanish 217

U
Uig Bay, North Skye 240
unit of length 177, 218
University of California 263

V
Van Millingen, Ben 251–2
Vatcher, Lance 251
Vatcher, Mrs Lance 249
Velikovsky 346, 350
Verel, Mr & Mrs 124
Vickers 254
*Victories of the Engineer* 65
*Vistas in Astronomy* 37, 202, 259, 280, 348
Von Braun, Wernher 191
Von Daniken 279
Vost, J 105
Voyager 78

W
Wales 176, 178, 202
Walkham, Harry 82
Wallace, Anne 16
Wallace, Barnes 107, 189
Wallace, CS 364
Wallace, Mark 267
*Washington Post* 203
Watkins, Alfred 364
West Loch Roag 217
White, Mrs Cooper 15
*White Heather* 134
Whiteford, Alex 16, 64
Wilcock, Bruce 206, 250
Williams, Lloyd 357
Wilson, Sir Alan 195
Wilson, Jim 104, 134
Wilson, Stuart 16, 17, 151, 195, 261
wind tunnel 103, 105, 106, 152, 184–7, 265, 341, 359
Wingate, Edmund 168

wobble 182
Wood, John Edwin 306
Woodhenge 224
Worsley, Cmndr FA 119
Wroth, Peter 15

XYZ
*Yorkshire Post* 252
Young, Fiona 16
Young, Tom 114
Young, Scottie 82
Yuille, Mr 120
zodiacal light 152

*Alexander Thom sitting on a stone while at work*
*on a survey at Carnac (1972)*
*(photo :Hamish Gorrie)*